The Troubled Vision

Also by Jerome Charyn

The Single Voice

AN ANTHOLOGY OF
CONTEMPORARY SHORT NOVELS
AND PASSAGES

The
Troubled
Vision

Edited by Jerome Charyn

COLLIER BOOKS
COLLIER-MACMILLAN LTD., LONDON

The Macmillan Company
866 Third Avenue, New York, N.Y. 10022
Collier-Macmillan Canada Ltd., Toronto, Ontario

Library of Congress Catalog Card Number: 72-109448

FIRST PRINTING

Printed in the United States of America

ACKNOWLEDGMENTS

For permission to reprint copyrighted material the following acknowledgments are gratefully made to:

Farrar, Straus & Giroux, Inc. for material from *Everything That Rises Must Converge* by Flannery O'Connor. Copyright © 1962, 1965 by the Estate of Mary Flannery O'Connor.

Farrar, Straus & Giroux, Inc. for "Pre-Game" from *The Natural* by Bernard Malamud. Copyright © 1952 by Bernard Malamud.

McGraw-Hill Book Company for material from *Absent Without Leave* by Heinrich Böll (translated by Leila Vennewitz). Copyright © 1965 by Heinrich Böll.

New Directions Publishing Corporation for material from *Miss Lonelyhearts* by Nathanael West. Copyright 1933 by Nathanael West.

Harper & Row, Publishers, Inc., for *The Pederson Kid* from *In the Heart of the Heart of the Country* by William H. Gass. Copyright © 1961 by William H. Gass.

Acknowledgments   v

McClelland & Stewart, Ltd., Toronto, for material from *Beautiful Losers* by Leonard Cohen. Copyright © 1966 by Leonard Cohen.

The Viking Press, Inc. for material from *Beautiful Losers* by Leonard Cohen. Copyright © 1966 by Leonard Cohen.

The Dial Press, Inc. for material from *Going to Meet the Man* by James Baldwin. Copyright © 1948, 1951, 1957, 1958, 1960, 1965 by James Baldwin.

MacGibbon & Kee for material from *The Third Policeman* by Flann O'Brien.

Walker & Company for material from *The Third Policeman* by Flann O'Brien. Copyright © 1967 by Evelyn O'Nolan. Reprinted by permission of Walker & Company and Lancer Books Inc.

G. P. Putnam's Sons for material from *Advertisements for Myself* by Norman Mailer. Copyright © 1959 by Norman Mailer.

Random House, Inc. for material from *Nog* by Rudolph Wurlitzer. Copyright © 1968 by Rudolph Wurlitzer.

Delacorte Press for material from *Trout Fishing in America* by Richard Brautigan. Copyright © 1967 by Richard Brautigan. First published by Four Seasons Foundation, San Francisco, in its Writing Series edited by Donald Allen. A Seymour Lawrence Book/Delacorte Press.

CONTENTS

INTRODUCTION

"Forget the epic, the masterwork," Nathanael West wrote in "Some Notes on *Miss Lonelyhearts*." "In America fortunes do not accumulate, the soil does not grow, families have no history. Leave slow growth to the book reviewers, you only have time to explode." More than any of his contemporaries, West felt the urge to explore and depict the obscenity, sterility, and violence of the American dream. And the short, nervous, highly compressed, and explosive novel, which West vitalized and perfected in *Miss Lonelyhearts* and *The Day of the Locust*, has remained a distinctive fictional form of our time. Abandoning character development and a strict linear perspective, and other props of the nineteenth-century novel of manners, no longer able to range through an entire society with the appetite and aplomb of Tolstoy or Balzac, to fit the individual motes and fragments of his own life within the continuum of a thousand-page novel, to feel rooted in a particular time, a particular place, a particular past, the contemporary writer has been left with little else than a sense of dislocation, a splintered reality, and the shards and bones of language. As John Bleibtreu has suggested in *The Parable of the Beast*:

The voice of the turtle is heard in the land, heard in all the arts—in literature, painting, and music—and in the voices of men and women speaking to one another. It is not the voice of the dove, that sweet and melancholy sound which the translators of the Authorized Version presumably had in mind; it is the croak of isolation and alienation issuing from within a vault of defensive armor—the voice of the reptilian turtle. This armor we wear —the armor of technology separating us from the rest of the natural word—has created us lately in the condition of exiles. Nature exists within as well as without, and we are become, therefore, exiled from ourselves. The style of the catatonic has become the style of Everyman.

And it is precisely the voice of the turtle, "the croak of isolation," that has cropped up so persistently in contemporary American fiction. The personae of our best writers drift through their fictive landscapes half-asleep, locked within the muted, disordered tones of the catatonic, in a dream-riddled, violent word. "In America," Nathanael West has warned us, "violence is idiomatic. . . . In America violence is daily." His own heroes are self-deluded sleepwalkers who invariably hover at the edge of violence. West says of his disillusioned Christ figure, Miss Lonelyhearts: "Like a dead man, only friction could make him warm or violence make him mobile." Tod Hackett, chasing seventeen-year-old Faye Greener through the cluttered dreamscape of Hollywood in *The Day of the Locust*, has his moment of consciousness: "He began to wonder if he himself didn't suffer from the ingrained, morbid apathy he liked to draw in others. Maybe he could only be galvanized into sensibility and that was why he was chasing Faye." And it is only after violence has erupted around him, after Homer Simpson is ravaged by a Hollywood mob, that Tod is allowed one pathetic croak. The siren of the police car he is sitting in "began to scream and at first he thought he was making the noise himself. He felt his lips with his hands. They were clamped tight. He knew then it was the siren. For some reason this made him laugh and he began to imitate the siren as loud as he could."

William Gass's heroes are adrift in the heart of the heart of the country, his own stylized version of the American Midwest, where: "Streets, sidewalks, faces, feelings—they are gray. Speech is gray, and the grass where it shows. Every flank and front, each top is gray. Everything is gray: hair, eyes, window glass, the hawkers' bills and touters' posters, lips, teeth, poles and metal signs—they're gray, quite gray."

The narrator of Rudolph Wurlitzer's *Nog*, having manufactured a sensibility and a landscape for himself, advises: "Narrow all possibilities. Develop and love your limitations." He is suspended in a perpetual fugue state in which he has "no memories, only vague symbols of separations: an overturned kitchen table, a ripped bed sheet, a broken battleship abandoned at the bottom of a bathtub."

And what of the contemporary writer himself? Isolated, skittery, eccentric, feeling less and less human in a mechanical, Americanized world that honors moonwalks, kill machines, and artificial hearts, having only words to play with, he has retreated within the borders of his own fiction, knowing full well the limitations of his work and the emptiness around him. And William Gass, who has written about madness, isolation, and the overwhelming grayness of human life, provides a kind of credo for the contemporary writer in his essay, "The Concept of Character in Fiction":

On the other side of a novel lies the void. Think, for instance, of a striding statue; imagine the purposeful inclination of the torso, the alert and penetrating gaze of the head, the outstretched arm and pointing finger; everything would appear to direct us toward some goal in front of it. Yet our eye travels only to the finger's end, and not beyond. Though pointing, the finger bids us stay instead, and we journey slowly back along the tension of the arm. In our hearts we know what actually surrounds that statue. The same surrounds every other work of art: empty space and silence.

The Troubled Vision

1 ❧ *Flannery O'Connor*

Flannery O'Connor was born in Savannah, Georgia, in 1925 and was educated at the Georgia State College for Women and the University of Iowa. She died in 1964. Her novels are Wise Blood (1952) and The Violent Bear It Away (1960); she also published two remarkable books of stories, A Good Man Is Hard to Find (1955) and Everything That Rises Must Converge (1965), the second of which Theodore Solotaroff has called "the best collection of shorter fiction to have been published in America during the past 20 years."

THE LAME
SHALL ENTER FIRST

Sheppard sat on a stool at the bar that divided the kitchen in half, eating his cereal out of the individual pasteboard box it came in. He ate mechanically, his eyes on the child, who was wandering from cabinet to cabinet in the panelled kitchen, collecting the ingredients for his breakfast. He was a stocky blond boy of ten. Sheppard kept his intense blue eyes fixed on him. The boy's future was written in his face. He would be a banker. No, worse. He would operate a small loan company. All he wanted for the child was that he be good and unselfish and neither seemed likely. Sheppard was a young man whose hair was already white. It stood up like a narrow brush halo over his pink sensitive face.

The boy approached the bar with the jar of peanut butter under his arm, a plate with a quarter of a small chocolate cake on it in one hand and the ketchup bottle in the other. He did not appear to notice his father. He climbed up on the stool and began to spread peanut butter on the cake. He had very large round ears that leaned away from his head and seemed to pull his eyes slightly too far apart. His shirt was green but so faded that the cowboy charging across the front of it was only a shadow.

"Norton," Sheppard said, "I saw Rufus Johnson yesterday. Do you know what he was doing?"

The child looked at him with a kind of half attention, his eyes forward but not yet engaged. They were a paler blue than his father's as if they might have faded like the shirt; one of them listed, almost imperceptibly, toward the outer rim.

"He was in an alley," Sheppard said, "and he had his hand in a garbage can. He was trying to get something to eat out of it." He paused to let this soak in. "He was hungry," he finished, and tried to pierce the child's conscience with his gaze.

The boy picked up the piece of chocolate cake and began to gnaw it from one corner.

"Norton," Sheppard said, "do you have any idea what it means to share?"

A flicker of attention. "Some of it's yours," Norton said.

"Some of it's *his*," Sheppard said heavily. It was hopeless. Almost any fault would have been preferable to selfishness— a violent temper, even a tendency to lie.

The child turned the bottle of ketchup upside-down and began thumping ketchup onto the cake.

Sheppard's look of pain increased. "You are ten and Rufus Johnson is fourteen," he said. "Yet I'm sure your shirts would fit Rufus." Rufus Johnson was a boy he had been trying to help at the reformatory for the past year. He had been re-leased two months ago. "When he was in the reformatory, he looked pretty good, but when I saw him yesterday, he was skin and bones. He hasn't been eating cake with peanut butter on it for breakfast."

The child paused. "It's stale," he said. "That's why I have to put stuff on it."

Sheppard turned his face to the window at the end of the bar. The side lawn, green and even, sloped fifty feet or so down to a small suburban wood. When his wife was living, they had often eaten outside, even breakfast, on the grass. He had never noticed then that the child was selfish. "Listen to me," he said, turning back to him, "look at me and listen."

The boy looked at him. At least his eyes were forward.

"I gave Rufus a key to this house when he left the reformatory—to show my confidence in him and so he would have a place he could come to and feel welcome any time. He didn't use it, but I think he'll use it now because he's seen me and he's hungry. And if he doesn't use it, I'm going out and find him and bring him here. I can't see a child eating out of garbage cans."

The boy frowned. It was dawning upon him that something of his was threatened.

Sheppard's mouth stretched in disgust. "Rufus's father died before he was born," he said. "His mother is in the state penitentiary. He was raised by his grandfather in a shack without water or electricity and the old man beat him every day. How would you like to belong to a family like that?"

"I don't know," the child said lamely.

"Well, you might think about it sometime," Sheppard said.

Sheppard was City Recreational Director. On Saturdays he worked at the reformatory as a counselor, receiving nothing for it but the satisfaction of knowing he was helping boys no one else cared about. Johnson was the most intelligent boy he had worked with and the most deprived.

Norton turned what was left of the cake over as if he no longer wanted it.

"You started that, now finish it," Sheppard said.

"Maybe he won't come," the child said and his eyes brightened slightly.

"Think of everything you have that he doesn't!" Sheppard said. "Suppose you had to root in garbage cans for food? Suppose you had a huge swollen foot and one side of you dropped lower than the other when you walked?"

The boy looked blank, obviously unable to imagine such a thing.

"You have a healthy body," Sheppard said, "a good home. You've never been taught anything but the truth. Your daddy gives you everything you need and want. You don't have a grandfather who beats you. And your mother is not in the state penitentiary."

The child pushed his plate away. Sheppard groaned aloud.

A knot of flesh appeared below the boy's suddenly distorted mouth. His face became a mass of lumps with slits for eyes. "If she was in the penitentiary," he began in a kind of racking bellow, "I could go to seeeeee her." Tears rolled down his face and the ketchup dribbled on his chin. He looked as if he had been hit in the mouth. He abandoned himself and howled.

Sheppard sat helpless and miserable, like a man lashed by some elemental force of nature. This was not a normal grief. It was all part of his selfishness. She had been dead for over a year and a child's grief should not last so long. "You're going on eleven years old," he said reproachfully.

The child began an agonizing high-pitched heaving noise.

"If you stop thinking about yourself and think what you can do for somebody else," Sheppard said, "then you'll stop missing your mother."

The boy was silent but his shoulders continued to shake. Then his face collapsed and he began to howl again.

"Don't you think I'm lonely without her too?" Sheppard said. "Don't you think I miss her at all? I do, but I'm not sitting around moping. I'm busy helping other people. When do you see me just sitting around thinking about my troubles?"

The boy slumped as if he were exhausted but fresh tears streaked his face.

"What are you going to do today?" Sheppard asked, to get his mind on something else.

The child ran his arm across his eyes. "Sell seeds," he mumbled.

Always selling something. He had four quart jars full of nickels and dimes he had saved and he took them out of his closet every few days and counted them. "What are you selling seeds for?"

"To win a prize."

"What's the prize?"

"A thousand dollars."

"And what would you do if you had a thousand dollars?"

"Keep it," the child said and wiped his nose on his shoulder.

"I feel sure you would," Sheppard said. "Listen," he said and lowered his voice to an almost pleading tone, "suppose by some chance you did win a thousand dollars. Wouldn't you like to spend it on children less fortunate than yourself? Wouldn't you like to give some swings and trapezes to the orphanage? Wouldn't you like to buy poor Rufus Johnson a new shoe?"

The boy began to back away from the bar. Then suddenly he leaned forward and hung with his mouth open over his plate. Sheppard groaned again. Everything came up, the cake, the peanut butter, the ketchup—a limp sweet batter. He hung over it gagging, more came, and he waited with his mouth open over the plate as if he expected his heart to come up next.

"It's all right," Sheppard said, "it's all right. You couldn't help it. Wipe your mouth and go lie down."

The child hung there a moment longer. Then he raised his face and looked blindly at his father.

"Go on," Sheppard said. "Go on and lie down."

The boy pulled up the end of his t-shirt and smeared his mouth with it. Then he climbed down off the stool and wandered out of the kitchen.

Sheppard sat there staring at the puddle of half-digested food. The sour odor reached him and he drew back. His gorge rose. He got up and carried the plate to the sink and turned the water on it and watched grimly as the mess ran down the drain. Johnson's sad thin hand rooted in garbage cans for food while his own child, selfish, unresponsive, greedy, had so much that he threw it up. He cut off the faucet with a thrust of his fist. Johnson had a capacity for real response and had been deprived of everything from birth; Norton was average or below and had had every advantage.

He went back to the bar to finish his breakfast. The cereal was soggy in the cardboard box but he paid no attention to what he was eating. Johnson was worth any amount of effort because he had the potential. He had seen it from the time the boy had limped in for his first interview.

Sheppard's office at the reformatory was a narrow closet with one window and a small table and two chairs in it. He had never been inside a confessional but he thought it must be the same kind of operation he had here, except that he explained, he did not absolve. His credentials were less dubious than a priest's; he had been trained for what he was doing.

When Johnson came in for his first interview, he had been reading over the boy's record—senseless destruction, windows smashed, city trash boxes set afire, tires slashed—the kind of thing he found where boys had been transplanted abruptly from the country to the city as this one had. He came to Johnson's I. Q. score. It was 140. He raised his eyes eagerly.

The boy sat slumped on the edge of his chair, his arms hanging between his thighs. The light from the window fell on his face. His eyes, steel-colored and very still, were trained narrowly forward. His thin dark hair hung in a flat forelock across the side of his forehead, not carelessly like a boy's, but fiercely like an old man's. A kind of fanatic intelligence was palpable in his face.

Sheppard smiled to diminish the distance between them.

The boy's expression did not soften. He leaned back in his chair and lifted a monstrous club foot to his knee. The foot was in a heavy black battered shoe with a sole four or five inches thick. The leather parted from it in one place and the end of an empty sock protruded like a grey tongue from a severed head. The case was clear to Sheppard instantly. His mischief was compensation for the foot.

"Well Rufus," he said, "I see by the record here that you don't have but a year to serve. What do you plan to do when you get out?"

"I don't make no plans," the boy said. His eyes shifted indifferently to something outside the window behind Sheppard in the far distance.

"Maybe you ought to," Sheppard said and smiled.

Johnson continued to gaze beyond him.

"I want to see you make the most of your intelligence," Sheppard said. "What's important to you? Let's talk about what's important to you." His eyes dropped involuntarily to the foot.

"Study it and git your fill," the boy drawled.

Sheppard reddened. The black deformed mass swelled before his eyes. He ignored the remark and the leer the boy was giving him. "Rufus," he said, "you've got into a lot of senseless trouble but I think when you understand why you do these things, you'll be less inclined to do them." He smiled. They had so few friends, saw so few pleasant faces, that half his effectiveness came from nothing more than smiling at them. "There are a lot of things about yourself that I think I can explain to you," he said.

Johnson looked at him stonily. "I ain't asked for no explanation," he said. "I already know why I do what I do."

"Well good!" Sheppard said. "Suppose you tell me what's made you do the things you've done?"

A black sheen appeared in the boy's eyes. "Satan," he said. "He has me in his power."

Sheppard looked at him steadily. There was no indication on the boy's face that he had said this to be funny. The line of his thin mouth was set with pride. Sheppard's eyes hardened. He would know the Bible with or without reading it. His some elemental warping of nature that had happened too long ago to be corrected now. This boy's questions about life had been answered by signs nailed on pine trees: DOES SATAN HAVE YOU IN HIS POWER? REPENT OR BURN IN HELL. JESUS SAVES. He would know the Bible with or without reading it. His despair gave way to outrage. "Rubbish!" he snorted. "We're living in the space age! You're too smart to give me an answer like that."

Johnson's mouth twisted slightly. His look was contemptuous but amused. There was a glint of challenge in his eyes.

Sheppard scrutinized his face. Where there was intelligence anything was possible. He smiled again, a smile that was like an invitation to the boy to come into a school room with all its windows thrown open to the light. "Rufus," he said, "I'm going to arrange for you to have a conference with me once a week. Maybe there's an explanation for your explanation. Maybe I can explain your devil to you."

After that he had talked to Johnson every Saturday for the rest of the year. He talked at random, the kind of talk the boy would never have heard before. He talked a little above him to give him something to reach for. He roamed from simple psychology and the dodges of the human mind to astronomy and the space capsules that were whirling around the earth faster than the speed of sound and would soon encircle the stars. Instinctively he concentrated on the stars. He wanted to give the boy something to reach for besides his neighbor's goods. He wanted to stretch his horizons. He wanted him to see the universe, to see that the darkest parts of it could be penetrated. He would have given anything to be able to put a telescope in Johnson's hands.

Johnson said little and what he did say, for the sake of his pride, was in dissent or senseless contradiction, with the club-foot raised always to his knee like a weapon ready for use, but Sheppard was not deceived. He watched his eyes and every week he saw something in them crumble. From the boy's face, hard but shocked, braced against the light that was ravaging him, he could see that he was hitting dead center.

Johnson was free now to live out of garbage cans and rediscover his old ignorance. The injustice of it was infuriating. He had been sent back to the grandfather; the old man's imbecility could only be imagined. Perhaps the boy had by now run away from him. The idea of getting custody of Johnson had occurred to Sheppard before, but the fact of the grandfather had stood in the way. Nothing excited him so much as thinking what he could do for such a boy. First he would have him fitted for a new orthopedic shoe. His back was thrown out of line every time he took a step. Then he would encourage him in some particular intellectual interest. He thought of the telescope. He could buy a second-hand one and they could set it up in the attic window. He sat for almost ten minutes thinking what he could do if he had Johnson here with him. What was wasted on Norton would cause Johnson to flourish. Yesterday when he had seen him with his hand in the garbage can, he had waved and started forward. Johnson had seen him, paused a split-second, then vanished with the swiftness of a rat, but not before Sheppard had seen his expression change. Something had kindled in the boy's eyes, he was sure of it, some memory of the lost light.

He got up and threw the cereal box in the garbage. Before he left the house, he looked into Norton's room to be sure he was not still sick. The child was sitting cross-legged on his bed. He had emptied the quart jars of change into one large pile in front of him, and was sorting it out by nickels and dimes and quarters.

That afternoon Norton was alone in the house, squatting on the floor of his room arranging packages of flower seeds in rows around himself. Rain slashed against the window panes and rattled in the gutters. The room had grown dark but every few minutes it was lit by silent lightning and the seed packages showed up gaily on the floor. He squatted motionless like a large pale frog in the midst of this potential garden. All at once his eyes became alert. Without warning the rain had stopped. The silence was heavy as if the downpour had been hushed by violence. He remained motionless, only his eyes turning.

Into the silence came the distinct click of a key turning in the front door lock. The sound was a very deliberate one. It drew attention to itself and held it as if it were controlled more by a mind than by a hand. The child leapt up and got into the closet.

The footsteps began to move in the hall. They were deliberate and irregular, a light and then a heavy one, then a silence as if the visitor had paused to listen himself or to examine something. In a minute the kitchen door screeked. The footsteps crossed the kitchen to the refrigerator. The closet wall and the kitchen wall were the same. Norton stood with his ear pressed against it. The refrigerator door opened. There was a prolonged silence.

He took off his shoes and then tiptoed out of the closet and stepped over the seed packages. In the middle of the room, he stopped and remained where he was, rigid. A thin bony-faced boy in a wet black suit stood in his door, blocking his escape. His hair was flattened to his skull by the rain. He stood there like an irate drenched crow. His look went through the child like a pin and paralyzed him. Then his eyes began to move over everything in the room—the unmade bed, the dirty curtain on the one large window, a photograph of a wide-faced young woman that stood up in the clutter on top of the dresser.

The child's tongue suddenly went wild. "He's been expecting you, he's going to give you a new shoe because you have to eat out of garbage cans!" he said in a kind of mouse-like shriek.

"I eat out of garbage cans," the boy said slowly with a beady stare, "because I like to eat out of garbage cans. See?"

The child nodded.

"And I got ways of getting my own shoe. See?"

The child nodded, mesmerized.

The boy limped in and sat down on the bed. He arranged a pillow behind him and stretched his short leg out so that the big black shoe rested conspicuously on a fold of the sheet.

Norton's gaze settled on it and remained immobile. The sole was as thick as a brick.

Johnson wiggled it slightly and smiled. "If I kick somebody

once with this," he said, "it learns them not to mess with me."

The child nodded.

"Go in the kitchen," Johnson said, "and make me a sandwich with some of that rye bread and ham and bring me a glass of milk.

Norton went off like a mechanical toy, pushed in the right direction. He made a large greasy sandwich with ham hanging out the sides of it and poured out a glass of milk. Then he returned to the room with the glass of milk in one hand and the sandwich in the other.

Johnson was leaning back regally against the pillow. "Thanks, waiter," he said and took the sandwich.

Norton stood by the side of the bed, holding the glass.

The boy tore into the sandwich and ate steadily until he finished it. Then he took the glass of milk. He held it with both hands like a child and when he lowered it for breath, there was a rim of milk around his mouth. He handed Norton the empty glass. "Go get me one of them oranges in there, waiter," he said hoarsely.

Norton went to the kitchen and returned with the orange. Johnson peeled it with his fingers and let the peeling drop in the bed. He ate it slowly, spitting the seeds out in front of him. When he finished, he wiped his hands on the sheet and gave Norton a long appraising stare. He appeared to have been softened by the service. "You're his kid all right," he said. "You got the same stupid face."

The child stood there stolidly as if he had not heard.

"He don't know his left hand from his right," Johnson said with a hoarse pleasure in his voice.

The child cast his eyes a little to the side of the boy's face and looked fixedly at the wall.

"Yaketty yaketty yak," Johnson said, "and never says a thing."

The child's upper lip lifted slightly but he didn't say anything.

"Gas," Johnson said. "Gas."

The child's face began to have a wary look of belligerence. He backed away slightly as if he were prepared to retreat instantly. "He's good," he mumbled. "He helps people."

"Good!" Johnson said savagely. He thrust his head forward. "Listen here," he hissed, "I don't care if he's good or not. He ain't *right!*"

Norton looked stunned.

The screen door in the kitchen banged and some one entered. Johnson sat forward instantly. "Is that him?" he said.

"It's the cook," Norton said. "She comes in the afternoon."

Johnson got up and limped into the hall and stood in the kitchen door and Norton followed him.

The colored girl was at the closet taking off a bright red raincoat. She was a tall light-yellow girl with a mouth like a large rose that had darkened and wilted. Her hair was dressed in tiers on top of her head and leaned to the side like the Tower of Pisa.

Johnson made a noise through his teeth. "Well look at Aunt Jemima," he said.

The girl paused and trained an insolent gaze on them. They might have been dust on the floor.

"Come on," Johnson said, "let's see what all you got besides a nigger." He opened the first door to his right in the hall and looked into a pink-tiled bathroom. "A pink can!" he murmured.

He turned a comical face to the child. "Does he sit on that?"

"It's for company," Norton said, "but he sits on it sometimes."

"He ought to empty his head in it," Johnson said.

The door was open to the next room. It was the room Sheppard had slept in since his wife died. An ascetic-looking iron bed stood on the bare floor. A heap of Little League baseball uniforms was piled in one corner. Papers were scattered over a large roll-top desk and held down in various places by his pipes, Johnson stood looking into the room silently. He wrinkled his nose. "Guess who?" he said.

The door to the next room was closed but Johnson opened it and thrust his head into the semi-darkness within. The shades were down and the air was close with a faint scent of perfume in it. There was a wide antique bed and a mammoth dresser whose mirror glinted in the half light. Johnson snapped the light switch by the door and crossed the room to the mirror and peered into it. A silver comb and brush lay on the linen runner. He picked up the comb and began to run it through his hair. He combed it straight down on his forehead. Then he swept it to the side, Hitler fashion.

"Leave her comb alone!" the child said. He stood in the door, pale and breathing heavily as if he were watching sacrilege in a holy place.

Johnson put the comb down and picked up the brush and gave his hair a swipe with it.

"She's dead," the child said.

"I ain't afraid of dead people's things," Johnson said. He opened the top drawer and slid his hand in.

"Take your big fat dirty hands off my mother's clothes!" the child said in a high suffocated voice.

"Keep your shirt on, sweetheart," Johnson murmured. He pulled up a wrinkled red polka dot blouse and dropped it back. Then he pulled out a green silk kerchief and whirled it over his head and let it float to the floor. His hand continued to plow deep into the drawer. After a moment it came up gripping a faded corset with four dangling metal supporters. "Thisyer must be her saddle," he observed.

He lifted it gingerly and shook it. Then he fastened it

around his waist and jumped up and down, making the metal supporters dance. He began to snap his fingers and turn his hips from side to side. "Gonter rock, rattle and roll," he sang. "Gonter rock, rattle and roll. Can't please that woman, to save my doggone soul." He began to move around, stamping the good foot down and slinging the heavy one to the side. He danced out the door, past the stricken child and down the hall toward the kitchen.

A half hour later Sheppard came home. He dropped his raincoat on a chair in the hall and came as far as the parlor door and stopped. His face was suddenly transformed. It shone with pleasure, Johnson sat, a dark figure, in a high-backed pink upholstered chair. The wall behind him was lined with books from floor to ceiling. He was reading one. Sheppard's eyes narrowed. It was a volume of the Encyclopedia Britannica. He was so engrossed in it that he did not look up. Sheppard held his breath. This was the perfect setting for the boy. He had to keep him here. He had to manage it somehow.

"Rufus!" he said, "it's good to see you boy!" and he bounded forward with his arm outstretched.

Johnson looked up, his face blank. "Oh hello," he said. He ignored the hand as long as he was able but when Sheppard did not withdraw it, he grudgingly shook it.

Sheppard was prepared for this kind of reaction. It was part of Johnson's make-up never to show enthusiasm.

"How are things?" he said. "How's your grandfather treating you?" He sat down on the edge of the sofa.

"He dropped dead," the boy said indifferently.

"You don't mean it!" Sheppard cried. He got up and sat down on the coffee table nearer the boy.

"Naw," Johnson said, "he ain't dropped dead. I wisht he had."

"Well where is he?" Sheppard muttered.

"He's gone with a remnant to the hills," Johnson said. "Him and some others. They're going to bury some Bibles in a cave and take two of different kinds of animals and all like that. Like Noah. Only this time it's going to be fire, not flood."

Sheppard's mouth stretched wryly. "I see," he said. Then he said, "In other words the old fool has abandoned you?"

"He ain't no fool," the boy said in an indignant tone.

"Has he abandoned you or not?" Sheppard asked impatiently.

The boy shrugged.

"Where's your probation officer?"

"I ain't supposed to keep up with him," Johnson said. "He's supposed to keep up with me."

Sheppard laughed. "Wait a minute," he said. He got up and went into the hall and got his raincoat off the chair and took it to the hall closet to hang it up. He had to give himself time to think, to decide how he could ask the boy so that he would stay. He couldn't force him to stay. It would have to be voluntary. Johnson pretended not to like him. That was only to uphold his pride, but he would have to ask him in such a way that his pride could still be upheld. He opened the closet door and took out a hanger. An old grey winter coat of his wife's still hung there. He pushed it aside but it didn't move. He pulled it open roughly and winced as if he had seen the larva inside a cocoon. Norton stood in it, his face swollen and pale, with a drugged look of misery on it. Sheppard stared at him. Suddenly he was confronted with a possibility. "Get out of there," he said. He caught him by the shoulder and propelled him firmly into the parlor and over to the pink chair where Johnson was sitting with the encyclopedia in his lap. He was going to risk everything in one blow.

"Rufus," he said, "I've got a problem. I need your help."

Johnson looked up suspiciously.

"Listen," Sheppard said, "we need another boy in the house." There was a genuine desperation in his voice. "Norton here has never had to divide anything in his life. He doesn't know what it means to share. And I need somebody to teach him. How about helping me out? Stay here for a while with us, Rufus. I need your help." The excitement in his voice made it thin.

The child suddenly came to life. His face swelled with fury. "He went in her room and used her comb!" he screamed, yanking Sheppard's arm. "He put on her corset and danced with Leola, he . . ."

"Stop this!" Sheppard said sharply. "Is tattling all you're capable of? I'm not asking you for a report on Rufus's conduct. I'm asking you to make him welcome here. Do you understand?

"You see how it is?" he asked, turning to Johnson.

Norton kicked the leg of the pink chair viciously, just missing Johnson's swollen foot. Sheppard yanked him back.

"He said you weren't nothing but gas!" the child shrieked.

A sly look of pleasure crossed Johnson's face.

Sheppard was not put back. These insults were part of the boy's defensive mechanism. "What about it, Rufus?" he said. "Will you stay with us for a while?"

Johnson looked straight in front of him and said nothing. He smiled slightly and appeared to gaze upon some vision of the future that pleased him.

"I don't care," he said and turned a page of the encyclopedia. "I can stand anywhere."

"Wonderful," Sheppard said. "Wonderful."

"He said," the child said in a throaty whisper, "you didn't know your left hand from your right."

There was a silence.

Johnson wet his finger and turned another page of the encyclopedia.

"I have something to say to both of you," Sheppard said in a voice without inflection. His eyes moved from one to the other of them and he spoke slowly as if what he was saying he would say only once and it behooved them to listen. "If it made any difference to me what Rufus thinks of me," he said, "then I wouldn't be asking him here. Rufus is going to help me out and I'm going to help him out and we're both going to help you out. I'd simply be selfish if I let what Rufus thinks of me interfere with what I can do for Rufus. If I can help a person, all I want is to do it. I'm above and beyond simple pettiness."

Neither of them made a sound. Norton stared at the chair cushion. Johnson peered closer at some fine print in the encyclopedia. Sheppard was looking at the tops of their heads. He smiled. After all, he had won. The boy was staying. He reached out and ruffled Norton's hair and slapped Johnson on the shoulder. "Now you fellows sit here and get acquainted," he said gaily and started toward the door. "I'm going to see what Leola left us for supper."

When he was gone, Johnson raised his head and looked at Norton. The child looked back at him bleakly. "God, kid," Johnson said in a cracked voice, "how do you stand it?" His face was stiff with outrage. "He thinks he's Jesus Christ!"

II

Sheppard's attic was a large unfinished room with exposed beams and no electric light. They had set the telescope up on a tripod in one of the dormer windows. It pointed now toward the dark sky where a sliver of moon, as fragile as an egg shell, had just emerged from behind a cloud with a brilliant silver edge. Inside, a kerosene lantern set on a trunk cast their shadows upward and tangled them, wavering slightly, in the joists overhead. Sheppard was sitting on a packing box, looking through the telescope, and Johnson was at his elbow, waiting to get at it. Sheppard had bought it for fifteen dollars two days before at a pawn shop.

"Quit hoggin it," Johnson said.

Sheppard got up and Johnson slid onto the box and put his eye to the instrument.

Sheppard sat down on a straight chair a few feet away. His face was flushed with pleasure. This much of his dream was a reality. Within a week he had made it possible for this boy's vision to pass through a slender channel to the stars. He looked at Johnson's bent back with complete satisfaction. The boy had on one of Norton's plaid shirts and some new khaki trousers he had bought him. The shoe would be ready next week. He had taken him to the brace shop the day after he came and had him fitted for a new shoe. Johnson was as touchy about the foot as if it were a sacred object. His face had been glum while the clerk, a young man with a bright pink bald head, measured the foot with his profane hands. The shoe was going to make the greatest difference in the boy's attitude. Even a child with normal feet was in love with the world after he had got a new pair of shoes. When Norton got a new pair, he walked around for days with his eyes on his feet.

Sheppard glanced across the room at the child. He was sitting on the floor against a trunk, trussed up in a rope he had found and wound around his legs from his ankles to his knees. He appeared so far away that Sheppard might have been looking through the wrong end of the telescope. He had had to whip him only once since Johnson had been with them—the first night when Norton had realized that Johnson was going to sleep in his mother's bed. He did not believe in whipping children, particularly in anger. In this case, he had done both and with good results. He had had no more trouble with Norton.

The child hadn't shown any positive generosity toward Johnson but what he couldn't help, he appeared to be resigned to. In the mornings Sheppard sent the two of them to the Y swimming pool, gave them money to get their lunch at the cafeteria and instructed them to meet him in the park in the afternoon to watch his Little League baseball practice. Every afternoon they had arrived at the park, shambling, silent, their faces closed each on his own thoughts as if neither were aware of the other's existence. At least he could be thankful there were no fights.

Norton showed no interest in the telescope. "Don't you want to get up and look through the telescope, Norton?" he said. It irritated him that the child showed no intellectual curiosity whatsoever. "Rufus is going to be way ahead of you."

Norton leaned forward absently and looked at Johnson's back.

Johnson turned around from the instrument. His face had begun to fill out again. The look of outrage had retreated from his hollow cheeks and was shored up now in the caves of his eyes, like a fugitive from Sheppard's kindness. "Don't waste your valuable time, kid," he said. "You seen the moon once, you seen it."

Sheppard was amused by these sudden turns of perversity. The boy resisted whatever he suspected was meant for his improvement and contrived when he was vitally interested in something to leave the impression he was bored. Sheppard was not deceived. Secretly Johnson was learning what he wanted him to learn—that his benefactor was impervious to insult and that there were no cracks in his armor of kindness and patience where a successful shaft could be driven. "Some day you may go to the moon," he said. "In ten years men will probably be making round trips there on schedule. Why you boys may be spacemen. Astronauts!"

"Astro-nuts," Johnson said.

"Nuts or nauts," Sheppard said, "it's perfectly possible that you, Rufus Johnson, will go to the moon."

Something in the depths of Johnson's eyes stirred. All day his humor had been glum. "I ain't going to the moon and get there alive," he said, "and when I die I'm going to hell."

"It's at least possible to get to the moon," Sheppard said dryly. The best way to handle this kind of thing was with gentle ridicule. "We can see it. We know it's there. Nobody has given any reliable evidence there's a hell."

"The Bible has give the evidence," Johnson said darkly, "and if you die and go there you burn forever."

The child leaned forward.

"Whoever says it ain't a hell," Johnson said, "is contradicting Jesus. The dead are judged and the wicked are damned. They weep and gnash their teeth while they burn," he continued, "and it's everlasting darkness."

The child's mouth opened. His eyes appeared to grow hollow.

"Satan runs it," Johnson said.

Norton lurched up and took a hobbled step toward Sheppard. "Is she there?" he said in a loud voice. "Is she there burning up?" He kicked the rope off his feet. "Is she on fire?"

"Oh my God," Sheppard muttered. "No no," he said, "of course she isn't. Rufus is mistaken. Your mother isn't anywhere. She's not unhappy. She just isn't." His lot would have been easier if when his wife died he had told Norton she had gone to heaven and that some day he would see her again, but he could not allow himself to bring him up on a lie.

Norton's face began to twist. A knot formed in his chin.

"Listen," Sheppard said quickly and pulled the child to him, "your mother's spirit lives on in other people and it'll live on in you if you're good and generous like she was."

The child's pale eyes hardened in disbelief.

Sheppard's pity turned to revulsion. The boy would rather she be in hell than nowhere. "Do you understand?" he said. "She doesn't exist." He put his hand on the child's shoulder. "That's all I have to give you," he said in a softer, exasperated tone, "the truth."

Instead of howling, the boy wrenched himself away and caught Johnson by the sleeve. "Is she there, Rufus?" he said. "Is she there, burning up?"

Johnson's eyes glittered. "Well," he said, "she is if she was evil. Was she a whore?"

"Your mother was not a whore," Sheppard said sharply. He had the sensation of driving a car without brakes. "Now let's have no more of this foolishness. We were talking about the moon."

"Did she believe in Jesus?" Johnson asked.

Norton looked blank. After a second he said, "Yes," as if he saw that this was necessary. "She did," he said. "All the time."

"She did not," Sheppard muttered.

"She did all the time," Norton said. "I heard her say she did all the time."

"She's saved," Johnson said.

The child still looked puzzled. "Where?" he said. "Where is she at?"

"On high," Johnson said.

"Where's that?" Norton gasped.

"It's in the sky somewhere," Johnson said, "but you got to be dead to get there. You can't go in no space ship." There was a narrow gleam in his eyes now like a beam holding steady on its target.

"Man's going to the moon," Sheppard said grimly, "is very much like the first fish crawling out of the water onto land billions and billions of years ago. He didn't have an earth suit. He had to grow his adjustments inside. He developed lungs."

"When I'm dead will I go to hell or where she is?" Norton asked.

"Right now you'd go where she is," Johnson said, "but if you live long enough, you'll go to hell."

Sheppard rose abruptly and picked up the lantern. "Close the window, Rufus," he said. "It's time we went to bed."

On the way down the attic stairs he heard Johnson say in a a loud whisper behind him, "I'll tell you all about it tomorrow, kid, when Himself has cleared out."

The next day when the boys came to the ball park, he watched them as they came from behind the bleachers and around the edge of the field. Johnson's hand was on Norton's shoulder, his head bent toward the younger boy's ear, and on the child's face there was a look of complete confidence, of dawning light. Sheppard's grimace hardened. This would be Johnson's way of trying to annoy him. But he would not be annoyed. Norton was not bright enough to be damaged much. He gazed at the child's dull absorbed little face. Why try to make him superior? Heaven and hell were for the mediocre, and he was that if he was anything.

The two boys came into the bleachers and sat down about ten feet away, facing him, but neither gave him any sign of recognition. He cast a glance behind him where the Little Leaguers were spread out in the field. Then he started for the bleachers. The hiss of Johnson's voice stopped as he approached.

"What have you fellows been doing today?" he asked genially.

"He's been telling me . . ." Norton started.

Johnson pushed the child in the ribs with his elbow. "We ain't been doing nothing," he said. His face appeared to be covered with a blank glaze but through it a look of complicity was blazoned forth insolently.

Sheppard felt his face grow warm, but he said nothing. A child in a Little League uniform had followed him and was nudging him in the back of the leg with a bat. He turned and put his arm around the boy's neck and went with him back to the game.

That night when he went to the attic to join the boys at the telescope, he found Norton there alone. He was sitting on the packing box, hunched over, looking intently through the instrument. Johnson was not there.

"Where's Rufus?" Sheppard asked.

"I said where's Rufus?" he said louder.

"Gone somewhere," the child said without turning around.

"Gone where?" Sheppard asked.

"He just said he was going somewhere. He said he was fed up looking at stars."

"I see," Sheppard said glumly. He turned and went back down the stairs. He searched the house without finding Johnson. Then he went to the living room and sat down. Yesterday he had been convinced of his success with the boy. Today he faced the possibility that he was failing with him. He had been over-lenient, too concerned to have Johnson like him. He felt a twinge of guilt. What difference did it make if Johnson liked him or not? What was that to him? When the boy came in, they would have a few things understood. As long as you stay here there'll be no going out at night by yourself, do you understand?

I don't have to stay here. It ain't nothing to me staying here.

Oh my God, he thought. He could not bring it to that. He would have to be firm but not make an issue of it. He picked

up the evening paper. Kindness and patience were always called
for but he had not been firm enough. He sat holding the paper
but not reading it. The boy would not respect him unless he
showed firmness. The doorbell rang and he went to answer it.
He opened it and stepped back, with a pained disappointed
face.

A large dour policeman stood on the stoop, holding Johnson
by the elbow. At the curb a patrolcar waited. Johnson looked
very white. His jaw was thrust forward as if to keep from
trembling.

"We brought him here first because he raised such a fit,"
the policeman said, "but now that you've seen him, we're going
to take him to the station and ask him a few questions."

"What happened?" Sheppard muttered.

"A house around the corner from here," the policeman said.
"A real smash job, dishes broken all over the floor, furniture
turned upside-down . . ."

"I didn't have a thing to do with it!" Johnson said. "I was
walking along minding my own bidnis when this cop came up
and grabbed me."

Sheppard looked at the boy grimly. He made no effort to
soften his expression.

Johnson flushed. "I was just walking along," he muttered,
but with no conviction in his voice.

"Come on, bud," the policeman said.

"You ain't going to let him take me, are you?" Johnson said.
"You believe me, don't you?" There was an appeal in his voice
that Sheppard had not heard there before.

This was crucial. The boy would have to learn that he could
not be protected when he was guilty. "You'll have to go with
him, Rufus," he said.

"You're going to let him take me and I tell you I ain't done
a thing?" Johnson said shrilly.

Sheppard's face became harder as his sense of injury grew.

The boy failed him even before he had had a chance to give
him the shoe. They were to have got it tomorrow. All his regret
turned suddenly on the shoe; his irritation at the sight of Johnson doubled.

"You made out like you had all this confidence in me," the
boy mumbled.

"I did have," Sheppard said. His face was wooden.

Johnson turned away with the policeman but before he
moved, a gleam of pure hatred flashed toward Sheppard from
the pits of his eyes.

Sheppard stood in the door and watched them get into the
patrolcar and drive away. He summoned his compassion. He
would go to the station tomorrow and see what he could do
about getting him out of trouble. The night in jail would not
hurt him and the experience would teach him that he could
not treat with impunity someone who had shown him nothing
but kindness. Then they would go get the shoe and perhaps
after a night in jail it would mean even more to the boy.

The next morning at eight o'clock the police sergeant called
and told him he could come pick Johnson up. "We booked a
nigger on that charge," he said. "Your boy didn't have nothing
to do with it."

Sheppard was at the station in ten minutes, his face hot
with shame. Johnson sat slouched on a bench in a drab outer
office, reading a police magazine. There was no one else in the
room. Sheppard sat down beside him and put his hand tenta-
tively on his shoulder.

The boy glanced up—his lip curled—and back to the magazine.

Sheppard felt physically sick. The ugliness of what he had
done bore in upon him with a sudden dull intensity. He had
failed him at just the point where he might have turned him

once and for all in the right direction. "Rufus," he said, "I apologize. I was wrong and you were right. I misjudged you."

The boy continued to read.

"I'm sorry."

The boy wet his finger and turned a page.

Sheppard braced himself. "I was a fool, Rufus," he said.

Johnson's mouth slid slightly to the side. He shrugged without raising his head from the magazine.

"Will you forget it, this time?" Sheppard said. "It won't happen again."

The boy looked up. His eyes were bright and unfriendly. "I'll forget it," he said, "but you better remember it." He got up and stalked toward the door. In the middle of the room, he turned and jerked his arm at Sheppard and Sheppard jumped up and followed him as if the boy had yanked an invisible leash.

"Your shoe," he said eagerly, "today is the day to get your shoe!" Thank God for the shoe!

But when they went to the brace shop, they found that the shoe had been made two sizes too small and a new one would not be ready for another ten days. Johnson's temper improved at once. The clerk had obviously made a mistake in the measurements but the boy insisted the foot had grown. He left the shop with a pleased expression, as if, in expanding, the foot had acted on some inspiration of its own. Sheppard's face was haggard.

After this he redoubled his efforts. Since Johnson had lost interest in the telescope, he bought a microscope and a box of prepared slides. If he couldn't impress the boy with immensity, he would try the infinitesimal. For two nights Johnson appeared absorbed in the new instrument, then he abruptly lost interest in it, but he seemed content to sit in the living room in the evening and read the encyclopedia. He devoured the encyclopedia as he devoured his dinner, steadily and without dint to his appetite. Each subject appeared to enter his head, be ravaged, and thrown out. Nothing pleased Sheppard more than to see the boy slouched on the sofa, his mouth shut, reading. After they had spent two or three evenings like this, he began to recover his vision. His confidence returned. He knew that some day he would be proud of Johnson.

On Thursday night Sheppard attended a city council meeting. He dropped the boys off at a movie on his way and picked them up on his way back. When they reached home, an automobile with a single red eye above its windshield was waiting in front of the house. Sheppard's lights as he turned into the driveway illuminated two dour faces in the car.

"The cops!" Johnson said. "Some nigger has broke in somewhere and they've come for me again."

"We'll see about that," Sheppard muttered. He stopped the car in the driveway and switched off the lights. "You boys go in the house and go to bed," he said. "I'll handle this."

He got out and strode toward the squad car. He thrust his head in the window. The two policemen were looking at him with silent knowledgeable faces. "A house on the corner of Shelton and Mills," the one in the driver's seat said. "It looks like a train run through it."

"He was in the picture show down town," Sheppard said. "My boy was with him. He had nothing to do with the other one and he had nothing to do with this one. I'll be responsible."

"If I was you," the one nearest him said, "I wouldn't be responsible for any little bastard like him."

"I said I'd be responsible," Sheppard repeated coldly. "You people made a mistake the last time. Don't make another."

The policemen looked at each other. "It ain't our funeral," the one in the driver's seat said, and turned the key in the ignition.

Sheppard went in the house and sat down in the living room in the dark. He did not suspect Johnson and he did not want the boy to think he did. If Johnson thought he suspected him again, he would lose everything. But he wanted to know if his alibi was airtight. He thought of going to Norton's room and asking him if Johnson had left the movie. But that would be worse. Johnson would know what he was doing and would be incensed. He decided to ask Johnson himself. He would be direct. He went over in his mind what he was going to say and then he got up and went to the boy's door.

It was open as if he had been expected but Johnson was in bed. Just enough light came in from the hall for Sheppard to see his shape under the sheet. He came in and stood at the foot of the bed. "They've gone," he said. "I told them you had nothing to do with it and that I'd be responsible."

There was a muttered "Yeah," from the pillow.

Sheppard hesitated. "Rufus," he said, "you didn't leave the movie for anything at all, did you?"

"You make out like you got all this confidence in me!" a sudden outraged voice cried, "and you ain't got any! You don't trust me no more now than you did then!" The voice, disembodied, seemed to come more surely from the depths of Johnson than when his face was visible. It was a cry of reproach, edged slightly with contempt.

"I do have confidence in you," Sheppard said intensely. "I have every confidence in you. I believe in you and I trust you completely."

"You got your eye on me all the time," the voice said sullenly. "When you get through asking me a bunch of questions, you're going across the hall and ask Norton a bunch of them."

"I have no intention of asking Norton anything and never did," Sheppard said gently. "And I don't suspect you at all.

You could hardly have got from the picture show down town and out here to break in a house and back to the picture show in the time you had."

"That's why you believe me!" the boy cried, "—because you think I couldn't have done it."

"No, no!" Sheppard said. "I believe you because I believe you've got the brains and the guts not to get in trouble again. I believe you know yourself well enough now to know that you don't have to do such things. I believe that you can make anything of yourself that you set your mind to."

Johnson sat up. A faint light shone on his forehead but the rest of his face was invisible. "And I could have broke in there if I'd wanted to in the time I had," he said.

"But I know you didn't," Sheppard said. "There's not the least trace of doubt in my mind."

There was a silence. Johnson lay back down. Then the voice, low and hoarse, as if it were being forced out with difficulty, said, "You don't want to steal and smash up things when you've got everything you want already."

Sheppard caught his breath. The boy was thanking him! He was thanking him! There was gratitude in his voice. There was appreciation. He stood there, smiling foolishly in the dark, trying to hold the moment in suspension. Involuntarily he took a step toward the pillow and stretched out his hand and touched Johnson's forehead. It was cold and dry like rusty iron.

"I understand. Good night, son," he said and turned quickly and left the room. He closed the door behind him and stood there, overcome with emotion.

Across the hall Norton's door was open. The child lay on the bed on his side, looking into the light from the hall.

After this, the road with Johnson would be smooth.

Norton sat up and beckoned to him.

He saw the child but after the first instant, he did not let his eyes focus directly on him. He could not go in and talk to Norton without breaking Johnson's trust. He hesitated, but remained where he was a moment as if he saw nothing. Tomorrow was the day they were to go back for the shoe. It would be a climax to the good feeling between them. He turned quickly and went back into his own room.

The child sat for some time looking at the spot where his father had stood. Finally his gaze became aimless and he lay back down.

The next day Johnson was glum and silent as if he were ashamed that he had revealed himself. His eyes had a hooded look. He seemed to have retired within himself and there to be going through some crisis of determination. Sheppard could not get to the brace shop quickly enough. He left Norton at home because he did not want his attention divided. He wanted to be free to observe Johnson's reaction minutely. The boy did not seem pleased or even interested in the prospect of the shoe, but when it became an actuality, certainly then he would be moved.

The brace shop was a small concrete warehouse lined and stacked with the equipment of affliction. Wheel chairs and walkers covered most of the floor. The walls were hung with every kind of crutch and brace. Artificial limbs were stacked on the shelves, legs and arms and hands, claws and hooks, straps and human harnesses and unidentifiable instruments for unnamed deformities. In a small clearing in the middle of the room there was a row of yellow plastic-cushioned chairs and a shoe-fitting stool. Johnson slouched down in one of the chairs and set his foot up on the stool and sat with his eyes on it moodily. What was roughly the toe had broken open again and he had patched it with a piece of canvas; another place he had patched with what appeared to be the tongue of the original shoe. The two sides were laced with twine.

There was an excited flush on Sheppard's face; his heart was beating unnaturally fast.

The clerk appeared from the back of the shop with the new shoe under his arm. "Got her right this time!" he said. He straddled the shoe-fitting stool and held the shoe up, smiling as if he had produced it by magic.

It was a black slick shapeless object, shining hideously. It looked like a blunt weapon, highly polished.

Johnson gazed at it darkly.

"With this shoe," the clerk said, "you won't know you're walking. You'll think you're riding!" He bent his bright pink bald head and began gingerly to unlace the twine. He removed the old shoe as if he were skinning an animal still half alive. His expression was strained. The unsheathed mass of foot in the dirty sock made Sheppard feel queasy. He turned his eyes away until the new shoe was on. The clerk laced it up rapidly. "Now stand up and walk around," he said, "and see if that ain't power glide." He winked at Sheppard. "In that shoe," he said, "he won't know he don't have a normal foot."

Sheppard's face was bright with pleasure.

Johnson stood up and walked a few yards away. He walked stiffly with almost no dip in his short side. He stood for a moment, rigid, with his back to them.

"Wonderful!" Sheppard said. "Wonderful." It was as if he had given the boy a new spine.

Johnson turned around. His mouth was set in a thin icy line. He came back to the seat and removed the shoe. He put his foot in the old one and began lacing it up.

"You want to take it home and see if it suits you first?" the clerk murmured.

"No," Johnson said. "I ain't going to wear it at all."

"What's wrong with it?" Sheppard said, his voice rising.

"I don't need no new shoe," Johnson said. "And when I do,

I got ways of getting my own." His face was stony but there was a glint of triumph in his eyes.

"Boy," the clerk said, "is your trouble in your foot or in your head?"

"Go soak your skull," Johnson said. "Your brains are on fire."

The clerk rose glumly but with dignity and asked Sheppard what he wanted done with the shoe, which he dangled dispiritedly by the lace.

Sheppard's face was a dark angry red. He was staring straight in front of him at a leather corset with an artificial arm attached.

The clerk asked him again.

"Wrap it up," Sheppard muttered. He turned his eyes to Johnson. "He's not mature enough for it yet," he said. "I had thought he was less of a child."

The boy leered. "You been wrong before," he said.

That night they sat in the living room and read as usual. Sheppard kept himself glumly entrenched behind the Sunday New York *Times*. He wanted to recover his good humor, but every time he thought of the rejected shoe, he felt a new charge of irritation. He did not trust himself even to look at Johnson. He realized that the boy had refused the shoe because he was insecure. Johnson had been frightened by his own gratitude. He didn't know what to make of the new self he was becoming conscious of. He understood that something he had been was threatened and he was facing himself and his possibilities for the first time. He was questioning his identity. Grudgingly, Sheppard felt a slight return of sympathy for the boy. In a few minutes, he lowered his paper and looked at him.

Johnson was sitting on the sofa, gazing over the top of the

encyclopedia. His expression was trancelike. He might have
been listening to something far away. Sheppard watched him
intently but the boy continued to listen, and did not turn
his head. The poor kid is lost, Sheppard thought. Here he
had sat all evening, sullenly reading the paper, and had not
said a word to break the tension. "Rufus," he said.

Johnson continued to sit, stock-still, listening.

"Rufus," Sheppard said in a slow hypnotic voice, "you can
be anything in the world you want to be. You can be a scientist or an architect or an engineer or whatever you set your
mind to, and whatever you set your mind to be, you can be
the best of its kind." He imagined his voice penetrating to
the boy in the black caverns of his psyche. Johnson leaned
forward but his eyes did not turn. On the street a car door
closed. There was a silence. Then a sudden blast from the
door bell.

Sheppard jumped up and went to the door and opened it.
The same policeman who had come before stood there. The
patrolcar waited at the curb.

"Lemme see that boy," he said.

Sheppard scowled and stood aside. "He's been here all
evening," he said. "I can vouch for it."

The policeman walked into the living room. Johnson appeared engrossed in his book. After a second he looked up
with an annoyed expression, like a great man interrupted at
his work.

"What was that you were looking at in that kitchen window
over on Winter Avenue about a half hour ago, bud?" the
policeman asked.

"Stop persecuting this boy!" Sheppard said. "I'll vouch for
the fact he was here. I was here with him."

"You heard him," Johnson said. "I been here all the time."

"It ain't everybody makes tracks like you," the policeman said and eyed the clubfoot.

"They couldn't be his tracks," Sheppard growled, infuriated. "He's been here all the time. You're wasting your own time and you're wasting ours." He felt the *ours* seal his solidarity with the boy. "I'm sick of this," he said. "You people are too damn lazy to go out and find whoever is doing these things. You come here automatically."

The policeman ignored this and continued looking through Johnson. His eyes were small and alert in his fleshy face. Finally he turned toward the door. "We'll get him sooner or later," he said, "with his head in a window and his tail out."

Sheppard followed him to the door and slammed it behind him. His spirits were soaring. This was exactly what he had needed. He returned with an expectant face.

Johnson had put the book down and was sitting there, looking at him slyly. "Thanks," he said.

Sheppard stopped. The boy's expression was predatory. He was openly leering.

"You ain't such a bad liar yourself," he said.

"Liar?" Sheppard murmured. Could the boy have left and come back? He felt himself sicken. Then a rush of anger sent him forward. "Did you leave?" he said furiously. "I didn't see you leave."

The boy only smiled.

"You went up in the attic to see Norton," Sheppard said.

"Naw," Johnson said, "that kid is crazy. He don't want to do nothing but look through that stinking telescope."

"I don't want to hear about Norton," Sheppard said harshly. "Where were you?"

"I was sitting on that pink can by my ownself," Johnson said. "There wasn't no witnesses."

Sheppard took out his handkerchief and wiped his forehead. He managed to smile.

Johnson rolled his eyes. "You don't believe in me," he said. His voice was cracked the way it had been in the dark room two nights before. "You make out like you got all this confidence in me but you ain't got any. When things get hot, you'll fade like the rest of them." The crack became exaggerated, comic. The mockery in it was blatant. "You don't believe in me. You ain't got no confidence," he wailed. "And you ain't any smarter than that cop. All that about tracks— that was a trap. There wasn't any tracks. That whole place is concreted in the back and my feet were dry."

Sheppard slowly put the handkerchief back in his pocket. He dropped down on the sofa and gazed at the rug beneath his feet. The boy's clubfoot was set within the circle of his vision. The pieced-together shoe appeared to grin at him with Johnson's own face. He caught hold of the edge of the sofa cushion and his knuckles turned white. A chill of hatred shook him. He hated the shoe, hated the foot, hated the boy. His face paled. Hatred choked him. He was aghast at himself.

He caught the boy's shoulder and gripped it fiercely as if to keep himself from falling. "Listen," he said, "you looked in that window to embarrass me. That was all you wanted— to shake my resolve to help you, but my resolve isn't shaken. I'm stronger than you are. I'm stronger than you are and I'm going to save you. The good will triumph."

"Not when it ain't true," the boy said. "Not when it ain't right."

"My resolve isn't shaken," Sheppard repeated. "I'm going to save you."

Johnson's look became sly again. "You ain't going to save me," he said. "You're going to tell me to leave this house. I

did those other two jobs too—the first one as well as the one
I done when I was supposed to be in the picture show."

"I'm not going to tell you to leave," Sheppard said. His
voice was toneless, mechanical. "I'm going to save you."

Johnson thrust his head forward. "Save yourself," he hissed.
"Nobody can save me but Jesus."

Sheppard laughed curtly. "You don't deceive me," he said.
"I flushed that out of your head in the reformatory. I saved
you from that, at least."

The muscles in Johnson's face stiffened. A look of such repulsion hardened on his face that Sheppard drew back. The
boy's eyes were like distorting mirrors in which he saw himself made hideous and grotesque. "I'll show you," Johnson
whispered. He rose abruptly and started headlong for the
door as if he could not get out of Sheppard's sight quick
enough, but it was the door to the back hall he went through,
not the front door. Sheppard turned on the sofa and looked
behind him where the boy had disappeared. He heard the
door to his room slam. He was not leaving. The intensity had
gone out of Sheppard's eyes. They looked flat and lifeless as
if the shock of the boy's revelation were only now reaching
the center of his consciousness. "If he would only leave," he
murmured. "If he would only leave now of his own accord."

The next morning Johnson appeared at the breakfast table
in the grandfather's suit he had come in. Sheppard pretended
not to notice but one look told him what he already knew,
that he was trapped, that there could be nothing now but
a battle of nerves and that Johnson would win it. He wished
he had never laid eyes on the boy. The failure of his compassion numbed him. He got out of the house as soon as he
could and all day he dreaded to go home in the evening. He

had a faint hope that the boy might be gone when he returned. The grandfather's suit might have meant he was leaving. The hope grew in the afternoon. When he came home and opened the front door, his heart was pounding.

He stopped in the hall and looked silently into the living room. His expectant expression faded. His face seemed suddenly as old as his white hair. The two boys were sitting close together on the sofa, reading the same book. Norton's cheek rested against the sleeve of Johnson's black suit. Johnson's finger moved under the lines they were reading. The elder brother and the younger. Sheppard looked woodenly at this scene for almost a minute. Then he walked into the room and took off his coat and dropped it on a chair. Neither boy noticed him. He went on to the kitchen.

Leola left the supper on the stove every afternoon before she left and he put it on the table. His head ached and his nerves were taut. He sat down on the kitchen stool and remained there, sunk in his depression. He wondered if he could infuriate Johnson enough to make him leave of his own accord. Last night what had enraged him was the Jesus business. It might enrage Johnson, but it depressed him. Why not simply tell the boy to go? Admit defeat. The thought of facing Johnson again sickened him. The boy looked at him as if he were the guilty one, as if he were a moral leper. He knew without conceit that he was a good man, that he had nothing to reproach himself with. His feelings about Johnson now were involuntary. He would like to feel compassion for him. He would like to be able to help him. He longed for the time when there would be no one but himself and Norton in the house, when the child's simple selfishness would be all he had to contend with, and his own loneliness.

He got up and took three serving dishes off the shelf and took them to the stove. Absently he began pouring the butter-beans and the hash into the dishes. When the food was on the table, he called them in.

They brought the book with them. Norton pushed his place setting around to the same side of the table as Johnson's and moved his chair next to Johnson's chair. They sat down and put the book between them. It was a black book with red edges.

"What's that you're reading?" Sheppard asked, sitting down.

"The Holy Bible," Johnson said.

God give me strength, Sheppard said under his breath.

"We lifted it from a ten cent store," Johnson said.

"We?" Sheppard muttered. He turned and glared at Norton. The child's face was bright and there was an excited sheen to his eyes. The change that had come over the boy struck him for the first time. He looked alert. He had on a blue plaid shirt and his eyes were a brighter blue than he had ever seen them before. There was a strange new life in him, the sign of new and more rugged vices. "So now you steal?" he said, glowering. "You haven't learned to be generous but you have learned to steal."

"No he ain't," Johnson said. "I was the one lifted it. He only watched. He can't sully himself. It don't make any difference about me. I'm going to hell anyway."

Sheppard held his tongue.

"Unless," Johnson said, "I repent."

"Repent, Rufus," Norton said in a pleading voice. "Repent, hear? You don't want to go to hell."

"Stop talking this nonsense," Sheppard said, looking sharply at the child.

"If I do repent, I'll be a preacher," Johnson said. "If you're going to do it, it's no sense in doing it half way."

"What are you going to be, Norton," Sheppard asked in a brittle voice, "a preacher too?"

There was a glitter of wild pleasure in the child's eyes. "A space man!" he shouted.

"Wonderful," Sheppard said bitterly.

"Those space ships ain't going to do you any good unless you believe in Jesus," Johnson said. He wet his finger and began to leaf through the pages of the Bible. "I'll read you where it says so," he said.

Sheppard leaned forward and said in a low furious voice, "Put that Bible up, Rufus, and eat your dinner."

Johnson continued searching for the passage.

"Put that Bible up!" Sheppard shouted.

The boy stopped and looked up. His expression was startled but pleased.

"That book is something for you to hide behind," Sheppard said. "It's for cowards, people who are afraid to stand on their own feet and figure things out for themselves."

Johnson's eyes snapped. He backed his chair a little way from the table. "Satan has you in his power," he said. "Not only me. You too."

Sheppard reached across the table to grab the book but Johnson snatched it and put it in his lap.

Sheppard laughed. "You don't believe in that book and you know you don't believe in it!"

"I believe it!" Johnson said. "You don't know what I believe and what I don't."

Sheppard shook his head. "You don't believe it. You're too intelligent."

"I ain't too intelligent," the boy muttered. "You don't know nothing about me. Even if I didn't believe it, it would still be true."

"You don't believe it!" Sheppard said. His face was a taunt.

"I believe it!" Johnson said breathlessly. "I'll show you I believe it!" He opened the book in his lap and tore out a page of it and thrust it into his mouth. He fixed his eyes on Sheppard. His jaws worked furiously and the paper crackled as he chewed it.

"Stop this," Sheppard said in a dry, burnt-out voice. "Stop it."

The boy raised the Bible and tore out a page with his teeth and began grinding it in his mouth, his eyes burning.

Sheppard reached across the table and knocked the book out of his hand. "Leave the table," he said coldly.

Johnson swallowed what was in his mouth. His eyes widened as if a vision of splendor were opening up before him. "I've eaten it!" he breathed. "I've eaten it like Ezekiel and it was honey to my mouth!"

"Leave this table," Sheppard said. His hands were clenched beside his plate.

"I've eaten it!" the boy cried. Wonder transformed his face. "I've eaten it like Ezekiel and I don't want none of your food after it nor no more ever."

"Go then," Sheppard said softly. "Go. Go."

The boy rose and picked up the Bible and started toward the hall with it. At the door he paused, a small black figure on the threshold of some dark apocalypse. "The Devil has you in his power," he said in a jubilant voice and disappeared.

After supper Sheppard sat in the living room alone. Johnson had left the house but he could not believe that the boy had simply gone. The first feeling of release had passed. He felt dull and cold as at the onset of an illness and dread had settled in him like a fog. Just to leave would be too anticlimactic an end for Johnson's taste; he would return and try to prove something. He might come back a week later and set fire to the place. Nothing seemed too outrageous now.

He picked up the paper and tried to read. In a moment he

threw it down and got up and went into the hall and listened. He might be hiding in the attic. He went to the attic door and opened it.

The lantern was lit, casting a dim light on the stairs. He didn't hear anything. "Norton," he called, "are you up there?" There was no answer. He mounted the narrow stairs to see.

Amid the strange vine-like shadows cast by the lantern, Norton sat with his eye to the telescope. "Norton," Sheppard said, "do you know where Rufus went?"

The child's back was to him. He was sitting hunched, intent, his large ears directly above his shoulders. Suddenly he waved his hand and crouched closer to the telescope as if he could not get near enough to what he saw.

"Norton!" Sheppard said in a loud voice.

The child didn't move.

"Norton!" Sheppard shouted.

Norton started. He turned around. There was an unnatural brightness about his eyes. After a moment he seemed to see that it was Sheppard. "I've found her!" he said breathlessly.

"Found who?" Sheppard said.

"Mamma!"

Sheppard steadied himself in the door way. The jungle of shadows around the child thickened.

"Come and look!" he cried. He wiped his sweaty face on the tail of his plaid shirt and then put his eye back to the telescope. His back became fixed in a rigid intensity. All at once he waved again.

"Norton," Sheppard said, "you don't see anything in the telescope but star clusters. Now you've had enough of that for one night. You'd better go to bed. Do you know where Rufus is?"

"She's there!" he cried, not turning around from the telescope. "She waved at me!"

"I want you in bed in fifteen minutes," Sheppard said. After a moment he said. "Do you hear me, Norton?"

The child began to wave frantically.

"I mean what I say," Sheppard said. "I'm going to call in fifteen minutes and see if you're in bed."

He went down the steps again and returned to the parlor. He went to the front door and cast a cursory glance out. The sky was crowded with the stars he had been fool enough to think Johnson could reach. Somewhere in the small wood behind the house, a bull frog sounded a low hollow note. He went back to his chair and sat a few minutes. He decided to go to bed. He put his hands on the arms of the chair and leaned forward and heard, like the first shrill note of a disaster warning, the siren of a police car, moving slowly into the neighborhood and nearer until it subsided with a moan outside the house.

He felt a cold weight on his shoulders as if an icy cloak had been thrown about him. He went to the door and opened it.

Two policemen were coming up the walk with a dark snarling Johnson between them, handcuffed to each. A reporter jogged alongside and another policeman waited in the patrolcar.

"Here's your boy," the dourest of the policemen said. "Didn't I tell you we'd get him?"

Johnson jerked his arm down savagely. "I was waitin for you!" he said. "You wouldn't have got me if I hadn't of wanted to get caught. It was my idea." He was addressing the policemen but leering at Sheppard.

Sheppard looked at him coldly.

"Why did you want to get caught?" the reporter asked, running around to get beside Johnson. "Why did you deliberately want to get caught?"

The question and the sight of Sheppard seemed to throw

the boy into a fury. "To show up that big tin Jesus!" he
hissed and kicked his leg out at Sheppard. "He thinks he's
God. I'd rather be in the reformatory than in his house, I'd
rather be in the pen! The Devil has him in his power. He
don't know his left hand from his right, he don't have as
much sense as his crazy kid!" He paused and then swept on
to his fantastic conclusion. "He made suggestions to me!"

Sheppard's face blanched. He caught hold of the door
facing.

"Suggestions?" the reporter said eagerly, "what kind of suggestions?"

"Immor'l suggestions!" Johnson said. "What kind of suggestions do you think? But I ain't having none of it, I'm a
Christian, I'm. . ."

Sheppard's face was tight with pain. "He knows that's not
true," he said in a shaken voice. "He knows he's lying. I did
everything I knew how for him. I did more for him than I
did for my own child. I hoped to save him and I failed, but
it was an honorable failure. I have nothing to reproach myself
with. I made no suggestions to him."

"Do you remember the suggestions?" the reporter asked.
"Can you tell us exactly what he said?"

"He's a dirty atheist," Johnson said. "He said there wasn't
no hell."

"Well, they seen each other now," one of the policemen
said with a knowing sigh. "Let's us go."

"Wait," Sheppard said. He came down one step and fixed
his eyes on Johnson's eyes in a last desperate effort to save
himself. "Tell the truth, Rufus," he said. "You don't want
to perpetrate this lie. You're not evil, you're mortally confused. You don't have to make up for that foot, you don't
have to. . ."

Johnson hurled himself forward. "Listen at him!" he screamed. "I lie and steal because I'm good at it! My foot don't have a thing to do with it! The lame shall enter first! The halt'll be gathered together. When I get ready to be saved, Jesus'll save me, not that lying stinking atheist, not that. . ."

"That'll be enough out of you," the policeman said and yanked him back. "We just wanted you to see we got him," he said to Sheppard, and the two of them turned around and dragged Johnson away, half turned and screaming back at Sheppard.

"The lame'll carry off the prey!" he screeched, but his voice was muffled inside the car. The reporter scarmbled into the front seat with the driver and slammed the door and the siren wailed into the darkness.

Sheppard remained there, bent slightly like a man who has been shot but continues to stand. After a minute he turned and went back in the house and sat down in the chair he had left. He closed his eyes on a picture of Johnson in a circle of reporters at the police station, elaborating his lies. "I have nothing to reproach myself with," he murmured. His every action had been selfless, his one aim had been to save Johnson for some decent kind of service, he had not spared himself, he had sacrificed his reputation, he had done more for Johnson than he had done for his own child. Foulness hung about him like an odor in the air, so close that it seemed to come from his own breath. "I have nothing to reproach myself with," he repeated. His voice sounded dry and harsh. "I did more for him than I did for my own child." He was swept with a sudden panic. He heard the boy's jubilant voice. Satan has you in his power.

"I have nothing to reproach myself with," he began again.

"I did more for him than I did for my own child." He heard his voice as if it were the voice of his accuser. He repeated the sentence silently.

Slowly his face drained of color. It became almost grey beneath the white halo of his hair. The sentence echoed in his mind, each syllable like a dull blow. His mouth twisted and he closed his eyes against the revelation. Norton's face rose before him, empty, forlorn, his left eye listing almost imperceptibly toward the outer rim as if it could not bear a full view of grief. His heart constricted with a repulsion for himself so clear and intense that he gasped for breath. He had stuffed his own emptiness with good works like a glutton. He had ignored his own child to feed his vision of himself. He saw the clear-eyed Devil, the sounder of hearts, leering at him from the eyes of Johnson. His image of himself shrivelled until everything was black before him. He sat there paralyzed, aghast.

He saw Norton at the telescope, all back and ears, saw his arm shoot up and wave frantically. A rush of agonizing love for the child rushed over him like a transfusion of life. The little boy's face appeared to him transformed; the image of his salvation; all light. He groaned with joy. He would make everything up to him. He would never let him suffer again. He would be mother and father. He jumped up and ran to his room, to kiss him, to tell him that he loved him, that he would never fail him again.

The light was on in Norton's room but the bed was empty. He turned and dashed up the attic stairs and at the top reeled back like a man on the edge of a pit. The tripod had fallen and the telescope lay on the floor. A few feet over it, the child hung in the jungle of shadows, just below the beam from which he had launched his flight into space.

2 ❧ Bernard Malamud

Bernard Malamud was born in Brooklyn in 1914. He has written two funny, sad, and superb collections of stories, The Magic Barrel (1958) and Idiots First (1963), and five novels, including The Natural (1952), The Assistant (1957), and The Fixer (1966). Alfred Kazin has said of Malamud: "There seems to me no writer of his background who comes so close to the bone of human feeling, who makes one feel so keenly the enigmatic quality of life, for the body of this world—for that which cannot be explained because it is too precious to turn into symbols."

PRE-GAME
(FROM *THE NATURAL*)

Roy Hobbs pawed at the glass before thinking to prick a match with his thumbnail and hold the spurting flame in his cupped palm close to the lower berth window, but by then he had figured it was a tunnel they were passing through and was no longer surprised at the bright sight of himself holding a yellow light over his head, peering back in. As the train yanked its long tail out of the thundering tunnel, the kneeling reflection dissolved and he felt a splurge of freedom at the view of the moon-hazed Western hills bulked against night broken by sprays of summer lightning, although the season was early spring. Lying back, elbowed up on his long side, sleepless still despite the lulling train, he watched the land flowing and waited with suppressed expectancy for a sight of the Mississippi, a thousand miles away.

Having no timepiece he appraised the night and decided it was moving toward dawn. As he was looking, there flowed along this bone-white farmhouse with sagging skeletal porch, alone in untold miles of moonlight, and before it this white-faced, long-boned boy whipped with train-whistle yowl a glowing ball to someone hidden under a dark oak, who shot it back without thought, and the kid once more wound and returned. Roy shut his eyes to the sight because if it wasn't real it was a way he sometimes had of observing himself, just as in this dream he could never shake off—that had hours ago waked him out of sound sleep—of him standing at night in a strange field with a golden baseball in his palm that all the time grew heavier as he sweated to settle whether to hold on or fling it away. But when he had made his decision it was too heavy to lift or let fall (who wanted a hole that deep?) so he changed his mind to keep it and the thing grew fluffy light, a white rose breaking out of its hide, and all but soared off by itself, but he had already sworn to hang on forever.

As dawn tilted the night, a gust of windblown rain blinded him—no, there was a window—but the sliding drops made him thirsty and from thirst sprang hunger. He reached into the hammock for his underwear to be first at breakfast in the dining car and make his blunders of ordering and eating more or less in private, since it was doubtful Sam would be up to tell him what to do. Roy peeled his gray sweatshirt and bunched down the white ducks he was wearing for pajamas in case there was a wreck and he didn't have time to dress. He acrobated into a shirt, pulled up the pants of his good suit, arching to draw them high, but he had crammed both feet into one leg and was trapped so tight wriggling got him nowhere. He worried because here he was straitjacketed in the berth without much room to twist around in and might bust his pants or have to buzz the porter, which he dreaded. Grunting, he contorted himself this way and that till he was at last able to grab and pull down the cuff and with a gasp loosened his feet and got the caught one where it belonged. Sitting up, he gartered his socks, tied laces, got on a necktie and even squirmed into a suit coat so that when he parted the curtains to step out he was fully dressed.

Dropping to all fours, he peered under the berth for his bassoon case. Though it was there he thought he had better open it and did but quickly snapped it shut as Eddie, the porter, came walking by.

"Morning, maestro, what's the tune today?"

"It ain't a musical instrument." Roy explained it was something he had made himself.

"Animal, vegetable, or mineral?"

"Just a practical thing."

"A pogo stick?"

"No."

"Foolproof lance?"

"No."

"Lemme guess," Eddie said, covering his eyes with his long-fingered hand and pawing the air with the other. "I have it —combination fishing rod, gun, and shovel."

Roy laughed. "How far to Chicago, Eddie?"

"Chi? Oh, a long, long ways. I wouldn't walk."

"I don't intend to."

"Why Chi?" Eddie asked. "Why not New Orleans? That's a lush and Frenchy city."

"Never been there."

"Or that hot and hilly town, San Francisco?"

Roy shook his head.

"Why not New York, colossus of colossuses?"

"Some day I'll visit there."

"Where have you visited?"

Roy was embarrassed. "Boise."

"That dusty sandstone quarry."

"Portland too when I was small."

"In Maine?"

"No, Oregon—where they hold the Festival of Roses."

"Oregon—where the refugees from Minnesota and the Dakotas go?"

"I wouldn't know," Roy said. "I'm going to Chicago, where the Cubs are."

"Lions and tigers in the zoo?"

"No, the ballplayers."

"Oh, the ball—" Eddie clapped a hand to his mouth. "Are you one of them?"

"I hope to be."

The porter bowed low. "My hero. Let me kiss your hand."

Roy couldn't help but smile yet the porter annoyed and worried him a little. He had forgotten to ask Sam when to tip him, morning or night, and how much? Roy had made it a point, since their funds were so low, not to ask for anything at all but last night Eddie had insisted on fixing a pillow behind his back, and once when he was trying to locate the men's room Eddie practically took him by the hand and led him to it. Did you hand him a dime after that or grunt a foolish thanks as he had done? He'd personally be glad when the trip was over, though he certainly hated to be left alone in a place like Chicago. Without Sam he'd feel shaky-kneed and unable to say or do simple things like ask for directions or know where to go once you had dropped a nickel into the subway.

After a troublesome shave in which he twice drew blood he used one thin towel to dry his hands, face, and neck, clean his razor and wipe up the wet of his toothbrush so as not to have to ask for another and this way keep the bill down. From the flaring sky out the window it looked around half-past five, but he couldn't be sure because somewhere near they left Mountain Time and lost—no, picked up—yes, it was lost an hour, what Sam called the twenty-three hour day. He packed his razor, toothbrush, and pocket comb into a chamois drawstring bag, rolled it up small and kept it handy in his coat pocket. Passing through the long sleeper, be entered the diner and would gladly have sat down to breakfast, for his stomach had contracted into a bean at the smell of food, but the shirtsleeved waiters in stocking caps were joshing around as they gobbled fried kippers and potatoes. Roy hurried through the large-windowed club car, empty for once, through several sleepers, coaches, a lounge and another long line of coaches, till he came to the last one, where amid the gloom of drawn shades and sleeping people tossed every which way, Sam Simpson also slept although Roy had last night begged him to take the berth but the soft-voiced Sam had insisted, "You take the bed, kiddo, you're the one that has to show what you have got on the ball when we pull into the city. It don't matter where I sleep."

Sam lay very still on his back, looking as if the breath of life had departed from him except that it was audible in the ripe snore that could be chased without waking him, Roy had discovered, if you hissed scat. His lean head was held up by a folded pillow and his scrawny legs, shoeless, hung limp over the arm of the double seat he had managed to acquire, for he had started out with a seat partner. He was an expert conniver where his comfort was concerned, and since that revolved mostly around the filled flat bottle his ability to raise them up was this side of amazing. He often said he would not die of thirst though he never failed to add, in Roy's presence, that he wished for nobody the drunkard's death. He seemed now to be dreaming, and his sharp nose was pointed in the direction of a scent that led perhaps to the perfumed presence of Dame Fortune, long past due in his bed. With dry lips puckered, he smiled in expectation of a spectacular kiss though he looked less like a lover than an old scarecrow with his comical, seamed face sprouting prickly stubble in the dark glow of the expiring bulb overhead. A trainman passed who, seeing Sam sniff in his sleep, pretended it was at his own reek and humorously held his nose. Roy frowned, but Sam, who had a moment before been getting in good licks against fate, saw in his sleep, and his expression changed. A tear broke from his eye and slowly slid down his cheek. Roy concluded not to wake Sam and left.

He returned to the vacant club car and sat there with a magazine on his knee, worrying whether the trip wasn't a mistake, when a puzzled Eddie came into the car and handed him a pair of red dice.

"Mate them," he said. "I can't believe my eyes."

Roy paired the dice. "They mate."

"Now roll them."

He rolled past his shoe. "Snake eyes."

"Try again," said Eddie, interested.

Roy rattled the red cubes. "Snake eyes once more."

"Amazing. Again, please."

Again he rolled on the rug. Roy whistled. "Holy cow, three in a row."

"Fantastic."

"Did they do the same for you?"

"No, for me they did sevens."

"Are they loaded?"

"Bewitched," Eddie muttered. "I found them in the washroom and I'm gonna get rid of them pronto."

"Why?—if you could win all the time?"

"I don't crave any outside assistance in games of chance."

The train had begun to slow down.

"Oh oh, duty." Eddie hurried out.

Watching through the double-paned glass, Roy saw the porter swing himself off the train and jog along with it a few paces as it pulled to a stop. The morning was high and bright but the desolate station—wherever they were— gave up a single passenger, a girl in a dressy black dress, who despite the morning chill waited with a coat over her arm, and two suitcases and a zippered golf bag at her feet. Hatless, too, her hair a froth of dark curls, she held by a loose cord a shiny black hat box which she wouldn't let Eddie touch when he gathered up her things. Her face was striking, a little drawn and pale, and when she stepped up into the train her nyloned legs made Roy's pulses dance. When he could no longer see her, he watched Eddie set down her bags, take the red dice out of his pocket, spit on them and fling them over the depot roof. He hurriedly grabbed the bags and hopped on the moving train.

The girl entered the club car and directed Eddie to carry her suitcases to her compartment and she would stay and have a cigarette. He mentioned the hat box again but she giggled nervously and said no.

"Never lost a female hat yet," Eddie muttered.

"Thank you but I'll carry it myself."

He shrugged and left.

She had dropped a flower. Roy thought it was a gardenia but it turned out to be a white rose she had worn pinned to her dress.

When he handed it to her, her eyes widened with fascination, as if she had recognized him from somewhere, but when she found she hadn't, to his horror her expression changed instantly to one of boredom. Sitting across the aisle from him she fished out of her purse a pack of cigarettes and a lighter.

She lit up, and crossing her heart-breaking legs, began to flip through a copy of *Life*.

He figured she was his own age, maybe a year or so older. She looked to him like one of those high-class college girls, only with more zip than most of them, and dressed for 6 A.M. as the girls back home never would. He was marvelously interested in her, so much had her first glance into his eyes meant to him, and already felt a great longing in his life. Anxious to get acquainted, he was flabbergasted how to begin. If she hadn't yet eaten breakfast and he could work up the nerve, he could talk to her in the diner—only he didn't dare.

People were sitting around now and the steward came out and said first call for breakfast.

She snubbed out her cigarette with a wriggling motion of the wrist—her bracelets tinkled—picked up the hat box and went into the diner. Her crumpled white rose lay in the ashtray. He took it out and quickly stuck it in his pants pocket. Though his hunger bit sharp he waited till everyone was maybe served, and then he entered.

Although he had tried to avoid it, for fear she would see how unsure he was of these things, he was put at the same table with her and her black hat box, which now occupied a seat of its own. She glanced up furtively when he sat down but went wordlessly back to her coffee. When the waiter handed Roy the pad, he absently printed his name and date of birth but the waiter imperceptibly nudged him (hey, hayseed) and indicated it was for ordering. He pointed on the menu with his yellow pencil (this is the buck breakfast) but the blushing ballplayer, squinting through the blur, could only think he was sitting on the lone four-bit piece he had in his back pocket. He tried to squelch the impulse but something forced him to look up at her as he attempted to pour water into his ice-filled (this'll kill the fever) glass, spilling some on the tablecloth (whose diapers you wetting, boy?), then all thumbs and butterfingers, the pitcher thumped the pitcher down, fished the fifty cents out of his pants, and after scratching out the vital statistics on the pad, plunked the coin down on the table.

"That's for you," he told the (what did I do to deserve this?) waiter, and though the silver-eyed mermaid was about to speak, he did not stay to listen but beat it fast out of the accursed car.

Tramping highways and byways, wandering everywhere bird dogging the sandlots for months without spotting so much as a fifth-rater he could telegraph about to the head scout of the Cubs, and maybe pick up a hundred bucks in the mail as a token of their appreciation, with also a word of thanks for his good bird dogging and maybe they would sometime again employ him as a scout on the regular payroll—well, after a disheartening long time in which he was not able to roust up a single specimen worthy to be called by the name of ballplayer, Sam had one day lost his way along a dusty country road and when he finally found out where he was, too weary to turn back, he crossed over to an old, dry barn and sat against the haypile in front, to drown his sorrows with a swig. On the verge of dozing he heard these shouts and opened his eyes, shielding them from the hot sun, and as he lived, a game of ball was being played in a pasture by twelve blond-bearded players, six on each side, and even from where Sam sat he could tell they were terrific the way they smacked the pill— one blow banging it so far out the fielder had to run a mile before he could jump high and snag it smack in his bare hand. Sam's mouth popped open, he got up whoozy and watched, finding it hard to believe his eyes, as the teams changed sides and the first hitter that batted the ball did so for a far-reaching distance before it was caught, and the same with the second, a wicked clout, but then the third came up, the one who had made the bare-handed catch, and he really laid on and powdered the pellet a thundering crack so that even the one who ran for it, his beard parted in the wind, before long looked like a pygmy chasing it and quit running, seeing the thing was a speck on the horizon.

Sweating and shivering by turns, Sam muttered if I could ketch the whole twelve of them—and staggered out on the field to cry out the good news but when they saw him they gathered bats and balls and ran in a dozen directions, and though Sam was smart enough to hang on to the fellow who had banged the sphere out to the horizon, frantically shouting to him, "Whoa—whoa," his lungs bursting with the effort to call a giant—he wouldn't stop so Sam never caught him.

He woke with a sob in his throat but swallowed before he could sound it, for by then Roy had come to mind and he mumbled, "Got someone just as good," so that for once waking was better than dreaming.

He yawned. His mouth felt unholy dry and his underclothes were crawling. Reaching down his battered valise from the rack, he pulled out a used bath towel and cake of white soap, and to the surprise of those who saw him go out that way, went through the baggage cars to the car between them and the tender. Once inside there, he peeled to the skin and stepped into the shower stall, where he enjoyed himself for ten minutes, soaping and resoaping his bony body under warm water. But then a trainman happened to come through and after sniffing around Sam's clothes yelled in to him, "Hey, bud, come outa there."

Sam stopped off the shower and poked out his head.

"What's that?"

"I said come outa there, that's only for the train crew."

"Excuse me," Sam said, and he began quickly to rub himself dry.

"You don't have to hurry. Just wanted you to know you made a mistake."

"Thought it went with the ticket."

"Not in the coaches it don't."

Sam sat on a metal stool and laced up his high brown shoes. Pointing to the cracked mirror on the wall, he said, "Mind if I use your glass?"

"Go ahead."

He parted his sandy hair, combed behind the ears, and managed to work in a shave and brushing of his yellow teeth before he apologized again to the trainman and left.

Going up a few cars to the lounge, he ordered a cup of hot coffee and a sandwich, ate quickly, and made for the club car. It was semi-officially out of bounds for coach travelers but Sam had told the passenger agent last night that he had a nephew riding on a sleeper, and the passenger agent had mentioned to the conductor not to bother him.

When he entered the club car, after making sure Roy was elsewhere Sam headed for the bar, already in a fluid state for the train was moving through wet territory, but then he changed his mind and sat down to size up the congregation over a newspaper and spot who looked particularly amiable. The headlines caught his eye at the same time as they did this short, somewhat popeyed gent's sitting next to him, who had just been greedily questioning the husky, massive-shouldered man on his right, who was wearing sun glasses. Popeyes nudged the big one and they all three stared at Sam's paper.

WEST COAST OLYMPIC ATHLETE SHOT

FOLLOWS 24 HOURS AFTER SLAYING OF
ALL-AMERICAN FOOTBALL ACE

The article went on to relate that both of these men had been shot under mysterious circumstances with silver bullets from a .22 caliber pistol by an unknown woman that police were on the hunt for.

"That makes the second sucker," the short man said.

"But why with silver bullets, Max?"

"Beats me. Maybe she set out after a ghost but couldn't find him."

The other fingered his tie knot. "Why do you suppose she goes around pickin' on athletes for?"

"Not only athletes but also the cream of the crop. She's knocked off a crack football boy, and now an Olympic runner. Better watch out, Whammer, she may be heading for a baseball player for the third victim." Max chuckled.

Sam looked up and almost hopped out of his seat as he recognized them both.

Hiding his hesitation, he touched the short one on the arm. "Excuse me, mister, but ain't you Max Mercy, the sportswriter? I know your face from your photo in the articles you write."

But the sportswriter, who wore a comical mustache and dressed in stripes that crisscrossed three ways—suit, shirt, and tie—a nervous man with voracious eyes, also had a sharp sense of smell and despite Sam's shower and toothbrushing nosed out an alcoholic fragrance that slowed his usual speedy response in acknowledging the spread of his fame.

"That's right," he finally said.

"Well, I'm happy to have the chance to say a few words to you. You're maybe a little after my time, but I am Sam Simpson—Bub Simpson, that is—who played for the St. Louis Browns in the seasons of 1919 to 1921."

Sam spoke with a grin though his insides were afry at the mention of his professional baseball career.

"Believe I've heard the name," Mercy said nervously. After a minute he nodded toward the man Sam knew all along as the leading hitter of the American League, three times winner

of the Most Valuable Player award, and announced, "This is
Walter (the Whammer) Wambold." It had been in the
papers that he was a holdout for $75,000 and was coming
East to squeeze it out of his boss.

"Howdy," Sam said. "You sure look different in street
clothes."

The Whammer, whose yellow hair was slicked flat, with
tie and socks to match, grunted.

Sam's ears reddened. He laughed embarrassedly and then
remarked sideways to Mercy that he was traveling with a
slambang young pitcher who'd soon be laying them low in
the big leagues. "Spoke to you because I thought you might
want to know about him."

"What's his name?"

"Roy Hobbs."

"Where'd he play?"

"Well, he's not exactly been in organized baseball."

"Where'd he learn to pitch?"

"His daddy taught him years ago—he was once a semipro—
and I have been polishin' him up."

"Where's he been pitching?"

"Well, like I said, he's young, but he certainly mowed
them down in the Northwest High School League last year.
Thought you might of heard of his eight no-hitters."

"Class D is as far down as I go," Mercy laughed. He lit one
of the cigars Sam had been looking at in his breast pocket.

"I'm personally taking him to Clarence Mulligan of the
Cubs for a tryout. They will probably pay me a few grand for
uncovering the coming pitcher of the century but the condition is—and Roy is backing me on this because he is more
devoted to me than a son—that I am to go back as regular
scout, like I was in 1925."

Roy popped his head into the car and searched around for

the girl with the black hat box (Miss Harriet Bird, Eddie had gratuitously told him, making a black fluttering of wings), and seeing her seated near the card tables restlessly thumbing through a magazine, popped out.

"That's him," said Sam. "Wait'll I bring him back." He got up and chased after Roy.

"Who's the gabber?" said the Whammer.

"Guy named Simpson who once caught for the Brownies. Funny thing, last night I was doing a Sunday piece on drunks in baseball and I had occasion to look up his record. He was in the game three years, batted .340, .260, and .198, but his catching was terrific—not one error listed."

"Get rid of him, he jaws too much."

"Sh, here he comes."

Sam returned with Roy in tow, gazing uncomfortably ahead.

"Max," said Sam, "this is Roy Hobbs that I mentioned to you. Say hello to Max Mercy, the syndicated sportswriter, kiddo."

"Hello," Roy nodded.

"This is the Whammer," Max said.

Roy extended his hand but the Whammer looked through him with no expression whatsoever. Seeing he had his eye hooked on Harriet, Roy conceived a strong dislike for the guy.

The Whammer got up. "Come on, Max, I wanna play cards."

Max rose. "Well, hang onto the water wagon, Bub," he said to Sam.

Sam turned red.

Roy shot the sportswriter a dirty look.

"Keep up with the no-hitters, kid," Max laughed.

Roy didn't answer. He took the Whammer's chair and Sam sat where he was, brooding.

"What'll it be?" they heard Mercy ask as he shuffled the cards. They had joined two men at one of the card tables.

The Whammer, who looked to Sam like an overgrown side of beef wrapped in gabardine, said, "Hearts." He stared at Harriet until she looked up from her magazine, and after a moment of doubt, smiled.

The Whammer fingered his necktie knot. As he scooped up the cards his diamond ring glinted in the sunlight.

"Goddamned millionaire," Sam thought.

"The hell with her," thought Roy.

"I dealt rummy," Max said, and though no one had called him, Sam promptly looked around.

Toward late afternoon the Whammer, droning on about his deeds on the playing field, got very chummy with Harriet Bird and before long had slipped his fat fingers around the back of her chair so Roy left the club car and sat in the sleeper, looking out of the window, across the aisle from where Eddie slept sitting up. Gosh, the size of the forest. He thought they had left it for good yesterday and here it still was. As he watched, the trees flowed together and so did the hills and clouds. He felt a kind of sadness, because he had lost the feeling of a particular place. Yesterday he had come from somewhere, a place he knew was there, but today it had thinned away in space—how vast he could not have guessed—and he felt like he would never see it again.

The forest stayed with them, climbing hills like an army, shooting down like waterfalls. As the train skirted close in, the trees leveled out and he could see within the woodland the only place he had been truly intimate with in his wanderings, a green world shot through with weird light and strange bird cries, muffled in silence that made the privacy so complete his inmost self had no shame of anything he thought there, and it eased the body-shaking beat of his ambitions. Then he thought of here and now and for the thousandth time wondered why they had come so far and for what. Did

Sam really know what he was doing? Sometimes Roy had his doubts. Sometimes he wanted to turn around and go back home, where he could at least predict what tomorrow would be like. Remembering the white rose in his pants pocket, he decided to get rid of it. But then the pine trees flowed away from the train and slowly swerved behind blue hills; all at once there was this beaten gold, snow-capped mountain in the distance, and on the plain several miles from its base lay a small city gleaming in the rays of the declining sun. Approaching it, the long train slowly pulled to a stop.

Eddie woke with a jump and stared out the window.

"Oh oh, trouble, we never stop here."

He looked again and called Roy.

"What do you make out of that?"

About a hundred yards ahead, where two dirt roads crossed, a moth-eaten model-T Ford was parked on the farther side of the road from town, and a fat old man wearing a broad-brimmed black hat and cowboy boots, who they could see was carrying a squat doctor's satchel, climbed down from it. To the conductor, who had impatiently swung off the train with a lit red lamp, he flourished a yellow telegram. They argued a minute, then the conductor, snapping open his watch, beckoned him along and they boarded the train. When they passed through Eddie's car the conductor's face was sizzling with irritation but the doctor was unruffled. Before disappearing through the door, the conductor called to Eddie, "Half hour."

"Half hour," Eddie yodeled and he got out the stool and set it outside the car so that anyone who wanted to stretch, could.

Only about a dozen passengers got off the train, including Harriet Bird, still hanging on to her precious hat box, the Whammer, and Max Mercy, all as thick as thieves. Roy hunted up the bassoon case just if the train should decide to take off without him, and when he had located Sam they both got off.

"Well, I'll be jiggered." Sam pointed down about a block beyond where the locomotive had halted. There, sprawled out at the outskirts of the city, a carnival was on. It was made up of try-your-skill booths, kiddie rides, a freak show and a gigantic Ferris wheel that looked like a stopped clock. Though there was still plenty of daylight, the carnival was lit up by twisted ropes of blinking bulbs, and many banners streamed in the breeze as the calliope played.

"Come on," said Roy, and they went along with the people from the train who were going toward the tents.

Once they had got there and fooled around a while. Sam stopped to have a crushed coconut drink which he privately spiked with a shot from a new bottle, while Roy wandered over to a place where you could throw three baseballs for a dime at three wooden pins, shaped like pint-size milk bottles and set in pyramids of one on top of two, on small raised platforms about twenty feet back from the counter. He changed the fifty-cent piece Sam had slipped him on leaving the train, and this pretty girl in yellow, a little hefty but with a sweet face and nice ways, who with her peanut of a father was waiting on trade, handed him three balls. Lobbing one of them, Roy easily knocked off the pyramid and won himself a naked kewpie doll. Enjoying the game, he laid down another dime, again clattering the pins to the floor in a single shot and now collecting an alarm clock. With the other three dimes he won a brand-new boxed baseball, a washboard, and baby potty, which he traded in for a six-inch harmonica. A few kids came over to watch and Sam, wandering by, indulgently changed another half into dimes for Roy. And Roy won a fine leather cigar case for Sam, a "God Bless America" banner, a flashlight, can of coffee, and a two-pound box of sweets. To

the kids' delight, Sam, after a slight hesitation, flipped Roy
another half dollar, but this time the little man behind the
counter nudged his daughter and she asked Roy if he would
now take a kiss for every three pins he tumbled.

Roy glanced at her breasts and she blushed. He got embarrassed too. "What do you say, Sam, it's your four bits?"

Sam bowed low to the girl. "Ma'am," he said, "now you
see how dang foolish it is to be a young feller."

The girl laughed and Roy began to throw for kisses, flush-
ing each pyramid in a shot or two while the girl counted aloud
the kisses she owed him.

Some of the people from the train passed by and stayed to
watch when they learned from the mocking kids what Roy
was throwing for.

The girl, pretending to be unconcerned, tolled off the third
and fourth kisses.

As Roy fingered the ball for the last throw the Whammer
came by holding over his shoulder a Louisville Slugger that
he had won for himself in the batting cage down a way. Harriet, her pretty face flushed, had a kewpie doll, and Max Mercy
carried a box of cigars. The Whammer had discarded his sun
glasses and all but strutted over his performance and the
prizes he had won.

Roy raised his arm to throw for the fifth kiss and a clean
sweep when the Whammer called out to him in a loud voice,
"Pitch it here, busher, and I will knock it into the moon."

Roy shot for the last kiss and missed. He missed with the
second and third balls. The crowd oohed its disappointment.

"Only four," said the girl in yellow as if she mourned the
fifth.

Angered at what had happened, Sam hoarsely piped, "I got
ten dollars that says he can strike you out with three pitched
balls, Wambold."

The Whammer looked at Sam with contempt.

"What d'ye say, Max?" he said.

Mercy shrugged.

"Oh, I love contests of skill," Harriet said excitedly. Roy's face went pale.

"What's the matter, hayfoot, you scared?" the Whammer taunted.

"Not of you," Roy said.

"Let's go across the tracks where nobody'll get hurt," Mercy suggested.

"Nobody but the busher and his bazooka. What's in it, busher?"

"None of your business." Roy picked up the bassoon case.

The crowd moved in a body across the tracks, the kids circling around to get a good view, and the engineer and fireman watching from their cab window.

Sam cornered one of the kids who lived nearby and sent him home for a fielder's glove and his friend's catcher's mitt. While they were waiting, for protection he buttoned underneath his coat the washboard Roy had won. Max drew a batter's box alongside a piece of slate. He said he would call the throws and they would count as one of the three pitches only if they were over or if the Whammer swung and missed.

When the boy returned with the gloves, the sun was going down, and though the sky was aflame with light all the way to the snowy mountain peak, it was chilly on the ground.

Breaking the seal, Sam squeezed the baseball box and the pill shot up like a greased egg. He tossed it to Mercy, who inspected the hide and stitches, then rubbed the shine off and flipped it to Roy.

"Better throw a couple of warm-ups."

"My arm is loose," said Roy.

"It's your funeral."

Placing his bassoon case out of the way in the grass, Roy shed his coat. One of the boys came forth to hold it.

"Be careful you don't spill the pockets," Roy told him.

Sam came forward with the catcher's glove on. It was too small for his big hand but he said it would do all right.

"Sam, I wish you hadn't bet that money on me," Roy said.

"I won't take it if we win, kiddo, but just let it stand if we lose," Sam said, embarrassed.

"We came by it too hard."

"Just let it stand so."

He cautioned Roy to keep his pitches inside, for the Whammer was known to gobble them on the outside corner.

Sam returned to the plate and crouched behind the batter, his knees spread wide because of the washboard. Roy drew on his glove and palmed the ball behind it. Mercy, rubbing his hands to warm them, edged back about six feet behind Sam.

The onlookers retreated to the other side of the tracks, except Harriet, who stood without fear of fouls up close. Her eyes shone at the sight of the two men facing one another.

Mercy called, "Batter up."

The Whammer crowded the left side of the plate, gripping the heavy bat low on the neck, his hands jammed together and legs plunked evenly apart. He hadn't bothered to take off his coat. His eye on Roy said it spied a left-handed monkey.

"Throw it, Rube, it won't get no lighter."

Though he stood about sixty feet away, he loomed up gigantic to Roy, with the wood held like a caveman's ax on his shoulder. His rocklike frame was motionless, his face impassive, unsmiling, dark.

Roy's heart skipped a beat. He turned to gaze at the mountain.

Sam whacked the leather with his fist. "Come on, kiddo, wham it down his whammy."

The Whammer out of the corner of his mouth told the drunk to keep his mouth shut.

"Burn it across his button."

"Close your trap," Mercy said.

"Cut his throat with it."

"If he tries to dust me, so help me I will smash his skull," the Whammer threatened.

Roy stretched loosely, rocked back on his left leg, twirling the right a little like a dancer, then strode forward and threw with such force his knuckles all but scraped the ground on the follow-through.

At thirty-three the Whammer still enjoyed exceptional eyesight. He saw the ball spin off Roy's fingertips and it reminded him of a white pigeon he had kept as a boy, that he would send into flight by flipping it into the air. The ball flew at him and he was conscious of its bird-form and white flapping wings, until it suddenly disappeared from view. He heard a noise like the bang of a firecracker at his feet and Sam had the ball in his mitt. Unable to believe his ears he heard Mercy intone a reluctant strike.

Sam flung off the glove and was wringing his hand.

"Hurt you, Sam?" Roy called.

"No, it's this dang glove."

Though he did not show it, the pitch had bothered the Whammer no end. Not just the speed of it but the sensation of surprise and strangeness that went with it—him batting here on the railroad tracks, the crazy carnival, the drunk catching and a clown pitching, and that queer dame Harriet, who had five minutes ago been patting him on the back for his skill in the batting cage, now eyeing him coldly for letting one pitch go by.

He noticed Max had moved farther back.

"How the hell you expect to call them out there?"

"He looks wild to me," Max moved in.

"Your knees are knockin'," Sam tittered.

"Mind your business, rednose," Max said.

"You better watch your talk, mister," Roy called to Mercy.

"Pitch it, greenhorn," warned the Whammer.

Sam crouched with his glove on. "Do it again, Roy. Give him something similar."

"Do it again," mimicked the Whammer. To the crowd, maybe to Harriet, he held up a vaunting finger showing there were other pitches to come.

Roy pumped, reared and flung.

The ball appeared to the batter to be a slow spinning planet looming toward the earth. For a long light-year he waited for this globe to whirl into the orbit of his swing so he could bust it to smithereens that would settle with dust and dead leaves into some distant cosmos. At last the unseeing eye, maybe a fortuneteller's lit crystal ball—anyway, a curious combination of circles—drifted within range of his weapon, or so he thought, because he lunged at it ferociously, twisting round like a top. He landed on both knees as the world floated by over his head and hit with a whup into the cave of Sam's glove.

"Hey, Max," Sam said, as he chased the ball after it had bounced out of the glove, "how do they pernounce Whammer if you leave out the W?"

"Strike," Mercy called long after a cheer (was it a jeer?) had burst from the crowd.

"What's he throwing," the Whammer howled, "spitters?"

"In the pig's poop." Sam thrust the ball at him. "It's drier than your granddaddy's scalp."

"I'm warning him not to try any dirty business."

Yet the Whammer felt oddly relieved. He liked to have his back crowding the wall, when there was a single pitch to worry about and a single pitch to hit. Then the sweat began to leak out of his pores as he stared at the hard, lanky figure of the pitiless pitcher, moving, despite his years, and a few waste motions, like a veteran undertaker of the diamond, and he experienced a moment of depression.

Sam must have sensed it, because he discovered an unexpected pity in his heart and even for a split second hoped the idol would not be tumbled. But only for a second, for the Whammer had regained confidence in his known talent and experience and was taunting the greenhorn to throw.

Someone in the crowd hooted and the Whammer raised aloft two fat fingers and pointed where he would murder the ball, where the gleaming rails converged on the horizon and beyond was invisible.

Roy raised his leg. He smelled the Whammer's blood and wanted it, and through him the worm's he had with him, for the way he had insulted Sam.

The third ball slithered at the batter like a meteor, the flame swallowing itself. He lifted his club to crush it into a universe of sparks but the heavy wood dragged, and though he willed to destroy the sound he heard a gong bong and realized with sadness that the ball he had expected to hit had long since been part of the past; and though Max could not cough the fatal word out of his throat, the Whammer understood he was, in the truest sense of it, out.

The crowd was silent as the violet evening fell on their shoulders.

For a night game, the Whammer harshly shouted, it was customary to turn on lights. Dropping the bat, he trotted off to the train, an old man.

The ball had caught Sam smack in the washboard and lifted him off his feet. He lay on the ground, extended on his back. Roy pushed everybody aside to get him air. Unbuttoning Sam's coat, he removed the dented washboard.

"Never meant to hurt you, Sam."

"Just knocked the wind outa me," Sam gasped, "Feel better now." He was pulled to his feet and stood steady.

The train whistle wailed, the echo banging far out against the black mountain.

Then the doctor in the broadbrimmed black hat appeared, flustered and morose, the conductor trying to pacify him, and Eddie hopping along behind.

The doctor waved the crumpled yellow paper around. "Got a telegram says somebody on this train took sick. Anybody out here?"

Roy tugged at Sam's sleeve.

"Ixnay."

"What's that?"

"Not me," said Roy.

The doctor stomped off. He climbed into his Ford, whipped it up and drove away.

The conductor popped open his watch. "Be a good hour late into the city."

"All aboard," he called.

"Aboard," Eddie echoed, carrying the bassoon case.

The buxom girl in yellow broke through the crowd and threw her ams around Roy's neck. He ducked but she hit him quick with her pucker four times upon the right eye, yet he could see with the other that Harriet Bird (certainly a snappy goddess) had her gaze fastened on him.

They sat, after dinner, in Eddie's dimmed and empty Pullman, Roy floating through drifts of clouds on his triumph as Harriet went on about the recent tourney, she put it, and the unreal forest outside swung forward like a gate shutting. The odd way she saw things interested him, yet he was aware of the tormented trees fronting the snaky lake they were passing, trees bent and clawing, plucked white by icy blasts from the black water, their bony branches twisting in many a broken direction.

Harriet's face was flushed, her eyes gleaming with new insights. Occasionally she stopped and giggled at herself for the breathless volume of words that flowed forth, to his growing astonishment, but after a pause was on her galloping way again—a girl on horseback—reviewing the inspiring sight (she said it was) of David jawboning the Goliath-Whammer, or was it Sir Percy lancing Sir Maldemer, or the first son (with a rock in his paw) ranged against the primitive papa?

Roy gulped. "My father? Well, maybe I did want to skull him sometimes. After my grandma died, the old man dumped me in one orphan home after the other, wherever he happened to be working—when he did—though he did used to take me out of there summers and teach me how to toss a ball."

No, that wasn't what she meant, Harriet said. Had he ever read Homer?

Try as he would he could only think of four bases and not a book. His head spun at her allusions. He found her lingo strange with all the college stuff and hoped she would stop it because he wanted to talk about baseball.

Then she took a breather. "My friends say I have a fantastic imagination."

He quickly remarked he wouldn't say that. "But the only thing I had on my mind when I was throwing out there was that Sam had bet this ten spot we couldn't afford to lose out on, so I had to make him whiff."

"To whiff—oh, Roy, how droll," and she laughed again.

He grinned, carried away by the memory of how he had done it, the hero, who with three pitched balls had nailed the best the American League had to offer. What didn't that say about the future? He felt himself falling into sentiment in

his thoughts and tried to steady himself but couldn't before
he had come forth with a pronouncement: "You have to have
the right stuff to play good ball and I have it. I bet some day
I'll break every record in the book for throwing and hitting."

Harriet appeared startled then gasped, hiding it like a cough
behind her tense fist, and vigorously applauded, her bracelets
bouncing on her wrists. "Bravo, Roy, how wonderful."

"What I mean," he insisted, "is I feel that I have got it
in me—that I am due for something very big. I have to do it.
I mean," he said modestly, "that's of course when I get in
the game."

Her mouth opened. "You mean you're not—" She seemed,
to his surprise, disappointed, almost on the verge of crying.

"No," he said, ashamed. "Sam's taking me for a tryout."

Her eyes grew vacant as she stared out the window. Then
she asked, "But Walter—he is a successful professional player,
isn't he?"

"The Whammer?" Roy nodded.

"And he has won that award three times—what was it?"

"The Most Valuable Player." He had a panicky feeling he
was losing her to the Whammer.

She bit her lip. "Yet you defeated him," she murmured.

He admitted it. "He won't last much longer I don't think
—the most a year or two. By then he'll be too old for the
game. Myself, I've got my whole life ahead of me."

Harriet brightened, saying sympathetically, "What will you
hope to accomplish, Roy?"

He had already told her but after a minute remarked,
"Sometimes when I walk down the street I bet people will
say there goes Roy Hobbs, the best there ever was in the
game."

She gazed at him with touched and troubled eyes. "Is that
all?"

He tried to penetrate her question. Twice he had answered

it and still she was unsatisfied. He couldn't be sure what she expected him to say. "Is that all?" he repeated. "What more is there?"

"Don't you know?" she said kindly.

Then he had an idea. "You mean the bucks? I'll get them too."

She slowly shook her head. "Isn't there something over and above earthly things—some more glorious meaning to one's life and activities?"

"In baseball?"

"Yes."

He racked his brain—

"Maybe I've not made myself clear, but surely you can see (I was saying this to Walter just before the train stopped) that yourself alone—alone in the sense that we are all terribly alone no matter what people say—I mean by that perhaps if you understood that our values must derive from—oh, I really suppose—" She dropped her head futilely. "Please forgive me. I sometimes confuse myself with the little I know."

Her eyes were sad. He felt a curious tenderness for her a little as if she might be his mother (That bird.) and tried very hard to come up with the answer she wanted—something you said about LIFE.

"I think I know what you mean," he said. "You mean the fun and satisfaction you get out of playing the best way that you know how?"

She did not respond to that.

Roy worried out some other things he might have said but had no confidence to put them into words. He felt curiously deflated and a little lost, as if he had just flunked a test. The worst of it was he still didn't know what she'd been driving at.

Harriet yawned. Never before had he felt so tongue-tied in front of a girl, a looker too. Now if he had her in bed—

Almost as if she had guessed what he was thinking and her

mood had changed to something more practical than asking
nutty questions that didn't count, she sighed and edged closer
to him, concealing the move behind a query about his bassoon
case. "Do you play?"

"Not any music," he answered, glad they were talking about
something different. "There's a thing in it that I made for
myself."

"What, for instance?"

He hesitated. "A baseball bat."

She was herself again, laughed merrily. "Roy, you are price-
less."

"I got the case because I don't want to get the stick all
banged up before I got the chance to use it."

"Oh, Roy." Her laughter grew. He smiled broadly.

She was now so close he felt bold. Reaching down he lifted
the hat box by the string and lightly hefted it.

"What's in it?"

She seemed breathless. "In it?" Then she mimicked,
"—Something I made for myself."

"Feels like a hat."

"Maybe a head?" Harriet shook a finger at him.

"Feels more like a hat." A little embarrassed, he set the box
down. "Will you come and see me play sometime?" he asked.

She nodded and then he was aware of her leg against his
and that she was all but on his lap. His heart slapped against
his ribs and he took it all to mean that she had dropped the
last of her interest in the Whammer and was putting it on
the guy who had buried him.

As they went through a tunnel, Roy placed his arm around
her shoulders, and when the train lurched on a curve, casually
he let his hand fall upon her full breast. The nipple rose between his fingers and before he could resist the impulse he
had tweaked it.

Her high-pitched scream lifted her up and twirling like a dancer down the aisle.

Stricken, he rose—had gone too far.

Crooking her arms like broken branches she whirled back to him, her head turned so far around her face hung between her shoulders.

"Look, I'm a twisted tree."

Sam had sneaked out on the squirming, apologetic Mercy, who, with his back to the Whammer—he with a newspaper raised in front of his sullen eyes—had kept up a leechlike prodding about Roy, asking where he had come from (oh, he's just a home town boy), how it was no major league scout had got at him (they did but he turned them down for me) even with the bonus cash that they are tossing around these days (yep), who's his father (like I said, just an old semipro who wanted awful bad to be in the big leagues) and what, for God's sake, does he carry around in that case (that's his bat, Wonderboy). The sportswriter was greedy to know more, hinting he could do great things for the kid, but Sam, rubbing his side where it pained, at last put him off and escaped into the coach to get some shuteye before they hit Chicago, sometime past 1 A.M.

After a long time trying to settle himself comfortably, he fell snoring asleep flat on his back and was at once sucked into a long dream that he had gone thirsty mad for a drink and was threatening the slickers in the car get him a bottle or else. Then this weasel of a Mercy, pretending he was writing on a pad, pointed him out with his pencil and the conductor snapped him up by the seat of his pants and ran his free-wheeling feet lickity-split through the sawdust, giving him the merry heave-ho off the train through the air on a floating trapeze, ploop into a bog where it rained buckets. He thought

he better get across the foaming river before it flooded the
bridge away so he set out, all bespattered, to cross it, only
this queer duck of a doctor in oilskins, an old man with a
washable white mustache and a yellow lamp he thrust straight
into your eyeballs, swore to him the bridge was gone. You're
plumb tootin' crazy, Sam shouted in the storm, I saw it
standin' with me own eyes, and he scuffled to get past the
geezer, who dropped the light setting the rails afire. They
wrestled in the rain until Sam slyly tripped and threw him,
and helter-skeltered for the bridge, to find to his crawling horror it was truly down and here he was scratching space till he
landed with a splishity-splash in the whirling waters, sobbing
(whoa whoa) and the white watchman on the embankment
flung him a flare but it was all too late because he heard the
roar of the falls below (and restless shifting of the sea) and
felt with his red hand where the knife had stabbed him . . .

Roy was dreaming of an enormous mountain—Christ, the
size of it—when he felt himself roughly shaken—Sam, he
thought, because they were there—only it was Eddie holding
a lit candle.

"The fuse blew and I've had no chance to fix it."

"What's the matter?"

"Trou-ble. Your friend has collapsed."

Roy hopped out of the berth, stepped into moccasins and
ran, with Eddie flying after him with the snuffed wax, into a
darkened car where a pool of people under a blue light hovered
over Sam, unconscious.

"What happened?" Roy cried.

"Sh," said the conductor, "he's got a raging fever."

"What from?"

"Can't say. We're picking up a doctor."

Sam was lying on a bench, wrapped in blankets with a

pillow tucked under his head, his gaunt face broken out in sweat. When Roy bent over him, his eyes opened.

"Hello, kiddo," he said in a cracked voice.

"What hurts you, Sam?"

"Where the washboard banged me—but it don't hurt so much now."

"Oh, Jesus."

"Don't take it so, Roy. I'll be better."

"Save his strength, son," the conductor said. "Don't talk now."

Roy got up. Sam shut his eyes.

The train whistled and ran slow at the next town then came to a draggy halt. The trainman brought a half-dressed doctor in. He examined Sam and straightened up. "We got to get him off and to the hospital."

Roy was wild with anxiety but Sam opened his eyes and told him to bend down.

Everyone moved away and Roy bent low.

"Take my wallet outa my rear pocket."

Roy pulled out the stuffed cowhide wallet. "Now you go to the Stevens Hotel—"

"No, oh no, Sam, not without you."

"Go on, kiddo, you got to. See Clarence Mulligan tomorrow and say I sent you—they are expecting you. Give them everything you have got on the ball—that'll make me happy."

"But, Sam—"

"You got to. Bend lower."

Roy bent lower and Sam stretched his withered neck and kissed him on the chin.

"Do like I say."

"Yes, Sam."

A tear splashed on Sam's nose.

Sam had something more in his eyes to say but though he tried, agitated, couldn't say it. Then the trainmen came in with a stretcher and they lifted the catcher and handed him down the steps, and overhead the stars were bright but he knew he was dead.

Roy trailed the anonymous crowd out of Northwest Station and clung to the shadowy part of the wall till he had the courage to call a cab.

"Do you go to the Stevens Hotel?" he asked, and the driver without a word shot off before he could rightly be seated, passed a red light and scuttled a cripple across the deserted street. They drove for miles in a shadow-infested, street-lamped jungle.

He had once seen some stereopticon pictures of Chicago and it was a boxed-up ant heap of stone and crumbling wood buildings in a many-miled spreading checkerboard of streets without much open space to speak of except the railroads, stockyards, and the shore of a windy lake. In the Loop, the offices went up high and the streets were jam-packed with people, and he wondered how so many of them could live together in any one place. Suppose there was a fire or something and they all ran out of their houses to see—how could they help but trample all over themselves? And Sam had warned him against strangers, because there were so many bums, sharpers, and gangsters around, people you were dirt to, who didn't know you and didn't want to, and for a dime they would slit your throat and leave you dying in the streets.

"Why did I come here?" he muttered and felt sick for home.

The cab swung into Michigan Avenue, which gave a view of the lake and a white-lit building spiring into the sky, then before he knew it he was standing flatfooted (Christ, the size of it) in front of the hotel, an enormous four-sectioned fortress. He hadn't the nerve to go through the whirling doors but had to because this bellhop grabbed his things—he wrested the bassoon case loose—and led him across the thick-carpeted lobby to a desk where he signed a card and had to count out five of the wallet's pulpy dollars for a room he would give up as soon as he found a house to board in.

But his cubbyhole on the seventeenth floor was neat and private, so after he had stored everything in the closet he lost his nervousness. Unlatching the window brought in the lake breeze. He stared down at the lit sprawl of Chicago, standing higher than he ever had in his life except for a night or two on a mountain. Gazing down upon the city, he felt as if bolts in his knees, wrists, and neck had loosened and he had spread up in height. Here, so high in the world, with the earth laid out in small squares so far below, he knew he would go in tomorrow and wow them with his fast one, and they would know him for the splendid pitcher he was.

The telephone rang. He was at first scared to answer it. In a strange place, so far from everybody he knew, it couldn't possibly be for him.

It rang again. He picked up the phone and listened.

"Hello, Roy? This is Harriet."

He wasn't sure he had got it right. "Excuse me?"

"Harriet Bird, silly."

"Oh, Harriet." He had completely forgotten her.

"Come down to my room," she giggled, "and let me say welcome to the city."

"You mean now?"

"Right away." She gave him the room number.

"Sure." He meant to ask her how she knew he was here but she had hung up.

Then he was elated. So that's how they did it in the city. He combed his hair and got out his bassoon case. In the

elevator a drunk tried to take it away from him but Roy was
too strong for him.

He walked—it seemed ages because he was impatient—
through a long corridor till he found her number and knocked.

"Come on in."

Opening the door, he was astonished at the enormous room.
Through the white-curtained window the sight of the endless
dark lake sent a shiver down his spine.

Then he saw her standing shyly in the far corner of the
room, naked under the gossamer thing she wore, held up on
her risen nipples and the puffed wedge of hair beneath her
white belly. A great weight went off his mind.

As he shut the door she reached into the hat box which
lay open next to a vase of white roses on the table and fitted
the black feathered hat on her head. A thick veil fell to her
breasts. In her hand she held a squat, shining pistol.

He was greatly confused and thought she was kidding but
a grating lump formed in his throat and his blood shed ice.
He cried out in a gruff voice. "What's wrong here?"

She said sweetly, "Roy, will you be the best there ever was
in the game?"

"That's right."

She pulled the trigger (thrum of bull fiddle). The bullet
cut a silver line across the water. He sought with his bare
hands to catch it, but it eluded him and, to his horror, bounced
into his gut. A twisted dagger of smoke drifted up from the
gun barrel. Fallen on one knee he groped for the bullet, sickened as it moved, and fell over as the forest flew upward, and
she, making muted noises of triumph and despair, danced on
her toes around the stricken hero.

3 ◈ *Heinrich Böll*

Heinrich Böll served in the German Army during World War II and was wounded, captured, and finally repatriated. His novels include The Train Was on Time, Billiards at Half-past Nine, *and* The Clown. *Daniel Stern has noted that Böll is "the first writer to speak from the heart of the German 'economic miracle' in a cold, ironic and unsentimental voice."*

ABSENT WITHOUT LEAVE

I

Before coming to the actual subject of this work (work to be understood here in the sense of clockwork), to the Bechtold family, of which I became a member on September 22, 1938, shortly before five in the afternoon, at the age of twenty-one, I would like to submit a few facts about myself which I trust will be misunderstood and arouse suspicion. The time is ripe to air at least some of the secrets to which I owe an upright demeanor, a sound mind in a sound body (although the latter is debatable), discipline and constancy, qualities which my friends deplore and my enemies resent, and which may represent a source of strength to unbiased, impartial citizens in an age which demands of each one of us perseverance at, in, or on behalf of: Here the reader may fill in, as if he were completing a printed form, whatever seems most essential at the moment: readiness to defend, to attack, to aid, to act with, on behalf of, in FC, JC, MSC, NATO, SEATO, the Warsaw Pact, East and West, East or West; the reader is even entitled to harbor the heretical notion that the compass also indicates such cardinal points as North and South; however, he is also at liberty to insert what are known as abstract terms: faith, lack of faith, hope, despair, and to those who feel they are totally deprived of any guiding hand and lacking both concrete and abstract terms, I recommend the most extensive encyclopedia available from which he can pick out anything he fancies from Aardvark to Zwingli. . . .

The reason I have not mentioned either the lenient church of believers or the intolerant church of unbelievers is not caution but sheer terror that I might be recalled to duty: the word duty ("I am on duty," "I have to go on duty," "official duty") has always alarmed me.

As long as I can remember, but particularly since that September 22, 1938, on which I underwent a kind of rebirth, my aim in life has been to become unfit for duty. I have never quite achieved this goal, although I have been close to it. I was prepared at any time not only to swallow pills, suffer injections, pretend I was crazy (most miserable failure of all), I even had people whom I did not regard as my enemies but who had reason to regard me as their enemy, shoot me in the right foot, push a sliver of wood through my left hand (not directly, but through the agency of a stoutly built German railway car that was blown up with me in it), I even had myself shot in the head and hip; dysentery, malaria, common diarrhea, nystagmus and neuralgia, migraine (Meunière) and mycosis—nothing worked. Each time the doctors made me fit for duty again. Only one doctor made any serious attempt to certify me as unfit for duty; the only good thing that led to was a ten-day tour of *official duty*, with official travel documents, official ration book, official hotel billeting in Paris—Rouen—Orléans—Amiens—Abbeville. A nice eye specialist (nystagmus) wangled the trip for me; armed with a detailed list I was to buy for him *les oeuvres complètes de Frédéric Chopin* who, he confessed, was to him what absinthe was to the early symbolists. He was not angry, just sad and disappointed, when the one series I was unable to complete was the waltzes, and the absence of Valse No. 9 in A-sharp, which I had not been able to find anywhere, was a bitter blow. I got nowhere by quickly concocting a sociology of sorts and explaining at great length that of course this piece was prized by the piano-playing ladies of every city, town and village for its exquisite melancholy; he was still disappointed, and when I suggested he send me to unoccupied France, when I explained—again at great length—that undoubtedly Marseilles, Toulouse, Toulon would not be influenced by the sultry inland air that made the Valse No. 9 in A-sharp such a sought-after drug—he gave a knowing smile and said: "I bet that's just what you'd like." I expect he meant that down there it would be easy for me to desert, and if he wanted to prevent that happening it was certainly not because he begrudged me the opportunity (we had played chess together for nights on end, we had discussed desertion for nights on end, he had played Chopin to me for nights on end), but probably because he did not want me to make a fool of myself. I solemnly swear that I would not have deserted down there in the South, for the simple reason that I had a loving wife waiting for me at home, later on wife and child, later still only a child. In any case, his efforts to cultivate my nystagmus abated, and a few days later he handed me over as "an interesting case"—I resented his using this term, it was the lowest form of betrayal—to the consulting ophthalmologist of the Western Division of the Army, whose shoulder braid I found

as depressing as his aura of professional importance. Prompted
by revenge, I suppose (he must have sensed my dislike), he in-
jected my eyes for two days in a row with some infernal stuff
that made it impossible for me to go to the movies. I could not
see more than ten or twelve feet, and I have always preferred
sitting far back at the movies. Anything further than ten or
twelve feet away appeared distorted and fuzzy, and I wandered
around Paris like a Hänsel without Gretel's comforting hand. I
was not rendered unfit for duty, I was merely sent back to my
unit as "exempt from shooting." My superior (delightful word,
it melts in my mouth) simply altered two letters in the spelling
and sentenced me to a job at which I had already had a good
deal of experience. Among veterans this occupation is commonly known as "shit duty." I hesitate to use this term and do
so only for the sake of historical accuracy and out of respect
for all technical jargon.

I had obtained my first experience in this honorable fecal
calling three years previously, during spade drill, when, at the
command "Down spades," I had suddenly—because up to then
I had been quite skillful—struck my superior officer in the back
of the knee with the edge of the spade. When I was asked
what my profession was, I answered truthfully and with naïve
insouciance that I was an "arts student," and on the basis of
the universally acknowledged German respect for every common and uncommon variety of intellectual activity, I was condemned to work in the ordure field, "to make a man of me."

So I still remembered how to put together a ladle out of an
old lard pail, a pole, some wire and nails, I was also familiar
with the physics and chemistry involved, and for several weeks,
between seven a.m. and half-past twelve, and between 2:30
and 5:30 in the afternoon, I walked through a straggling
French village not far from Mers-les Bains, a lard pail in each
hand, and fertilized the neat vegetable patch of the battalion
commander. This man, in civilian life the principal of a rural

elementary school, had planted an exact replica of his school garden at home: cabbages, onions, leeks, carrots, a sizable colony of corn stalks ("for my chicks"). What embarrassed me about this battalion commander was his habit when off duty of turning into "a regular guy," of coming over to "strike up a conversation" with me. In order to prevent this faux pas—superiors who turn into regular guys have always revolted me—in order to preserve my dignity and draw his attention to his own, it was necessary every time for me to sacrifice a whole bucketful of ordure, tipping it over at his feet, taking care not to give the impression of clumsiness and yet at the same time not making my real purpose too obvious, for my aim was to make him understand our difference in rank. I had nothing against him personally; he was an object of complete indifference to me. It is clear that, in the execution of even the humblest calling, style is vitally important. In any event, by spreading a belt of ordure around I managed to stay out of his reach. The fact that he was so overcome by nausea (a few minute particles splashed into his face) that he suffered a bilious attack, is not my fault: as a captain in the reserve he shouldn't have been *that* sensitive. His mistress (whom he undoubtedly would not have been able to afford at home, she was listed in the battalion payroll as a mess aid on special duty) consoled him by playing the piano as he lay in bed—the Valse No. 9 in A-sharp, as it happened, and I suspected her, and still suspect her, of being the one who snatched the music from under my very nose in Abbeville, thus ruining my nystagmus career. On mild autumn evenings she sometimes went for walks through the village, dressed all in mauve and carrying a riding whip; pale, more corrupted than corrupt, the personification of Madame Bovary collaborateuse.

At this point the patient reader may pause for breath. I shall not digress, I shall regress, I solemnly promise: the subject of

ordure has not yet been quite exhausted, while we have finished
with Chopin—qualitatively at least, although quantitatively I
shall have to resort to him now and again, if only for the sake
of literary composition. It won't occur again. Humbly I beat
my breast, the quantitative measure of which can be ascertained
from my tailor but the quality of which is so hard to define. I
would like nothing better than to introduce myself here with a
clear statement relevant to my duty; for instance—political
affiliation: democrat, but would this still apply to someone who
has refused to be "a regular guy" with army captains, someone
who, be it only with ordure, keeps his distance? Or take another category: religious affiliation. It would be easy to use one
of the common abbreviations; the choice is limited: Prot.,
Luth., Calv., Cath., R.C., Orth., Isr., Hebr., "other." I have
always found it embarrassing that religions, which their ad-
herents and others have been struggling to define for 2,000, for
6,000—for 400 years, should be reducible to pitiful abbreviations, but even if I wanted to I could not supply a single one
of these abbreviations.

I must not proceed without revealing an error which
amounts almost to a congenital defect and has involved me in
all kinds of difficulties and misunderstandings. My parents,
united in a mixed marriage, were far too devoted for one to
burden the other with the ordeal of deciding once and for all
which church I should belong to (it was only at my mother's
funeral that I found out that she had been the Protestant
one). They had worked out a highly involved system of mutual
respect: on Sundays they would take turns for one to go to
Trinity Church and the other to St. Mary's; a kind of exalted
religious courtesy, whose nicest little touch was that every
third Sunday neither of them went to either church. Although
my father assured me repeatedly that I had been baptized into
the Christian community, I never took part in any religious

instruction. Though I am getting on for fifty, I am still groping
in the dark; the Income Tax Department, inasmuch as I do
not pay church taxes, has me listed as an atheist. I would like
very much to become a Jew so as to get rid of that embarrassing "other" in this column, but my father feels that then
when he dies and finally exposes the secret, I would have to
resign from the Jewish community, and that would be open to
misinterpretation. So I prefer to call myself unofficially a "coming Christian," which exposes me to the unfounded suspicion
of being an Adventist. As far as religion is concerned I am an
unknown quantity, a cause for despair, a thorn in the flesh for
the atheists, an "obscure case" for the Christians, not eager to
proclaim a faith, immature, too courteous toward my deceased
mother; after all—as one man of God recently put it—"Courtesy is not a theological category." Which is a pity, otherwise
I might easily be a very religious man.

I wish to present this work, not only as far as I am concerned but also in regard to all other persons appearing in it,
less as a completed record than as one of those coloring books
with which we are all familiar from our happy childhood days:
you could get them for a nickel (at the dime store they were
even two for a nickel). They were the standard gift of un-
imaginative and parsimonious aunts and uncles who simply
took it for granted that you owned a paintbox or a set of
crayons. In these books only some of the lines were drawn in,
and often only dots which you joined together to form lines.
Freedom of expression was yours even in the joining of the
lines, and *full* freedom of expression could be enjoyed by filling
in the spaces with color. A figure whose collar or tonsure obviously suggested a priest could, while permitting of many
variations, be colored with the standard clerical black, but you
could also make him white, red, brown or even purple. Since
the top half of each page left room for further artistry, you

could draw in the head covering, making it anything from a
biretta to a miter. You could also turn him into a rabbi or, by
the addition of white clerical bands, clearly indicate a post-
Reformation denomination. If all else failed you got hold of
an encyclopedia, opened it at "priest's clothing," and knew
then exactly which neck, head and foot covering (such as
sandals for a Franciscan monk) were required in order to
achieve the man of God you had in mind. It was also possible,
of course, simply to ignore the suggested "priest" in his meager
outlines and construct a bumpkin, baker or bartender, or a
Caesar, chiromancer or clown. A figure armed with a ticket
punch, its dots and outlines somewhat obviously indicating a
ticket-taker, could be turned into a streetcar, train or bus conductor, and if with a few deft strokes (not prohibited by the
printed instructions) you turned the ticket punch into a pipe,
or extended it into the crook of a walking stick, you could
make him into a museum guard, a factory janitor, or a veteran
gallantly marching along at a regimental reunion. I for one
made full use of this metamorphic scope and horrified my
mother by transforming figures that were clearly supposed to
be chefs into surgeons at operations, by turning the spoon into
a scalpel and making the cap look flatter by widening the face.
With female outlines I was even more ruthless: because I was
so good at drawing grilles, I turned all these figures into nuns,
though I must admit my father sometimes mistook them for
ladies in a harem.

There is no question about it: a few outlines, given a certain
direction by a few skillfully scattered dots, permit of much
greater freedom than the yearned for absolute freedom, for this
absolute freedom is at the mercy of the imagination of the individual who, as we all know, has no ideas at all, none whatever,
and in whom a blank sheet of paper can provoke just as much
despair as that empty hour when the television set is out of

order. It is not merely to blur my portrait that I have devoted
a few parting tears and thoughts to the dying art of coloring.
Now that our children have learned to take blank paper and
paint exhibition-level pictures, and at the age of fourteen can
discuss Kafka, some adult exhibitions have become as embarrassing as some adult literary comments. Obviously a lamb
that is truly naïve, as well as capable of interpreting the oracle's
smile, knows how to arrange its entrails, before it is slaughtered,
in an interesting and ambiguous pattern, and by previously
swallowing pins, needles and paper clips, party and other
badges or church tax statements, how to furbish the contents
of its woolly fleece; while a lamb that is neither naïve nor
capable of interpreting the oracle's smile offers its entrails "just
as they are": pathetic little intestines, from which it is impossible to conjure up any kind of future at all. I therefore offer a
few strokes, a few dots, which the reader is at liberty to use
as an outline to decorate the brickwork of the memorial chapel
which this little work is intended to become: he may apply it
to the bare walls in the form of either a fresco or a graffito, or
even a mosaic.

Foreground and background will be left quite free: for raised
fingers, hands wrung in indignation or despair, for shaken
heads, lips compressed in grandfatherly severity and superior
wisdom, for furrowed brows, held noses, burst collars (with or
without ties, clerical bands, etc.), for St. Vitus' dance and
foaming mouths, discarded or scattered gall or kidney stones
for whose emergence into the light of day I may be to blame.

Like a miserly uncle or a thrifty aunt, I take for granted the
possession of a paintbox or a set of crayons. Those who have
nothing but a pencil, a ballpoint, or the remains of some ink,
are free to try it in monochrome.

In place of the dual, triple or quadruple levels of ambiguity
which may be missed by some, I suggest multiple levels: the

humus of the ages, which we can have for nothing, the rubble of history, to be had for even less than nothing. I have no objection to anyone extending my, that is, my model's feet, or adding an archeologist's hook to my hand, so as to dredge up all kinds of amusing objects: one of Agrippina's bracelets, the one she lost during a brawl with some drunken Roman sailors of the Rhine fleet—she was drunk too—at the precise spot where my parents' house used to stand (and now stands again), or one of St. Ursula's shoes, perhaps even a button from General de Gaulle's coat, ripped off by the enthusiastic mob and washed down into modern sewers, thence into historically more interesting layers. What I have fished out so far has been well worth the trouble: a sword pommel belonging to Germanicus Caesar when he pulled too violently, almost wildly (perhaps even hysterically) at his scabbard in order to display to a muttering crowd of Roman-Germanic mutineers the sword with which he had so often led them to victory. A well-preserved lock of Germanic hair, which I was able without the slightest difficulty to identify as originating from the head of Thumelicus, together with a number of other objects which I will not enumerate so as not to arouse the envy of tourists and their desire to dredge and rake.

But now we will neither digress nor regress: we will forge straight ahead and at last draw near a certain reality—Cologne. A stupendous heritage, an immense historical cargo (immense in proportion to its latitude, anyway). Let us, as sailors say, "clear the decks" before we sink down into the mire of history. Mere mention of the fact that from here, in order to win a fame that was both illusory and delusory, Caligula deliberately provoked hostile engagements with the Tencterians and Sugambrians would be enough to swamp us and make us try in vain to erect dikes. To penetrate to the Caligula layer, the fourth from the bottom, I would have to remove all the upper layers entirely, some twelve or so, and the top one would already be a mass of rubble, stucco, broken furniture, human bones, steel helmets, gas-mask containers, buckles, squashed or trodden flat only on the surface, and how would I explain to the younger generation—apart from everything else—what the inscription on the buckle, "Gott mit uns," can have meant?

Since I have already admitted to being born in Cologne (a fact which will make Leftist, Rightist, Center and Diaspora Catholics wring their hands in despair, as it will Rhineland and other Protestants, as well as doctrinarians of every hue, in other words: practically everyone), I would like, so as at least to encourage suspicion as well as misunderstanding, to offer a selection of at least four streets as the one in which I was born: Rheinau-Strasse, Grosse-Witsch-Gasse, Filzengraben, and Rhein-Gasse, and in case anyone should feel I have moved my parents' house perilously close to those environs where Nietzsche foundered but Scheler flourished, let me inform him that in none of these streets was or is that calling pursued of which the drunken Roman sailors took Agrippina to be an exponent, and should practiced snoopers set out to try and determine where Agrippina *really* got into a brawl, where Thumelicus *really* landed, where Germanicus gave his famous speech, then I will merely add, in order to compound the confusion, that when visitors come across the ivory box in my glass cabinet and ask me whose hair is inside it, I sometimes ascribe its origin to the head of one of Lochner's models or St. Engelbert: in holy places like Cologne, such mistakes are permissible and customary.

When asked about my racial background I frankly supply the following information: Jewish, Germanic, Christian. The central link in this trinity may be replaced by any one of the numerous pure or mixed racial categories that Cologne has to offer: but whether it be pure Samoyed, mixed Swedish-

Samoyed, or Slovenian-Italian, I cannot sacrifice the two outer
brackets—Jewish-Christian—holding my racial blend together;
those who are none of these things, or only one of them
(mixed Slavic-Germanic only, for instance), are hereby declared fit for active duty and ordered to report for military
inspection forthwith. The requirements are well known: properly washed, and ready at any time to strip to the skin.

I I

This concludes the interior outline; let us pass on quickly to
the exterior: height—five foot eleven; coloring—medium fair;
weight—normal. Distinguishing features: slightly lopsided walk
due to hip wound.

When on September 22, 1938, about four forty-five in the
afternoon, I boarded a Number 7 streetcar in front of the main
railway station in Cologne, I was wearing a white shirt, olive-
drab trousers recognizable to the informed (of those days) as
part of a uniform. Anyone who did not come too close, in
other words could not detect my odor, would have said I
looked "quite all right." A source of surprise to those who
knew me (because all my friends are aware that, from my
paternal great-great-grandfather, who came from a village near
Nimwegen, I suffer from anancastia (obsessional hand-washing), yet another detail leading to a limbo of uncertainty and
infinity)—and probably for that reason rather touching—were
my dirty fingernails. For the dirty nails I offer a simple explanation: as a sharer in our national destiny and a member of that
compulsory mutual fellowship whose uniform I was supposed
to be wearing (as soon as the train pulled out I had taken it
off in the washroom and packed it away in my suitcase, except
for the trousers which, for reasons of decency, and the shoes,
for reasons of necessity, I could not remove)—in this com-

pulsory mutual fellowship I had adopted the common practice, when our nails were inspected for cleanliness before dinner, of cleaning them quickly with a fork. So that day, which I spent almost entirely in the train (no money to eat in the dining car, so no fork to clean my nails with) I was still at large, late in the afternoon, with dirty nails. To this day, twenty-seven years later, at both formal and informal meals, I have to restrain myself from quickly cleaning my nails with a fork, and I have often provoked angry looks from waiters who took me for a boor, but sometimes respectful looks from people who took me for a snob. In acquainting the reader with this habit, I would like to point out the ineradicable effects of military training. So when your children come to table with dirty nails, the best thing to do is to pack them off right away to the army. Should the reader be overcome with nausea, or be concerned about hygiene, let me add that of course I and my fellow-sharers in our national destiny wiped our forks on our trouserlegs and then rinsed them off in the hot soup. Now and again when— as rarely happens—I am alone, that is, neither accompanied nor watched over by my mother-in-law or my grandfather, nor having a bite to eat with business friends on the terrace of the Café Reichard, I reach naturally and instinctively for the fork and do indeed use it to clean my nails. I was recently asked by an Italian tourist sitting at the next table whether this was a German custom, a fact which I unhesitatingly confirmed. I even referred him to Tacitus and the well-known expression in Italian Renaissance literature, "forcalismo teutonico"—he made a note of it then and there in his travel diary, and when he whispered again: "formalismo tautonico?" I let it pass, because I thought it sounded so nice.

So except for my dirty nails I really looked quite all right.

Even my shoes had been shined. Not by my own hand (I have consistently refused to do this) but by the hand of one of my fellow-sharers in our national destiny, who knew no other way of expressing his gratitude for services I had rendered to him. Money, tobacco, material objects of any kind—these he was tactful enough not to offer me; he was illiterate, and I wrote ardent letters for him to two girls in Cologne, whose address, although not far from my parents' house (only two to seven streets away) was in a milieu totally unfamiliar to me (in fact, the very one that had caused the mix-up about Agrippina, the one where Nietzsche got into trouble and Scheler was quite at home). This fellow-sharer in our national destiny, a pimp by the name of Schmenz, always seized on my shoes and boots in frantic gratitude, washed my shirts and socks for me, sewed on my buttons, ironed my trousers—because my ardent letters evoked rapturous responses in the recipients. The letters were on a very high plane, almost esoteric, markedly stylized, and in that milieu this kind of thing is as popular as a permanent wave. Once Schmenz even gave me half his share of the caramel pudding with which our Sundays used to be enhanced, and for a long time I imagined he did not like caramel pudding (pimps are the fussiest kind of people I have ever had anything to do with), until I later received convincing proof that caramel pudding was one of his favorite dishes. As word soon got round that I knew how to write ardent letters, I soon, less from necessity than by force, built up a clientele as a letter-composer if not actually as an author. Fees usually consisted of strange favors: *not* to pinch tobacco from my locker and meat from my plate, *not* to push me into the muddy ditch when we took our morning exercise, *not* to trip me up during night marches, and various other favors which exist among such fellow-sharers in national destiny. Some of my friends, Marxists and anti-Marxists, have since accused me of wrongful behavior in the writing of these love letters. It was my duty, they said, "to allow this pent-up ardor to bring about a change of awareness in these illiterate persons, resulting possibly in a revolt," and it was my duty as an upright man to look around for support every morning in the muddy ditch. I am ashamed to admit that I did indeed act wrongly, and was inconsistent, for two totally unrelated reasons, of which the first is a congenital and the second an environmental defect: courtesy, and fear of getting beaten up. Actually I would have been happier if Schmenz had not cleaned my boots and the others had gone on pushing me into the ditch or dunking my cigarette paper in my breakfast coffee, but I lacked both the discourtesy and the courage to prevent them granting me these favors. I blame myself, I acknowledge that it is entirely my faut, and now perhaps the hands which were about to be wrung in despair will fall, the furrowed brows will become smooth again, and here and there someone will wipe the foam from the corners of his mouth. I solemnly promise that at the end of this work I will make a full confession and offer a ready-made moral, as well as an interpretation which will spare all interpreters, from high school student to university professor, the trouble of sighing and wondering. It will be presented in such a way that even the unsophisticated reader can "digest it," not nearly as involved as the directions on how to complete an application for an income tax refund. Patience, patience, we're not there yet. I must confess that, in our free, pluralistic, industrial society, I naturally prefer a free shoeshine man with a lordly contempt for tips.

Let us now leave me to myself for a few minutes, with my dirty nails, my well-polished shoes, in Streetcar Number 7. Endearing and old-fashioned (nowadays streetcars are nothing but machines for bundling people in and out), the Number

7 wobbles around the east nave of the Cathedral, swings into
Unter-Taschenmacher-Strasse in the direction of the Alter-
markt, is already approaching the Heumarkt, and no sooner
than the Malzmühle but no later than the curve by the
Malzbüchel, where I always used to jump off, I shall have to
make up my mind whether to go home first and console my
father (or my parents. My father's telegram, "Mother passed
away," to which I owed my temporary release from this
compulsory mutual fellowship, might easily have been a bluff.
My mother would have been quite capable of feigning death),
or whether I should go right on to the Perlengraben and visit
the Bechtolds first. We will leave this question unanswered
for the moment, till the streetcar reaches the Malzmühle, and
turn back to the ordure section of that sharers-in-our-national-
destiny camp where I first met Engelbert Bechtold, from now
on to be called, like every Engelbert in Cologne: Angel. That's
what he was known as at home, in camp, by me, and that's
what he looked like.

The fervent desire of that superior officer whom I had
struck in the back of the knee during spade drill with the
sharp edge of my spade (and I did not plan it that way, as
my Marxist and other friends would have it: on the contrary
—a confession that will fill them and everyone else with despair—I was impelled by an invisible and celestial common
sense)—the fervent desire of that superior to make a man of
me had banished me with all possible speed to those fields
where Angel, a mythical figure in the camp, had for three
months been steadily and steadfastly pursuing the most varied
assortment of dirty jobs: every day he had to empty the huge
latrine, which was not connected with the sewer (I will spare
myself and the reader the statistical details), he had to empty
the kitchen garbage into pig buckets, clean out and light the
stoves in the officers' mess, fill the coal scuttles, remove the

traces of their carousings (consisting mainly of vomited potato salad mixed with beer and liquor), and look through the mountainous supply of potatoes in the cellar for rotten potatoes to prevent the spread of decay.

The moment I came face to face with Angel I knew that what had sent me here to make a man of me had not been my own volition, still less something as absurd as a plan, nor my superior's curses, but, as I say, that invisible power of celestial common sense. When I saw Angel I also knew: If he had to perform any kind of duty at all, it was bound to be carrying ordure, and it was an honor for me to do likewise in his company.

Wherever people are forced to become sharers in national destiny, the noble state of manhood is conferred not by advantage but by disadvantage. (Patience: I am well aware of how disadvantage can be turned into advantage and will watch out accordingly.) I still regard my Chopin tour of official duty as something of a black mark against me, although my comparative youth—I was twenty-two—may help to exonerate me. Other advantages (which were not "transformed disadvantages" but genuine advantages), I do not regard as black marks —for instance, that in my capacity of battalion coal heaver— it will be seen from this that I did not carry only ordure—I conducted involved and, for reasons of sublimated eroticism, protracted negotiations with the mother superior of a Benedictine convent of the Eternal Adoration in a little town near Rouen, lengthy conversations lasting for over a week (I had, among other things, to allay her fears that I might be a *provocateur*), in order to get permission for two baths a week in exchange for the coal she so desperately needed for the convent laundry. Between us, she and I worked out an advanced mathematical system of diplomacy and eroticism, under the patronage of Pascal and Péguy. And although the nuns

knew my church affiliation to be obscure, they invited me to
a special service on Assumption Day, entertaining me afterwards with tea and streusel cake (the mother superior was
aware of my dislike of coffee). I chivalrously returned the
honor with an extra hundredweight of coal and three snow-
white officer's handkerchiefs which I had stolen with my own
hands—I was especially proud of this feat—from a German
Army depot and which at my own expense had been embroidered by a crippled schoolteacher with the words: "Make
to yourselves friends of the mammon of unrighteousness. Votre
ami allemand." It would complicate this work unnecessarily
were I to enumerate other, let alone all, advantages which I
enjoyed, for instance: that a very pretty Rumanian Jewish girl
in a dry goods shop in Jassy kissed me on both cheeks, mouth
and forehead, with the strange remark, murmured in Yiddish:
"Because you belong to such a poor people"—the affair had
a prologue and an epilogue, I am merely giving the central
section because the rest would be too hard to explain. As for
a Hungarian colonel who assisted me in falsifying a document,
I shall not even begin to go into that.

Let us quickly double back, first to Streetcar Number 7,
which has just passed the Malzmühle and is toiling protest-
ingly up the Mühlenbach toward the Waidmarkt—then back
to the ordure section in the camp where I suddenly found
myself face to face with Angel, who was sitting on a ledge
between the kitchen, the sick bay and the latrine having his
lunch: a piece of dry bread, a cigarette he had rolled himself,
a mug of ersatz coffee. The way he was sitting there reminded
me of the streetcleaners at home, whose dignified style of
lunch while they sat beside the Tauzieher monument I had
always admired and always envied. Angel, like all Lochner's
angels, had fair, almost golden hair, he was short and stocky,
and although his features—a broad nose, mouth too small,

an almost uncannily high forehead—had nothing classical about them, they seemed radiant. In his dark eyes not a trace of melancholy. When I stopped in front of him, he said: "Morning," nodded as if we had arranged to meet there four hundred years ago and I was a trifle late, and said, without putting down his coffee mug: "You should marry my sister"; setting his mug down on the ledge he added: "She's a pretty girl, although she looks like me. She's called Hildegard."

I was silent, as only a man can be silent who has received an angel's annunciation and command. Angel stubbed out his cigarette on the wall, put the butt into his pocket, picked up the two empty lard pails, and proceeded to give me some practical instructions on my impending occupation, mainly scientific details as to how much would go into a ladle, measured in kilos, the load capacity of the pole the ladle was attached to. He threw in a few chemical details but refrained from mentioning the hygienic aspects, no doubt because there was a large sign over the latrine saying: "Bowel movement over, meal time ahead,/ Hands should be washed before you are fed!" It will be observed that those who pack their children off to the army right away need not be afraid the army will overlook anything. If one bears in mind that there is a sign in the mess hall saying: "Work makes us free," it will immediately be seen that the army takes as much thought for poetry as for a man's ethical views.

I spent only two weeks working with Angel at the duties which still enable me to earn my living any day as a sewer worker or a potato sorter. Never again have I seen so many potatoes at any one time as were stored in the cellar under the kitchen: daylight fell dimly through tiny slits onto enormous brown piles that seemed to heave like a seething swamp, sickly alcoholic vapors filled the cellar when we had finished sorting a great heap of rotten potatoes and set them aside to be carried away. The positive side of our labors consisted in carrying the precious fruit upstairs in buckets (I might add, for the peace of mind of all mothers, in *different* buckets) into the kitchen, where it was tipped into the tubs which had been set up for the communal evening potato-peeling.

When we brought the first buckets up into the kitchen, the first thing we were given was what the kitchen supervisor (one of the few people in this compulsory mutual fellowship with no previous conviction) called the snail's blessing, i.e.: we had to throw ourselves down on the greasy dirty floor and crawl right round the huge stove, we were only allowed to raise our heads above the floor just far enough to keep from scraping our faces. The only way we were allowed to help propel ourselves along was to push with our toes; if we used our hands or knees, or stopped moving from exhaustion, our punishment was having to sing, and we were ordered to do this with the words: "A song, a merry song!" and to this day I am not sure whether it was sheer inspiration or whether there was some unconscious rapport between Angel and myself: in any case, the very first time I immediately began singing the song that seems to have been part of Angel's repertoire: "*Deutschland, Deutschland über alles.*" It is to be observed that, while they were making men of us, the patriotic side of our feelings was not neglected either, and anyone who is afraid his sons might ever forget they were Germans should pack them off to the army with even greater dispatch than was proposed on Page 93, in the hope that they receive the toughest possible training. Like the conscientious person I have always been, I wondered while I sang whether our song could really be called merry. Incidentally, the method described here—I offer this as an advance on my promised interpreta-tion—is the best and most effective one for drilling a young man's nationality or racial origin into him in a manner he will never forget. I recommend it also for the Swiss, the French, and other nations. For not everyone has the good fortune to be kissed by pretty Jewish girls in Rumanian shops.

It will surprise no one to learn that we were too worn out to sing consistently with the perfection customary among choral societies. We simply mumbled the unforgettable and unforgotten text in a kind of singsong chant into the sticky tiled floor. Later on they forbade me—me, of all people!— to sing the Deutschland song, after our camp commandant looked me up one day in the potato cellar, bawled me out for not having a baptism certificate, and, unexpectedly—whether unjustifiably or not, I still don't know, the matter was never cleared up—bellowed the words "lousy Jew" at me, which I have always regarded as a kind of baptism or circumcision. After that I was no longer allowed to sing the Deutschland song, instead I sang the song about the Lorelei.

It will also surprise no one to learn that Angel and I hardly spoke any more, and not at all about Hildegard. We were usually so exhausted by nine-thirty in the morning that we went staggering about our various duties, vomiting from fatigue and nausea. As a result, our sole means of communication was nodding or shaking our heads. Moreover, our vomiting, headaches and fatigue made us more aware of how little chance there was of our disadvantages turning into advantages. When Angel shrugged his shoulders in a certain way—half apologetic, half submissive—I knew he was going to sit down on a pile of potato sacks and say his rosary ("I promised my mother I would").

Needless to say, in this compulsory mutual fellowship there were also "off-duty regular guys," and even an "on-duty" variety in the person of a young officer, a former Protestant theology student of noble bearing who sometimes approached us to "strike up a conversation." I always had a special blend of rotten potatoes and ordure ready for this man, and I would during those two weeks, each time for three minutes—humbly actually "got into conversation" with him and—about twice during those two weeks, each time for three minutes—humbly accepted words like "necessity," "spirit of the age," "destiny," the way a beggar accepts a slice of dry bread.

By now the Number 7 was not far from the Waidmarkt, and all I could think about was Hildegard Bechtold. There had been times during the past two weeks when I had planned to just go ahead and write her a letter "asking for her hand" (in those days I knew of no other way of putting it, and I still know of no better), but just at this time my evening letter clients were pressing me inordinately, threatening me because they were beginning to find my vocabulary too "refined" after all. The crude endearments which my clients wished to convey to their partners (both primary and secondary sex organs were combined, and these combinations in turn combined with various other physical attributes), were shifted by me onto a still more elevated plane and developed into a mannerist style that still enables me to write letters from every sort of male correspondent to every sort of female recipient which would pass any censorship without suppressing a single thing. In other words, I could earn my living any day as a letter composer. Inasmuch as I have always liked using the blackest possible ink or the softest possible pencil to write on the whitest possible paper, I include my letter composing among the advantages of which I am not ashamed.

By the time we reached the Waidmarkt my anxiety was verging on trepidation, barely another minute and I would be getting out at the Perlengraben. The decision was made. (My mother was dead, that I knew.) Since here, too, on the plat-

form of Number 7, the belt of ordure odor kept me a prisoner
in my ivory tower, I perceived what is known as one's environment with the dream-like indistinctness (or distinctness)
obtained by looking through high prison windows. A member
of the S.A. (how could anyone wear a uniform like that!),
a man wearing a silk tie (obviously an upper-class type), a
girl eating grapes with innocent fingers out of a paper bag,
and the conductress, the beauty of whose young, slightly coarse
features was enhanced by that frank eroticism which used to
be the mark of Cologne streetcar conductresses—they all
avoided me like the plague. I pushed my way through to the
exit, jumped off, raced along the Perlengraben, and three
minutes later was climbing the stairs to the fourth floor of
a block of cheap flats. To the interpreter seeking for reality,
I suggest he draw a semicircle of three minutes radius west
of Severin-Strasse from the Perlengraben streetcar stop, and
choose one of the streets caught in his semicircle—of course,
in order to give the radius correctly I ought also to state my
speed: I suggest any speed between Jesse Owens and an above-
average amateur. I was not surprised to see a transparency
over the Bechtolds' front door with the words: "Behold him!
Who? The bridegroom. Behold him! How? As he were a
lamb." Just as I was about to press the bell—it is hardly necessary to mention this, but it is better to be on the safe side—
Hildegard opened the door, fell into my arms, and all my bad
odor was taken from me.

III

It is neither my purpose nor within the scope of my capa-
bilities even to try and describe, let alone explain, the power
of love. One thing is certain: it was not love at first sight. It
was not till an hour later, when I had survived the initiation

rites of the Bechtold clan, the betrothal coffee had been drunk
and the betrothal cake half consumed, that I got around to
having a proper look at Hildegard. I found her much more
beautiful that her resemblance to Angel might have led one
to expect, and this was a relief. Although I had been in love
with her for two weeks, it was nice to find she was beautiful.
If I say that from now on we, Hildegard and I, embraced, not
very often but as often as we could, and if I say again that
I attribute this to the guidance of that celestial common sense
which inspired me, at the words "Down spades," suddenly
to forget everything I had ever learned, I am afraid that parents who are worried about their sons will now consider packing them off to the army not only for educational purposes
but also in the hope that, by the roundabout means of doing
the wrong thing at the command "Down rifles" (for of course
they don't use spades nowadays), they may win a wife as
wonderful, clever and beautiful as mine. So I would like to
warn the reader, by reminding him of various relevant fairy
tales, that the person who unintentionally does good reaps
a richer reward than the person who intentionally imitates
him, and I would like to reiterate: I did not do it intentionally.
(I will leave room here for the gnashing teeth of those angry
people who, intoxicated with intentions as they unfortunately
are, refuse to admit that a celestial common sense can work
to the benefit of those who have no intentions at all.) Needless to say, I am not acquainted with all the intentions of that
guiding common sense: undoubtedly one of them was that
the Bechtold family be kept supplied with coffee not only
for the duration of the war but as long as they lived (my father owned a wholesale coffee business, which I have meanwhile inherited). A secondary intention: to bring to my notice, in the form of my two brothers-in-law, that diabolism of

the twenties of which until September 22, 1938, I had no inkling (child of middle-class parents, graduated from high school, one semester under Ernst Bertram, not yet a member of either National Socialist or any other organizations). Possible further intentions: to give me, at the moment of my mother's death, my mother-in-law (she would have been capable not only of feigning death: later, in her forthright fashion, she even forced her way up to the area commander and called him a "feebleminded, pigheaded, idiotic thing" because on one occasion he refused to extend my leave, when my little daughter had scarlet fever). Additional intentions: to provide my father, in the person of old Mr. Bechtold, with someone to talk to for the rest of his life, someone with whom he could grumble about the Nazis; and to use my cigarette coupons to keep Angel's youngest brother Johann, an inveterate smoker, in cigarettes throughout the tobacco-rationing period —i.e., nearly eleven years. It is possible that this guiding common sense also had an economic balance in mind: we had money, the Bechtolds did not. The coffee is the only thing I am sure about: in the times we knew were in store for us, no family would have been so completely at a loss without coffee as the Bechtolds. At the slightest excuse every single member of the family would ask: "Shall I put on some more coffee?" Although one could be sure at any given time that four or five pots of coffee had already been made. Later on, when war actually broke out, I committed two cardinal sins at once: I indulged in both statistics and psychology—I reduced the Bechtold family's consumption of coffee from some two hundred pounds a year to seventy-five, estimating that the war would last seven years (whether out of pessimism or a mystical passion for the number seven I don't know), and persuaded my father to lay in stocks of raw coffee accordingly.

And I goaded my mother-in-law into economizing on coffee, conjuring up before her horrified eyes the vision of a coffee-less era if she failed to economize.

I V

Before I continue I wish to give solemn assurance that from now on the subject of ordure is as closed as Chopin was back on Page 86. I have also come to the end of my portrayal of training methods in military establishments. The suspicion might be too easily aroused that this work is anti-militarist or even pro-disarmament or anti-armament. Oh no, I am concerned with something much more exalted, with—as every unprejudiced reader is already aware—with love and innocence. The fact that the circumstances under and the details with which I am now attempting to depict these things necessitate the mention of certain formations, organizations and institutions, is not my fault but the fault of a destiny with which anyone may quarrel to his heart's content. It is not my fault that I write in German, that in the potato cellar of a German fellowship of national destiny I was made a Jew by the commandant bellowing at me, that in the back room of a cheap Rumanian shop I was made a German by a pretty Jewish girl kissing me. Had I been born in Ballaghaderreen I would be writing—with the darkest possible ink or the softest possible pencils on the whitest possible paper—about love and innocence under quite different circumstances and with quite different details. I would be singing about dogs and horses and donkeys, about fair maidens I kissed behind the hedge after a dance, to whom I had promised what I intended to keep but then could not keep: marriage. I would sing of the moors, the bog, the wind whining in the peat ditches, whipping up dark water in the peat ditches and making them billow

like the dark tweed skirt of a maiden who has drowned herself because the one who kissed her and promised to marry
her became a priest and went his way. I would fill many
pages to sing the praises of the dogs of Dukinella; those clever
faithful beasts, thoroughbreds and mongrels alike, have long
deserved a monument in words. But, things being what they
are, I sharpen my pencil again, not to relate anything unpleasant but to tell what happened—so let us return with a
sigh to Cologne, to that street to be found inside a western
semicircle of three minutes around the Perlengraben, if it is
to be found at all. It has not been swallowed up by the ground,
it has been swept away, scraped away, and in order not to
leave this page in the coloring book completely blank, thus
opening wide the gates to nonsense, I offer three small land-
marks: a tobacco shop, a fur store, a school, and a number
of yellowish-white house fronts, almost the same color, though
not the same size, as the ones I saw in Pilsen. I suggest that
intelligent and obedient art students draw three steam-shovels,
one carrying away the fur store, one the tobacco shop, and
one the school, and that they write across the top of the page
the motto: "Work makes us free."

The trouble is, though, that no one will know where to
hang the plaque when one day Angel acquires the odor of
sanctity. I don't have to be told that I cannot represent the
Congregation of Rites, or raise the question of canonization
without a devil's advocate, but, inasmuch as my church affiliation is obscure, it will not, I hope, hurt anyone's feelings if
I procure a saint for a church to which I probably do not belong. Like everything else in this work, it is not done deliberately. Naturally the fact that Angel has been both match-
maker and brother-in-law to me is enough to make uncharit-
able people say "Aha," but may I not, since the column
"church affiliation" has to remain blank, at least point out

that I spent two weeks with Angel and therefore use a little
of the odor of sanctity to chase away the odor of ordure from
these pages? I can see I shall have no such luck, I am suspected
of ulterior motives. Never mind, I won't bother, if only because courtesy (so they say) is not a theological category.
Besides, my father is still alive, has long ceased to go to alter-
nate churches, he doesn't go to church at all, won't let me
see his tax return, still grumbles about the Nazis with old Mr.
Bechtold, my father-in-law.

The two of them are now completely absorbed in a new
interest: exploring the layers of Cologne. They dig away in
a shaft my father has had sunk in our courtyard and roofed
over, and they assure us plausibly, although with a good deal
of snickering, that they have discovered the remains of a
temple of Venus. My mother-in-law is in her charming way
a Catholic, like the Cologne motto: "We are the ones who
decide whether something is Catholic or not." When I am
forced to discuss religious matters with her (I am the father
of a twenty-four-year-old daughter, who at the fervent wish
of my deceased wife was brought up a Catholic, then married
a Protestant, becoming in turn the mother of a three-year-old
daughter who at her fervent wish is being brought up a Catholic), and present convincing evidence that her view does not
coincide with the official one of her church, she dismisses this
with a pronouncement I hesitate to repeat: "Then all I can
say is, the Pope was wrong." And when—as is sometimes un-
avoidable—there are church dignitaries present who contradict
her personal brand of Papism, she refuses to budge and relies
on a statement which it is as impossible to prove as it is to
refute: "We Kerkhoffs (her maiden name was Kerkhoff) have
always been Catholics by instinct." It is not up to me to dis-
suade her of this. I am too fond of her. To augment the confusion about this kind soul (who once during the war threw,

literally threw, a military policeman—who was searching for her deserter son, Anton—down the stairs singlehanded), let me add the following touch for the coloring book: that for six weeks she was the leader of a Communist Party cell, till she realized that "this business" was incompatible with her instinctive Catholicism, and she was also, and is still, chairman of a Rosary Fellowship.

As a background for at least one of the pages to be devoted to her in the coloring book, I suggest a blue which anyone who has ever painted the sky above Naples is sure to have. If the reader now "hasn't the slightest idea what to make of her," I have achieved my object, and now everyone may take their crayons, paintbox or palette and color my mother-in-law whatever color seems to convey "dubious" or "scandalous." I suggest a soft mauve shading to red. I shall not have a great deal more to say about my mother-in-law, I value her too much to expose her to the light, I am keeping the greater part of her to myself in my private dark-room. I will gladly reveal a few of her external features: she is short, was at one time slim but now "has put on a lot of weight," she still drinks staggering quantities of coffee; at an advanced age, seventy-two, she has become a confirmed smoker and occupies herself with her grandchildren "quite outrageously"; the children of my deceased brother-in-law Anton, who was "a declared atheist and an out-and-out Leftist," two girls between eighteen and twenty-one, she drags off to the kitchen, says the rosary with them, and goes through the Creed; the children of my surviving brother-in-law Johann (a boy and girl, ten and twelve), who are being brought up in strict observance of church discipline, she is "injecting with obstinacy and rebellion." (All the quotation marks denote her own words.)

For her I am still "that nice boy who made my Hilde so happy and who for months on end (it was actually only two weeks) carried shit with my Angel." (Once again I am forced, in the interest of historical accuracy, to utter the blunt word.) She has no more forgotten these two facts than that "he kept me supplied with coffee in war and peace." It is perhaps to her credit that she always mentions my material services last. But otherwise she considers me "terribly naïve," if only for the fact that I was "witless enough to let them shoot at him, and even hit him."

This is something she cannot understand. She feels that "any intelligent person, who really and truly had nothing to do with that business (in this case she means the Nazi business), ought to have been able to avoid it." She is probably right, and when I begin arguing with her and remind her how Angel died, she will say: "You know perfectly well that Angel was not intelligent, or that he was more than that," and there she is right. I don't know why I actually allowed myself to be shot at, what's more to be hit, or why, although I was "exempt from shooting," I exposed myself to the line of fire without doing any shooting myself. It remains a stain on my consciousness and my conscience. Probably I was just tired of listening to Chopin; or perhaps I was just tired of the West and longed for the East; I don't quite know what it was that caused me simply to ignore the certificate of the consulting ophthalmologist of the Western Army division. Hildegard wrote me at the time that she understood, but I didn't understand myself. My mother-in-law is right to associate the word witless with my behavior then and now. It remains totally obscure, dark, and I authorize anyone to take some black ink and a piece of cotton and dab a nice big blot onto the coloring book just where my consciousness should be. In any event, I had given up the idea of deserting, I saw nothing attractive about exchanging my present captivity for any other. "What kind of music do the Russians play on the piano?" asked my mother-in-law when I came home on leave from the front. I told her what was true, that I had only heard the piano played a few times, and it had always been Beethoven. "That's good," she said, "that's very good."

Here, in the midst of our idyll, I wish to perform a neglected duty and propose a page or two for the erection of a memorial niche where I shall fill in only the commemorative tablets for those persons in this work who are now dead.

1. Hildegard Schmölder, née Bechtold, born January 6, 1920, died May 31, 1942, during an air raid on Cologne in a street in the vicinity of Clovis Square. Her mortal remains were never found.

2. Engelbert Bechtold, known as Angel, born September 15, 1917, shot on December 30, 1939, between Forbach and St. Avold by a French sentry who must have thought he was going to attack, although all he wanted to do was to give himself up. His mortal remains were never found.

3. Anton Bechtold, born May 12, 1915, executed one day in February 1945 behind the terrace of the Café Reichard in Cologne, between what are now the headquarters of the radio station and the cathedral residences, not far from the tourist bureau, "just opposite the cathedral," where today unsuspecting tourists and still more unsuspecting radio producers sip their iced coffee. Although his mortal remains were never found, his dossier was. He was listed as having "deserted twice," accused of stealing from and black-marketing in army supplies, and of organizing a group of deserters in the cellars of bombed-out houses in the Old Town and staging regular battles against the "police units of the German Wehrmacht." His widow, Monika Bechtold, used to talk a lot about "it," now she doesn't talk about "it" any more.

I offer this little funeral chapel in the midst of our idyll un-adorned, just the bare brickwork, so to speak. Anyone is free to follow his bent or taste and decorate it with dog roses, pansies or privet. Even roses are allowed, prayers may be said, and there is no objection to meditating on the transitoriness of man's mortal self. And I ask those who wish to pray not to forget Anton: I never liked him, but, when the trumpets sound on the Day of Judgment, I wish him a kiss from the gentlest of all the angels of Judgment, from an auxiliary angel who is not entitled to blow trumpets, just to polish them. I wish Anton redemption from his simulated wickedness, from his failure to be understood and his failure to understand. May the angel give him back what even he must once have had: innocence.

V

This more or less exhausts the topic of war too, at least for the duration of this work, and we return to the deep, too deep peace of that September afternoon when I kissed Hilde-gard for the first time and all my bad odor was suddenly taken from me.

What the Bechtolds called their hallway was an unlighted rectangle about nine feet square with five doors leading off it: three to bedrooms, one to the kitchen, one to the bathroom. Clothes hooks had been hammered directly into the narrow strips of wall between the doors. Dresses, coats, jackets, scarves, shabby dressing gowns and "Mother's funny hats" dangled from them, and a number of these things were always getting caught in doors as they opened and had to be shoved aside, sometimes from the inside, which led to hands getting caught.

At the very moment when I was embracing Hildegard, three doors opened: Mrs. Bechtold came out of the kitchen, Mr.

Bechtold out of the bedroom, Anton and Johann out of their room, and all four struck up the hymn—Hilde, the fifth, wept in silent bliss against my chest—"Behold him! How? As he were a lamb."

By this time, if not before, the astute reader will know what we—he and I—ought no longer to withhold from the less astute reader: namely, that this work is really designed as an idyll pure and simple, to fulfill the same function among the aromas of sewage as elsewhere the perfume of roses, by avoiding or at least greatly reducing the necessity of dealing with the war, and dismissing the Nazi business as something between a cold and a hail of brimstone; and although on a later page Angel and I, despite our geographical separation, became Stormtroopers and joined the S.A. simultaneously (even if only fictitiously, for we did our service elsewhere and never wore the terrible S.A. uniform) everyone knows that I would have done better to be born in Ballaghaderreen and chosen a lyre rather than the crest of Cologne as a watermark for my letter paper. I am a German to no purpose, a native of Cologne to no avail, and when I confess that after the war I took over my father's coffee business and now steadfastly refuse to be either shocked or concerned over the fact that last year's turnover has risen 3.7 per cent less than the turnover of the preceding year, which rose 4.9 per cent as compared with that of the year before that, it will become apparent that my brothers-in-law were justified in referring to me as "Buttercup." In vain do I try to soothe my manager with bonuses. He understands neither my allusions to the fiery chariot that carried Elijah off to heaven, nor the fact that I allow my three-year-old granddaughter to play with our complicated and costly accounting machines; and when I let the Income Tax Department look after the repair bills he is indignant, shocked, just as he is at the fact that I refer to these

achievements of science as a mere improvement on the loom.
His fear that the business is going "downhill" does not alarm
me. Where else should it go? When I walk down to the Leystapel by the river and along the Frankenwerft, I have to restrain myself from plunging into the dark waters of the Rhine.
Only my granddaughter's hand holds me back, and the thought
of my mother-in-law. I am a tea drinker, so why should I
worry about the coffee business?

My father and father-in-law do not hold me back. Their age
has carried them over a new threshold of pleasure, as old as
the rubble they burrow in. They have "become one with
Cologne," and it is vanished potency, not wisdom, that prevents them from crowning their snickering voluptuousness
with the joys of Venus. Old man Bechtold, whose proletarian
bravura used to impress me, has become quite soigné, and
when the two old men climb up out of their shaft and bring
to light a stone or a fragment of scribbled pottery, it is not
only their panting tongues that remind me of dogs. Their
snickering adds to my suspicion that all we have been is bait:
Angel, Hildegard, myself, each of us bait for the other—and
in the background there must have always been someone
snickering. Whatever happened to us or whatever we did always suited someone: whether we weighed coffee, carried ordure, let ourselves be shot at, lived or died. My mother's
death suited many people extremely well: the Bechtolds, me,
even my father, who "couldn't bear to go on watching her
suffer"; even herself, she couldn't stand the dreadful faces
and the uniforms, she was not religious and not innocent, not
sophisticated and not sufficiently corrupted to live in a sewer.
The Protestant pastor's words at her graveside were so embarrassing that I prefer not to repeat them. There are certain
manifestations of hypocrisy that I pass over with celestial
courtesy. When the trumpets sound on the Day of Judgment,

I hope the angels will not take all the words he ever spoke during his lifetime and stuff them back into his mouth like a mountain of candy floss.

When he expressed his condolences to my father and me after the funeral, he looked disapprovingly at my civilian clothes and whispered severely: "Why aren't you wearing your country's uniform?" and because of this remark I herewith dub him the most unpleasant character in this work, infinitely more unpleasant than the officer who gave us the snail's blessing while wearing his country's uniform. Silently I held out my dirty nails to the pastor, as we used to at inspection. This is the only deliberate impertinence I can boast of. Twenty years later I saw him again as my son-in-law's uncle at my daughter's wedding, I held out my—this time clean—nails to him, and that was not a deliberate impertinence but merely, as every psychologist knows, a reflex movement. He went scarlet, stammered when he started talking again, refused our invitation to the wedding reception, and my son-in-law is still angry with me for having ruined "the harmony of the day."

I hope these flashes back and forth will not upset the reader. By grade 7, if not before, the merest child knows that this is called changing the narrational level. It is the same thing as change of shift in a factory, except that in my case these changes mark the places where I have to sharpen my pencil before supplying more strokes and dots. Here I am seen at the age of twenty-one, twenty-three, I shall appear at the age of twenty, and then not until I am almost fifty. I am seen as a bridegroom, as a husband, then not again until I am a widower and a grandfather—nearly twenty years are blank pages for which I shall supply a few decorative outlines but no contents. Let us hurry back with freshly sharpened pencil to the level "Afternoon of September 22, 1938, about quarter past five."

VI

The song of welcome has died away, I feel Hildegard's tears
damp on my neck and cheeks, a few of her long hairs lie,
golden as the hair of Lochner's angels, on my white shirt.
From the open kitchen door comes the smell of fresh coffee
—who is going to make tea for me in this house?—freshly
baked Rodons (elsewhere known as Gugelhupf cake). Through
the open bedroom door I can see Anton Bechtold's easel, on
which a chaotic painting done entirely in purples and yellows
explicitly (for my taste too explicitly) represents a naked
woman reclining on a purple couch. Through the other open
door I can see a whole pile of leather, some eighteen by thirty
inches square, reddish yellow, a cobbler's stool, and a still
burning cigar lying in an enormous ashtray made to look like
a pond with swans. After unsuccessful settlement proceedings
and a successful, but not fraudulent, bankruptcy, old Mr.
Bechtold had to shut down his shoemaker's business, and he
now had a modest shoe-repair shop in the living room, as well
as earning "you can't call it a living, let's just say an existence"
(quotation from my mother-in-law) as a leather salesman.

An embarrassed silence follows, to be expected, no doubt,
after a miracle. Should anyone wish to ask at this point: "How
did the Bechtolds know you were coming, and even if they
knew your mother had died—what exactly did she die of,
anyway?—how could Engelbert let you know so fast that they
could prepare such a wonderful welcome for you?" the only
honest reply I can give is that shrug of the shoulders a person
gives who hasn't the faintest idea of the answer and with
which I have reduced many a questioner to despair. And when
I go on to add that our camp of fellow-sharers in national
destiny was situated more than 200 miles from Cologne, in

the heart of the forest from which came most of Grimms'
fairy tales, that Angel was permanently confined to barracks,
that, although the Bechtolds must have known I was coming,
they were demonstrably unaware that my mother had died—
I can only point to angelic messengers or the tom-tom as a
source of news; I at any rate know no other explanation—and
in the midst of this embarrassed silence old man Bechtold said
to his sons, with a motion of his head I found quite uncanny
(it reminded me of a myrmidon's nod): "You might as well
settle it with him right away." I was torn from Hildegard's
arms and led off in the direction of the easel, a door was
slammed shut behind me. I saw two untidy beds, two dressers,
a bookshelf with suspiciously few books (some seven to ten),
but a lot of painting gear, also a dozen or so fresh canvasses
of Anton's all based on a series of sins ("Sin among the Middle
Classes," "Sin among the Lower Middle Classes," "Sin in the
Proletariat," "Sin in the Church," etc.).

I was made to sit down on a wooden chest, Johann pressed
a leather dice box into my hand and told me "to try my luck
on the floor." I shook the dice box, turned it upside down on
the floor—although it was my first and last dice game, Anton
and Johann nodded approval at my technique. I threw two
fives and a six, which made Johann flip his cigarette into the
air in fury and shout "Oh shit!" (I quote). Here I must add
that these two male Bechtolds, unlike Angel and their father,
were dark-haired, short and tough, and wore little Mephisto-
phelean mustaches. When after they had both thrown pitiful
twos and threes, I shyly asked what the stake was, they indicated dumbly that I was to throw again, and this time I threw
two fives and a four, which provoked them both to such lurid
utterances that I shall pass over them with the same celestial
courtesy as over the pastor's hypocrisy. I find certain forms
of male frankness in sexual terminology as suspect as candy

floss, unless they have a place in professional jargon—pimps, for example. Perhaps my association with pimps had made me rather choosy in this respect, sensitive to style: anyway, I did not blush, which is what the other two had evidently expected. I started to sweat, I felt the bad odor suddenly cling to me again, but it was not till I had won the third round by an easy margin that it dawned on me what the stake was: which of the three Bechtold brothers was to make the sacrifice of joining the S.A. They had picked me to shake the dice box in Angel's place. One of old man Bechtold's former school-mates, who among other things was in charge of supplying leather to the S.A. units of Cologne South, West and North, had hinted that Bechtold could "count on a sizable order if at least one of your sons decides to join our ranks." That de-spite my mother-in-law's protests one of them did join, that despite my victorious throws it was Angel who applied for admission in the S.A., and I did not want him to be there all by himself so I applied for admission at the same time as he did; that we both had the misfortune to be accepted although our commanding officer issued a very bad report on us, I couldn't even produce a baptism certificate—to elab-orate on such complicated procedures, let alone render them credible, is beyond me: for this page in the coloring book I suggest a frenzied pencil scrawl, standing for a stylized dense forest. When I go on to admit that every Christmas, every single year, regardless of where I happened to be (once I spent it in prison), I received a little parcel containing half a pound of Speculatius cookies, three cigarettes, and two chocolate wafers, from the "Stormtroopers' unit, Cologne South," accompanied by a mimeographed letter that started off "To our S.A. comrades at the front" and was signed "Thinking of you all, Your Unit Leader," it becomes obvious that I was justly included in the category of exploiters of the system, in spite of the fact that old man Bechtold never got his order and never sold so much as a single ounce of leather to the S.A. It is galling enough to commit acts of stupidity, but it is even more galling to commit them uselessly. However, this confession makes it possible for me to supply a splendid contribution for the pages covering six years of my life: for each page, a little box about three by five inches square.

I must not forget to mention the sole survivor, apart from my father, mother-in-law and father-in-law, from the year 1938: my brother-in-law Johann. After a sinful youth, war actually made a man of him and cleansed him; fully restored to the (Catholic) religion of his fathers, he came home with the rank of infantry sergeant, went to university, got his degree, took up the respected career of textile merchant (doctor of political science), and today dismisses his deceased brother as "a queer fish, a radical Leftist." He regards me with suspicion because the blemish of membership in the S.A. still clings to me. Naturally I have too much celestial courtesy to remind him of the dice scene in the bedroom of my brothers-in-law. I believe if I actually did try to remind him he would look at me as if I were a liar.

If I fail to mention either my daughter or granddaughter, my son-in-law or mother-in-law, as being still alive, or even merely alive, it is because I have something else in store for them. In order of my affection I shall make use of them as keystones in the closing pages of this idyllic coloring book. I shall chip away at them a bit and stylize them, to make them fit in and look decorative.

My mother-in-law's insistence on a speedy wedding was not a matter of calculation, although she admitted to me time and again how glad she was to get her daughter married off

so satisfactorily. It was her anxiety to legalize and sanction
something she calld "unmistakable sensuality" and "this forever being together." Furthermore, she confessed quite frankly
that she was afraid of "illegitimate grandchildren or those
born too soon after the wedding." Inasmuch as I was of age
and the photocopying machines were running at full speed
to keep up with the demand for proof of Aryan origin, and
any document was readily obtainable at low cost (except for
my baptism certificate), after a hasty and depressing funeral
(my mother's) there was a hasty wedding, of which there is
even a photo. In this photo Hildegard looks strangely despondent, and the faces of my two brothers-in-law show mocking
grins. A civil marriage certificate exists with swastikas and
German eagles, in which I am described as an "arts student,
at present laborer." Since Hildegard desired our union to be
blessed in church, there is also a church marriage certificate
bearing the stamp of the parish of St. John the Baptist. A
wedding breakfast was held in the Bechtolds' apartment ("I'm
certainly not going to be done out of that"), a quadrille and
a polka were improvised before we were allowed to withdraw
to the hastily rented furnished room near Clovis Square (rent,
twenty-five marks a month), for a marriage which was supposed to last about twenty-three hours but actually lasted
nearly a week. Should youthful or even mature readers regard
this period as too short for a marriage, allow me to point out
that many a marriage that has gone on for twenty years has
not lasted a week, and if the fact that I was arrested, not on
the first day but on the seventh, and taken away to a (different) compulsory body of mutual fellowship, should arouse
suspicion toward or contempt for the authorities, I must point
to the loyalty of the Bechtold clan and my father, who stated
that we had "left town, destination unknown." We never
discovered who actually betrayed us. I was arrested in Batteux'

dairy in the Severin-Strasse while, still in my olive-drab trousers
and carrying a blue-and-white-striped shopping bag, I was buying some butter and eggs (rationed now) for our breakfast
(the fresh rolls were already in my shopping bag), and Hildegard was tidying up our room. Witless, lost in a kind of bliss-
ful timelessness, I mistook the two fellows in olive-drab uniforms, who suddenly grabbed my arms, for a bad dream, the
cries of the nice salesgirls at Batteux' for demonstrations of
sympathy (which is what they were). I resisted, shouted abuse
(contrary to my usual practice), and at the subsequent hearing
displayed not only no remorse but something which was entered in the files rather engagingly as "obstinate pride." The
remaining weeks which I should otherwise have spent among
my fellow-sharers in national destiny, I spent in a variety of
prisons and dungeons, a few days in the Cologne municipal
jail where I made my written application for admission into
the S.A. Angel I never saw again, and Hildegard not for nearly
two years. We were permitted to exchange a few censored
letters; to my mind a censored letter is not a letter at all, except as a sign of life. The few illegal visits Hildegard paid me
and I paid her cannot be called marriage, they were merely
assignations.

Meanwhile, equipped now with a proper dossier, I was
shifted from one mutual-fellowship camp to another, spent
a further five days of marriage in 1940, when my daughter was
born, and another two weeks again early in 1941, after I had
recovered from the head wound I received from a Frenchman,
who had every reason to take me for his enemy: I ran into
him as he was hurrying across the road one night with two
machine guns which obviously emanated from the armory of
the mutual-fellowship camp I was in at the time. In my best
mother-superior French I begged him not to put me in a position which might compel me to be discourteous—in what way

I had no idea; I suggested he just throw the things down and run away or, for all I cared, run away *with* the things in such a way that, without being discourteous, I could follow him without catching him up, since I was not interested in active combat—but he never let me finish, he shot me in the head with his automatic, left me lying in a pool of blood on the road, and put me in the awkward position of "turning out, much to everyone's surprise, to be a hero," as the commandant of the mutual-fellowship camp later put it. I find this incident highly embarrassing, I only mention it for the sake of literary composition.

This brings me to the end of the topics of war and marriage, and from now on only the rose perfume of peace shall prevail. Any wartime or postwar elements which, for quantitative reasons, I may be obliged to mention, will be presented in stylized form: either as art nouveau, genre art, or the mannerist style. In any case, they will be transposed back into art-historical periods with picture-postcard appeal. My feelings toward the war are not so much those of the tea drinker toward the coffee business as those of a pedestrian toward motorcars.

VII

As such—as a pedestrian toward motorcars—I now offer some historical material all by itself. I offer it raw, naked, using not my pencil but only my scissors. Let each person do with it or make out of it what he likes: cut out ornaments for his children or paper the walls with it. Nor is the material complete—on the contrary, it is very incomplete; anyone so inclined may stick the pieces together and make a kite and let it sail way up into the air, or he may bend over it with a magnifying glass and count the flyspecks. Magnified or reduced: the material I offer is genuine; what anyone does with it is not my business. It might serve as a kind of mourning edge to be stuck around the pages of the coloring book. I realized it all at the time, yet it was not real to me—and so I leave to each reader to form his own reality out of it.

In Aachen, the first Reich chess tournament was held, sponsored by the "Strength Through Joy" movement. A player called John used the French defense, a player called Lehmann the Queen Indian, Zabiensky the Dutch. A certain Tiltju defeated a certain Rüsken, who never got moving with his Sicilian defense.

In London a meeting took place between German and English veterans who expressed their common wish, their desire, for a true peace.

In Berlin there was a convention of animal psychologists. It was declared during this gathering that animal psychologists were linked to human psychology in ideals, strife, and work. A Professor Jaensch spoke with particular emphasis on the psychology of the domestic chicken and said many problems in human psychology could be greatly aided by studying the psychology of the chicken, because the chicken's life perspective, like the human one, is determined by the sense of sight. The chicken—he said—was the psychologist's pet, while the rabbit might be called the physiologist's pet.

On the same day a convention took place in Berlin on heating and ventilation, in the course of which some principles of ventilation as well as the ventilation regulations of the Standards Association were discussed in detail.

"The time of your life" was promised by a Cologne beer-hall called Zillertal. Millowitsch was appearing in "The Skunk," and the civic theater was doing "The Taming of the Shrew."

In Cologne there was also a meeting that day of thirty-five "Hitler-holidaymakers," who were warmly welcomed by some president or other who pointed out to them that during those days the whole world was looking toward the Rhineland.

Needless to say, the birth rate was declining in Europe.

Comrades of the former 460th Infantry Regiment and the 237th Infantry Division announced their next reunion. In Salzrümpchen at the law school.

As for football, the great question that day was: Will the teams now heading the leagues be able to maintain their position?

A reporter gives a lively account of the progress in the building of the fortifications in the Western part of the Reich:

As we turn the corner, we see the steaming field kitchen coming up the hill toward us drawn by two powerful horses. It smells of sauerkraut and boiled pork.

It is not easy to find a particular place. Everything is so new here. No one here can give any information. The workman knows nothing about the surrounding area. He knows his place of work, he knows the way to his camp. That is all he is interested in. Anyone giving information does so unwillingly and hesitatingly. Everyone displays a healthy distrust.

Everywhere there are camps; we have passed quite a lot of them on our way here, but we want to go to where Dr. Ley was yesterday.

Over there is a fellowship camp in the truest sense of the

words. Men from all parts of Germany have gathered together
here: from Mecklenburg, from Pomerania, Hamburg, West-
phalia, Thüringia, Berlin, and from Cologne a goodly number
too. We remember from the war that humor and cheerfulness
always prevailed wherever there were men from Cologne in a
unit. This is just as true here, but that is not the only reason.
The cheerfulness here, says the head cook, is the best sign
that the men's stomachs are being well looked after. We have
no reason to doubt him, for the leftovers from the midday
meal which have been kept for us are very tasty. The Labor
Front has the food distribution well in hand, and looks after
these things just as well as it does the spiritual needs of the
workmen, and one is bound to admit that

EVERYTHING HUMANLY POSSIBLE IS BEING DONE

Each man receives per day: 4 oz. of meat, 28 oz. of potatoes,
8 to 16 oz. of vegetables (according to the variety), 28 oz. of
bread, 2 to 3 oz. of butter, 4 oz. of sausage, cheese, etc., as
well as chocolate, cigars, cigarettes or canned fruit.

The movie truck is in constant use, the camps are provided
with radios and libraries, also chess and other indoor games,
as well as athletic equipment.

We have seen for ourselves: our Western front stands. These
fortifications are being built by Germans. It is the entire German nation which is building its wall of defense here.

With Strength Through Joy through Greece and Yugoslavia.
Five ocean giants will cruise to the South during 1938/39.
The National Socialist "Strength Through Joy" movement
has organized a series of Mediterranean cruises for the coming
winter of 1938/39 surpassing all previous programs.

A colonel of the General Staff by the name of Foertsch

has published a detailed study of the significance of reserve
training. In sober language he gave as his opinion that the
military manpower resources of a nation lie primarily in its
trained reserve units. Certain negative feelings existing temporarily among those recalled for duty would, he said, quickly
disappear when people came once again to that realization
which on Memorial Day, 1935, had caused the whole nation
with one accord to breathe a sigh of relief at the reintroduc-
tion of conscription. The understanding of the security needs
of the state and the nation's spirit of self-sacrifice, he said,
were the two poles governing the extent to which security
could be maintained. If an entire generation, he went on, was
able for four years to carry on a struggle of indescribable
heroism, it was only because for that generation four weeks
of reserve duty had not been too much.

The Legal Advice Bureau of the German Labor Front has
announced a decision of the Reich Labor Tribunal (No.
154/37) that refusal to join the German Labor Front is cause
for dismissal without notice. The Legal Advice Bureau con-
curred with this decision—that such refusal is cause for dismissal without notice, dismissal with notice on grounds of
nonmembership in the German Labor Front having long been
regarded as justifiable; furthermore, dismissal without notice
is permissible in cases where nonmembership arises from an
antisocial attitude.

CUT OUT—KEEP—PIN UP

Every house must be prepared for fire-fighting during air raids
and contain at least the minimum air-raid-precaution equipment.

1. As many buckets as possible.
2. Water tub of at least twenty-five gallons capacity.

3. A mop for extinguishing flames and hard-to-reach fire spots. This is to consist of a pole with a piece of cloth on the end to be dipped in water before use.

4. A sandbox with at least two cubic feet of sand or earth and a simple sand shovel (e.g., coal shovel) or

5. Scoops, spades, shovels.

6. Axes and hatchets.

7. Demolition pole (wooden pole with steel hook).

8. Rope (a long, sturdy washing-line).

Most of such items are to be found in the home or can be made at little cost. As soon as the ARP siren is sounded, this equipment is to be placed in the hallways and passages and distributed according to the air-raid warden's instructions.

Weather forecast: Winds southerly, light to moderate, some fog patches in the morning, otherwise sunny, cloudy at times and moderately warm. Further outlook: fair and dry. Due to an interaction of warm subtropical air and mild sea air, there was some precipitation yesterday over northwest France and the English Channel. However, this weak ridge of disturbance was unable to extend its influence appreciably toward the east. On the other hand, owing to a general rise in barometric pressure over western and central Europe, the eastern European high-pressure area was able to advance in a westerly direction. Atmospheric disturbances over the Atlantic which made themselves felt this morning by winds of hurricane force between Ireland and Newfoundland will for the time being have no effect on West Germany. Maximum temperature: 72 degrees; average temperature: 68 degrees; last night's low: 60 degrees. No precipitation.

A sculptor found it necessary to notify the public that an official government emblem showing the German eagle, commissioned by the Army for a military headquarters building, was produced by an old-established firm of art metalworkers —but had been designed by *him*.

To give those readers who are not from the Rhineland some idea of the mother-poetry of those days, here is a translation from a poem written at that time in the local Cologne dialect:

> Go out into the world, my lad,
> No harm can come to you,
> Mother does not feel too sad,
> Your former comrades, too
>
> Have left their parents' hearth and home,
> And traveled south and west,
> Mother knows you have to roam,
> "My son, you were the best.
>
> What'er betide you, good or ill,
> You never must forget
> That home, sweet home, awaits you still,
> And that I miss you yet."
>
> How brave is such a mother's heart,
> Braver than soldiers all.
> And yet one thing is sure,
> When you're out there and far apart
> Her tears will freely fall.

The announcement that the International Hairdressers' Convention was to be held in Cologne, that twenty different nations had agreed to participate, that the first world hairdressing championship was to take place and a contest announced for the challenge trophy donated by Dr. Ley, will fill everyone—at least, all the inhabitants of Cologne—with legitimate pride.

In going on to report some activities of the Bergisch-Gladbach Rabbit Breeders Association, my purpose is not to hold

these worthy people up to ridicule. Nor is it for the sake of
any literary considerations apropos the above-mentioned convention of animal psychologists: it is based on a certain sense
of justice, and especially because some of my friends used to
live in this little town. The Bergisch-Gladbach Rabbit Breeders Association announced its annual family outing, which this
year was to be a "mystery trip." Friends and supporters were
heartily invited to avail themselves of the fun in store for them.

The announcement in the same town of the Veterans' and
Home Guard Association's monthly reunion, and the promise
of the local branch of the National Socialist "Strength Through
Joy" movement of a gay and enjoyable evening, are mentioned here merely for the sake of completeness.

There are a few minor items which I must take care not
to overlook, for, although they are known to "the merest
child," there is reason to believe they are not known to the
merest grown-up, and so I am taking pains to reiterate what
is known to "the merest child":

That in the weeks surrounding September 22, perhaps even
on that very day, the discovery was made in the Kaiser Wilhelm Institute in Berlin-Dahlem of that new type of nuclear
reaction with which we are all familiar. A few months later,
with the caution so characteristic of science, the first research
reports were published; and a month after that nuclear phys-
icists all over the world knew that the atom bomb was a technical possibility and that a new era was dawning.

The fact that on that day, September 22, 1938, the Prime
Minister of England, Neville Chamberlain, arrived in Bad
Godesberg to discuss the so-called Sudeten crisis, is familiar
not only to the merest child but virtually to every infant, and

I reiterate it now for grown-ups only. "After Chamberlain,"
wrote one chronicler of that historic day, "had arrived from
Cologne, he looked with evident pleasure out of his window
across to the Rhine valley basking in the sunshine, and expressed his complete satisfaction with the choice of this symbolically unrestricted view. He allowed himself to be photog-
raphed with that open, friendly smile which his bold flight
made world-famous practically overnight."

VIII

My three-year-old granddaughter never calls me Grandfather, just Wilhelm; when she talks about me to other people,
she says "he has" or "Wilhelm has." So I am never prepared
for it when she asks me about her grandmother. While we
walk along the Leystapel and the Frankenwerft as far as the
Kaiser Friedrich Embankment and back (slowly, I am not
too steady on my legs), I tell her about Anna Bechtold, my
mother-in-law: how she was sent to prison because of her row
with the military police, how she broke out twice, the first
time managed to get as far as Gremberghoven and the second
time as far as Cologne-Deutz, but was caught both times. I
tell it like a folk ballad, letting the bombs whine as they fall,
the shells burst, the M.P.'s appear in all their martial fierceness.
My little granddaughter Hilde then tugs impatiently at my
hand, pointing out that she wants me to tell her about her
grandmother, not her great-grandmother. I clamber up and
down the genealogical tree till I think I have reached the right
branch and tell her about Katharina Berthen, the mother of
her father (my son-in-law), a person I avoid as much as possible although she is a beautiful woman, the same age as I am,
and at one time efforts were underway to couple me with her:
she reminds me too much of all my skittish cousins, whose

parlor games I still have lurid memories of, more lurid than the professional love nest of the lady called Hertha with whom I so often exchanged letters, although not on my own behalf. The appalling lassitude of professional vice—after five years of professional practice it reverts to something almost like innocence. (Is he really dead? Yes. Did you see it with your own eyes? Yes. Where? How sad—no muffled drums. And he was so fond of caramel pudding.) "Of course, the Berthens come from a very old Cologne family, way back in. . . ." No, she tugs at my arm with both hands, as if she were pulling on a bell rope. Grandmother means Hildegard. It is not easy to imagine that there is someone who thinks of Hildegard as a grandmother. What can I tell about her? Nothing. That she was fair and very sweet, that she liked curtains as much as books and geraniums; that at Batteux' they always gave her more eggs than her ration? Who can describe innocence? Not me. Who can describe the happiness and ecstasies of love? Not me. Am I to present Hildegard to my three-year-old granddaughter as if for inspection: properly washed and naked? No thanks. Give a detailed account of some three dozen breakfasts? Not me. It is not so difficult to explain to a three-year-old child what absent without leave means, but absent from *what*, I doubt if I can explain that. You become human when you go absent without leave from your unit: I found this out, and offer it as candid advice to later generations. (But watch out when they start shooting! There are some idiots who aim to hit!) For my granddaughter I just portray her as a genre painter might: a pretty young woman leaning over the sill of her attic window, watering her geraniums with a yellow watering-can. Visible in the background are Dostoevsky's "Idiot" next to Christian Morgenstern, Grimms' Fairy Tales, and "Michael Kohlhaas" in the kitchen closet between two china jars marked RICE and SUGAR, in front of the

closet a buggy containing a babbling infant for whom someone (me! I beat my breast in remorse) has made a rattle
out of some old uniform buckles and string. With the snoop-
er's telescope, one would be able to see on the buckles a spade
flanked by wheat ears. (Was that my mother? Yes.) Whenever I choose the Holzmarkt and the Bayen-Strasse for our
walk, instead of the Leystapel and the Frankenwerft, and
consent to go along the boulevard beside the Ubier Ring, a
child's persistence drags me relentlessly to the street whose
name I once revealed, whose location I once betrayed. (Where
was the house? Over there. Which was your room? Just about
there. How come my mother wasn't hit by the bomb? She
was at Grandmother's. You mean Great-Grandmother? Yes.)
I solemnly make her a promise I intend to keep: to read to
her from "The Idiot," from "Michael Kohlhaas" and Christian Morgenstern; I have already read to her from Grimms'
Fairy Tales. Our walks in the direction of the Bayen-Strasse
usually end up at Great-Grandmother's. Coffee is drunk (not
by me), cake is eaten (Rodons, elsewhere known as Gugelhupf, not by me), cigarettes are smoked (not by me), rosaries
are said (not by me). While all this is going on, I clasp my
hands behind my back, walk to the window, look across to
the Severin Gate. Whenever airplanes appear over the city
or—as the newspapers so charmingly put it—skim over it, I
suddenly find myself in the grip of that almost epileptic
twitching that is at the bottom of all the dispute over my
health, and by this time, if not before, everyone must have
realized what astute readers have perceived long ago: that I
am a neurotic. These attacks often go on for a long time, on
the way home I begin to drag my legs, jerk my arms. Recently
a mother explained to her five-year-old son in a loud clear
voice, pointing at me as she did so: "See that man? That's a
typical case of Parkinson's disease"—which I am not. Some-

times the sight of steam-shovels sets me off jerking like that, and whispering to myself "Work makes us free," and this recently caused a young man behind me to say: "There's another one of those." Since—as a result of my head wound— I also stammer, and the only words that flow smoothly from my lips are those I sing, and what is more suitable for singing than the lines "German women, German honor, German wine and German song"? I have to hear "There's another one of those" quite frequently. I am used to it. The fact that my clean hands usually have dirty nails, that I have never applied for a disabled veteran's pension, which means I have no document to prove the origin of my palpable impairments, gives rise to additional "There's another one of those." I have no intention whatever of making this concession to sound common sense.

The only advice I accept is my mother-in-law's. "You need a shave. Pay more attention to your business. Don't get annoyed over that fellow Berthen your daughter was silly enough to marry. Doesn't anyone sew your buttons on for you? Come here!"

It's true: I am not very good at sewing, and I shall be glad to supply the coloring book with a dozen torn-off buttons, both round and oblong, for each year of my life from twenty-one to forty-eight. The reader may transform and color the round buttons any way he likes, and the oblong ones too. If he feels so inclined, he may turn the round ones into daisies or asters, he can also make them into coins or clocks, into full moons, into pepper pots or wall plugs seen from above, any round object is a legitimate button-variation for his imagination. He can turn them into party badges, or St. Christopher medals. The oblong ones, the kind which are always sewn much too loosely onto duffel coats and related garments, can easily be turned into half-moons, croissants or commas, Christ-

mas decorations or sickles. For each year up to 1949 I will
generously fork out a dozen round and oblong buttons, and
for each year after 1949 half a dozen, and I will also throw in
a few worn-out zippers, excellent for turning into tangled
undergrowth or barbed wire. Then the tiny shirt buttons—
round ones only, I am afraid—we will just take a few hand-
fuls of these and sprinkle them like sugar on a doughnut.
Sock holes, shirt holes, even the great big ones, there are
plenty of those, especially suitable for snoopers too, for, as the
merest child knows (I repeat it here for the benefit of grown-
ups with their short memories), there is nothing so archae-
ologically pregnant as a hole. A widower like me, who has always steadfastly refused to sew anything, just as he had steadfastly refused to clean his shoes, has holes to offer in abundance. Not long ago, one of the few shoeshine men to be
found around here told me reproachfully: "I see you don't
know how to look after your shoes." I am sure he used to be
a sergeant-major, and Germans are born pedagogues. My
mother-in-law is not a pedagogue, she just tugs gently at my
clothes, picks fluff off my coat, straightens my shoulders by
"arranging" the padding in my jacket and coat, she bends
down (not to undo but) to tighten my shoelaces and tuck
them in. She places my hat on my head at the angle she considers smart (meaning, the angle that used to be smart in
the twenties), bursts into tears without warning, puts her
arms around me, kisses me on both cheeks, and maintains I
have always been more of a son to her than all her sons, except of course for Angel, "who was much more than a son."
Her son Johannes she always refers to simply as a "sourpuss,"
her daughters-in-law as "nothing but nuisances" and her husband as a "renegade proletarian" who, now that he has even
acquired a poodle (yellow collar, yellow leash) has ceased to
exist for her. "If we were divorced, we couldn't be more di-

vorced." And when she adds: "You're still absent without leave," I know what she means.

Now and again I invite her out to lunch, followed by a taxi ride through Cologne to give her a good look at how a destroyed city can destroy. I get a receipt for the dinner (she has a healthy appetite and appreciates "something special") and the taxi ride, and write on the receipt "discussion among business associates." My manager, who is as upright as he is accurate, suffers a slight bilious attack every time, first because it should be *with* instead of *among*, and then "because it is unethical." Recently when we were in a taxi my mother-in-law gave me a "penetrating" look with her dark eyes and said: "You know what you really could do, what you could take up?" "No," I said nervously. "You could go back to university," she said. And with that she managed to make me laugh for the first time in eighteen years, in a way which I can only describe as hearty. The last time I laughed that heartily was when an American lieutenant called me a "fuckin' German Nazi." Probably both are (were) right: my mother-in-law and the American lieutenant. At the time I sang in an undertone the words I now so often sing to myself almost compulsively, especially when I am sitting on the terrace of the Café Reichard: "German women, German honor, German wine and German song. . . ."

Sometimes we sit together on the café terrace, and, without expecting or making any comments, much less offering consolation, I let her cry quietly to herself, for her children who have died, and reflect on the fact that not one of her dead children has found a resting place in a churchyard. No grave to put flowers on, no dream or vision of that gentle, flowery peace which makes churchyards so appealing to romantics (like me), so full of healing to neurotics (like me), where under trees and shrubs, with widows weeding near by (strangely enough one hardly ever sees widowers weeding), they can meditate on the transitoriness of man's mortal self.

"Just opposite the cathedral," on the terrace of the Café Reichard, I have every reason to wish I was standing in the market square of Ballaghaderreen and could wait there for the next circus, due to arrive in about eight months.

When my granddaughter asks why her great-grandmother is crying, she has more in common with the waiters and their customers, who are embarrassed by an "oddly dressed, weeping old woman," than with us, and by asking such a question she puts us in the Neanderthal category. My daughter and son-in-law "flatly refuse" to go out with us. My daughter is sufficiently respectful not to analyze the reasons for this refusal, but my son-in-law describes us as being "something between half-witted and antisocial." My granddaughter still possesses the innocence that renders us fit company in her eyes. If I were to answer her question and tell her that here, six or eight feet away from us, one of her great-uncles had been executed, she would believe me less than her two great-grandfathers, who are so expert at dating their archaeological finds. And if I were to tell her that there are people who weep at gravesides, at places of execution, especially when one of those who were executed was her son, the child would probably already have learned that such sentiments derive merely from complexes or feelings of hostility. Even mention of the Blessed Virgin, who is said to have wept beside the Cross, would not preserve my mother-in-law from listening to such phrases, or my brother-in-law's execution from being vaguely seen by her in terms of a movie. Not because but although she is being brought up a Catholic, the child is past saving. She will wear her religion like a rare perfume that in a few years will have become a connoisseur's item.

While my mother-in-law is crying quietly, drying her tears

with a handkerchief which is much too large, and my granddaughter is eating ice cream, I am busy inventing a genuinely Brazilian-sounding name for our bill which I intend to present to my conscientious manager for a tax voucher. I hesitate between Oliveira and Espinhaco, whom I hereby declare to be coffee planters or wholesalers and with whom I shall swear at any time to have had business discussions. I shall raise my right hand and swear to the authenticity of Oliveira or Espinhaço. I shall probably also add a Margarita or a Juanita, for whom I shall likewise swear to have ordered flowers sent to their hotel.

Is it necessary, since I have already confessed to being a tea drinker, to enlarge on what the coffee business means to me? Nothing, of course. I do not feel the slightest moral tie with this branch of business. I sign anything my manager puts before me without even looking at it. Now and again I am forced to participate in meetings with planters, wholesalers, or bankers, and needless to say I have hanging in my wardrobe for such purposes what is known as a "business suit." My stammering and nervous twitching seem not only attractive but positively elegant. They lend me a certain air of decadence, enhanced by the fact that I ostentatiously drink tea. As soon as the conversation shows the faintest sign of becoming personal, I cut it off with a brief gesture and an expression meriting the epithet disgusted. I have never been one for familiarity, and "the human touch" has always reminded me too much of the inhuman touch. My son-in-law, who is present at these meetings and naturally admires my style in one way but in another way (understandably enough) detests it, looks at me as if I were an excavated statue which suddenly begins to move.

I am soon going to move in altogether with my mother-in-law, and probably follow her inspired advice to "go back to

university." But I must wait till the business has been transferred to my son-in-law de jure and de facto. He has warned
me himself, he has urged me, to read each paragraph in our
contract very carefully "and not to rely on humanitarian feelings which in business life simply don't exist." This warning
is almost humane, at any rate it is conscientious, and since
I do not trust conscientious people who have no style, I shall
read the contract carefully. Old Mr. Bechtold gave up his
room long ago, but there are still some leather samples lying
around in it, and his cobbler's stool is still there (he carted
it around with him each of the five times they moved house),
although from the day I threw dice with his sons over who
should join the S.A. he never repaired another shoe. The walls
will have to be repapered, my furniture will have to be moved
in there. Anna Bechtold has set up a program for our life
together: "Studying while absent without leave." I have promised her that finally, after more than twenty years, I will find
out what was meant by the "Rhenish florin" Hildegard was
so excited about the evening before she was killed, when she
brought little Hildegard over to her grandmother's. We shall,
of course, be "at home to relatives," we have no intention, if
only because of the necessity of obtaining food supplies, of
walling up our front door. Johannes, the "sourpuss," will come,
her "tiresome daughters-in-law," her grandchildren and great-
grandchildren. My son-in-law will come now and again and
with a crafty smile give me to understand that he has managed to cheat me, and his conscience will be perfectly clear
for, after all, he did warn me. I shall even put up with my
mother-in-law's romantic notions of "student's digs." As she
is experienced in dealing with "furnished gentlemen," I accept her ideas, since I have none myself, of "smartness" (as
it was in the twenties) which so far she has only been able
to put into practice with my hats. She has even agreed to
make a study of the preparation of tea.

Have I already mentioned that, although she is not illiterate, she can hardly write at all, and that she has chosen me as the one to whom she wishes to dictate her memoirs: with the blackest possible ink on the whitest possible paper? If I have not mentioned it before, I do so now.

IX

My son-in-law has requested that, since I am giving away family secrets, I insert "a little more publicity, even if it is negative," for him and his wife. As far as my daughter is concerned, I find myself in an awkward situation: by the end of the war, when she was four years old, she had been through one thousand air raids (my mother-in-law refused to leave Cologne, "you see, two of my children died here")—and I have no right to object to a certain hunger for life on the part of my daughter which manifests itself outwardly in an anxious materialism. Even her very best qualities—she doesn't talk much, and she is generous—are rooted in anxiety. She has little patience with me (owing to certain injuries I am slow—dressing and undressing, eating, and my occasional attacks fill her with ill-concealed disgust), but I am only too willing to forgive her ten embarrassments for every air raid, and in this way she has an inexhaustible credit. The disappointing fact that she resembles me rather than Hildegard (which gives her more grounds for annoyance than it does me) increases her credit. Her piety is also anxiety-ridden: precise, law-abiding, and because of her mixed marriage she is at present wrapped up in a church council euphoria which will gradually abate like the effect of a drug. The smile we exchange whenever we meet is merely another way of shrugging our shoulders. She is completely under the influence of my father and father-in-law, and already assiduously collecting "little antique pieces" with which to furnish my rooms when

I leave. With the eye of an interior decorator she is already moving my furniture out and her own in, measuring distances, gauging effects, matching colors, and I would be neither surprised nor hurt if I came home unexpectedly one day and found her with a tape measure in her hand. That is unlikely; my lopsided walk, coupled with a leg injury, make me both slow and noisy when I climb the stairs and give ample notice of my arrival. Apropos of my stair-climbing technique, I have more than once heard the word "snail." But no one has given me the snail's blessing yet, and there has been no talk of making a man of me or carrying ordure. Sometimes I am also called an "idealist" because I have not claimed a disabled veteran's pension. I am of the modest opinion that my motives are of a more realistic nature and have to do with my anancastia. Even the study of masculine absurdity—equally useful both quantitatively and qualitatively speaking—which I could not avoid making during the war, is something I regard as an unpleasant enrichment. I am still capable of pity for this masculine absurdity, but not of respect. I shall not become resigned, I shall study, which is perhaps—and not only in my case—a form of resignation.

Anyone looking for me will find me at the spot where, without having to crane one's neck, it is possible to look across to the Severin Gate.

POSTSCRIPTA

A JEW BY A BELLOW, A GERMAN BY A KISS,
A CHRISTIAN BY BAPTISM

1. *Detailed Confession.* I did not succeed in describing the expression on the faces of the two Bechtolds when I had beaten them at the dice game: respect, amazement, mingled with hysterical mortification and resignation, and when I suggested that as a son-in-law I take over the function of a son and

join the S.A., they howled with rage: what they wanted was to see Angel sullied with the stain of being a Stormtrooper.

That all I offer of my mother is one or two dots has its reason: she was too fragile, she might fall apart, or the result might be too unsatisfactory, so I would rather each person stick a cliché, a decal, or something of the sort, into the coloring book: middle-class lady circa 1938, mid-forties, delicate but not languishing. Nauseated yes, but not for sociological reasons.

I have already acknowledged to being a romantic, a neurotic, an idyllist; I reiterate it here for the benefit of grown-ups.

I have known for twenty years what was meant by the "Rhenish florin" Hildegard was so excited about. The compulsory mutual-fellowship camp where I received the snail's blessing, became a Jew by being bellowed at, was banished to the ordure section to become a man, and met Angel, was situated in the heart of the forest in which many of the Grimm fairy tales originate. I received most of the commands, punishments and blessings meted out by the officers there in the dialect which must have been spoken by the peasant woman who told the Grimm brothers the fairy tales. Is it any wonder that I gave Hildegard "Michael Kohlhaas" and Grimms' Fairy Tales for a wedding present ("The Idiot" and Christian Morgenstern were part of her dowry), that she read them a great deal and that the story called "How the Children Played at Butchering" made the deepest impression on her, that is to say, seemed to her the most topical. She must have known it by heart, the story about the innocent child reaching for the apple instead of the coin, for she used to repeat over and over again the phrase my mother-in-law could never understand: "They're taking the Rhenish florin—the Rhenish florin!" So I know the background, a rather involved one—but I can't bring myself to explain it to my mother-in-law. Even in my own

mind, a lot of it is *supposition*. But I have no doubt whatever
as to the topical nature of the "Rhenish florin." Who would
choose the apple, when the merest child knows that for a
florin you could probably buy a hundred apples? Everyone has
been playing at Butchering, and they were not children, and
innocence is not a coin. By adding that since my wife's death
I have lived chastely, I have at least put the finishing touch to
the embarrassment, and the reader may laugh long and lustily.
And when I add that my favorite fairy tale is the one about the
Singing Bone, the laughter will grow louder still.

2. *Moral.* I urge everyone to go absent without leave. De-
fection and desertion I would advise in favor of rather than
against, for as I said: there are idiots who aim to hit, and
everyone ought to realize the risk they are running. Firearms
are instruments completely lacking in humor. I recall Angel,
and Anton Bechtold.

To go absent without leave from irregular troops is particularly dangerous because this—most thinking people do not
think far enough—gives rise automatically, as it were, to the
suspicion that the would-be absentee wishes to join the regular troops; so, watch out.

3. *Interpretation* (a) The three (white) officers' handkerchiefs given to the nuns are transmuted lilies, like the ones
found in front of the altars of St. Joseph, the Blessed Virgin,
and virgin saints in general. They stand in direct relationship
to the whitest *possible* paper, to the obsessional hand-washing,
and the aversion to inspections and cleaning one's own shoes,
to the manifest passion for cleanliness. How otherwise would
anyone perpetrate a theft of army property for the sake of a
few baths—for, although the coal came from the Lorraine, it
belonged *by rights* to the German Army—and to carry on such

complicated negotiations with nuns of all people denotes a complete and utter Platonism.

On the other hand, the frequent mention of ordure, dirty nails, and the well-nigh ecstatic portrayal of his own weaknesses: attacks of near-epilepsy, severe difficulty in walking, the morbid dislike of airplane noises which precipitate such attacks —all this permits the conclusion that the narrator is right to call himself a neurotic, and is right to describe himself as romantic and resigned. The élitist elements—even when the subject is an élite among ordure carriers—are also unmistakable. And has the dislike for the "Rhenish florin" anything to do with the (totally incomprehensible) refusal to apply for and accept whatever is "due" to him for his war injuries and disabilities?

(b) The mention of Hänsel and Gretel is traceable to a simple set of facts: in the forest the narrator absented himself several times from the group of workers, wandered around with a piece of bread in his pocket—and it was on these occasions that he missed "Gretel's comforting hand." The fact that the author mentions "The Singing Bone" as a third and favorite fairy tale denotes a connection with the "Rhenish florin."

(c) The attempt to equate study with resignation, or at least to imply their identity, is attributable to an early deep-seated dislike of botanical specimen boxes.

(d) Engel(bert) is not meant to symbolize an angel, although that is what he was called and what he is described as looking like.

(e) The narrator is concealing something. What?

4 ◈ *Nathanael West*

Nathanael West was born in New York City in 1903. He attended De Witt Clinton High School in the Bronx and was graduated from Brown University in 1924. He wrote two short, experimental novels, The Dream Life of Balso Snell (1931) and A Cool Million (1934), and two bitter, tragi-comic masterpieces, Miss Lonelyhearts (1933) and The Day of the Locust (1939), which have had a profound influence on the fiction of the past thirty years. He was killed in an automobile accident in 1940.

"SHRIKE AND MRS. SHRIKE" (FROM *MISS LONELYHEARTS*)

MISS LONELYHEARTS,
HELP ME, HELP ME

The Miss Lonelyhearts of the New York *Post-Dispatch* (Are you in trouble?—Do-you-need-advice?—Write-to-Miss-Lonely-hearts-and-she-will-help-you) sat at his desk and stared at a piece of white cardboard. On it a prayer had been printed by Shrike, the feature editor.

> "Soul of Miss L, glorify me.
> Body of Miss L, nourish me
> Blood of Miss L, intoxicate me.
> Tears of Miss L, wash me.
> Oh good Miss L, excuse my plea,
> And hide me in your heart,
> And defend me from mine enemies.
> Help me, Miss L, help me, help me.
> In sæcula sæculorum. Amen."

Although the deadline was less than a quarter of an hour away, he was still working on his leader. He had gone as far as: "Life is worth while, for it is full of dreams and peace, gentleness and ecstasy, and faith that burns like a clear white flame on a grim dark altar." But he found it impossible to continue. The letters were no longer funny. He could not go on finding the same joke funny thirty times a day for months on end. And on most days he received more than thirty letters, all of them alike, stamped from the dough of suffering with a heart-shaped cookie knife.

On his desk were piled those he had received this morning. He started through them again, searching for some clew to a sincere answer.

Dear Miss Lonelyhearts—
I am in such pain I dont know what to do sometimes
I think I will kill myself my kidneys hurt so much. My
husband thinks no woman can be a good catholic and not
have children irregardless of the pain. I was married honor-
able from our church but I never knew what married life
meant as I never was told about man and wife. My grand-
mother never told me and she was the only mother I had
but made a big mistake by not telling me as it dont pay
to be inocent and is only a big disapointment. I have 7
children in 12 yrs and ever since the last 2 I have been so
sick. I was operatored on twice and my husband promised
no more children on the doctors advice as he said I might
die but when I got back from the hospital he broke his
promise and now I am going to have a baby and I don't
think I can stand it my kidneys hurt so much. I am so sick
and scared because I cant have an abortion on account of
being a catholic and my husband so religious. I cry all the
time it hurts so much and I dont know what to do.
                                        Yours respectfully
                                        Sick-of-it-all

Miss Lonelyhearts threw the letter into an open drawer and lit a cigarette.

Dear Miss Lonelyhearts
   I am sixteen years old now and I dont know what to do and would appreciate it if you could tell me what to do. When I was a little girl it was not so bad because I got used to the kids on the block makeing fun of me, but now I would like to have boy friends like the other girls and go out on Saturday nites, but no boy will take me because I was born without a nose—although I am a good dancer and have a nice shape and my father buys me pretty clothes.
   I sit and look at myself all day and cry. I have a big hole in the middle of my face that scares people even myself so I cant blame the boys for not wanting to take me out. My mother loves me, but she crys terrible when she looks at me.
   What did I do to deserve such a terrible bad fate? Even if I did do some bad things I didnt do any before I was a year old and I was born this way. I asked Papa and he says he doesn't know, but that maybe I did something in the other world before I was born or that maybe I was being punished for his sins. I dont believe that because he is a very nice man. Ought I commit suicide?
                                                  Sincerely yours,
                                                     Desperate

The cigarette was imperfect and refused to draw. Miss Lonelyhearts took it out of his mouth and stared at it furiously. He fought himself quiet, then lit another one.

Dear Miss Lonelyhearts—
   I am writing to you for my little sister Gracie because something awfull hapened to her and I am afraid to tell mother about it. I am 15 years old and Gracie is 13 and

we live in Brooklyn. Gracie is deaf and dumb and biger
than me but not very smart on account of being deaf and
dumb. She plays on the roof of our house and dont go to
school except to deaf and dumb school twice a week on
tuesdays and thursdays. Mother makes her play on the roof
because we dont want her to get run over as she aint very
smart. Last week a man came on the roof and did something dirty to her. She told me about it and I dont know
what to do as I am afraid to tell mother on account of her
being lible to beat Gracie up. I am afraid that Gracie is
going to have a baby and I listened to her stomach last
night for a long time to see if I could hear the baby but I
couldn't. If I tell mother she will beat Gracie up awfull
because I am the only one who loves her and last time
when she tore her dress they loked her in the closet for
2 days and if the boys on the blok hear about it they will
say dirty things like they did on Peewee Conors sister the
time she got caught in the lots. So please what would you
do if the same hapened in your family.

Yours truly,
Harold S.

He stopped reading. Christ was the answer, but, if he did
not want to get sick, he had to stay away from the Christ
business. Besides, Christ was Shrike's particular joke. "Soul of
Miss L, glorify me. Body of Miss L, save me. Blood of . . ." He
turned to his typewriter.

Although his cheap clothes had too much style, he still
looked like the son of a Baptist minister. A beard would become him, would accent his Old-Testament look. But even
without a beard no one could fail to recognize the New
England puritan. His forehead was high and narrow. His nose
was long and fleshless. His bony chin was shaped and cleft
like a hoof. On seeing him for the first time, Shrike had smiled
and said, "The Susan Chesters, the Beatrice Fairfaxes and

the Miss Lonelyhearts are the priests of twentieth-century America."

A copy boy came up to tell him that Shrike wanted to know if the stuff was ready. He bent over the typewriter and began pounding its keys.

But before he had written a dozen words. Shrike leaned over his shoulder. "The same old stuff," Shrike said. "Why don't you give them something new and hopeful? Tell them about art. Here, I'll dictate:

"*Art Is a Way Out.*

"Do not let life overwhelm you. When the old paths are choked with the débris of failure, look for newer and fresher paths. Art is just such a path. Art is distilled from suffering. As Mr. Polnikoff exclaimed through his fine Russian beard, when, at the age of eighty-six, he gave up his business to learn Chinese, 'We are, as yet, only at the beginning. . . .'

"*Art Is One of Life's Richest Offerings.*

"For those who have not the talent to create, there is appreciation. For those . . .

"Go on from there."

MISS LONELYHEARTS
AND THE DEAD PAN

When Miss Lonelyhearts quit work, he found that the weather had turned warm and that the air smelt as though it had been artificially heated. He decided to walk to Delehanty's speakeasy for a drink. In order to get there, it was necessary to cross a little park.

He entered the park at the North Gate and swallowed mouthfuls of the heavy shade that curtained its arch. He walked into the shadow of a lamp-post that lay on the path like a spear. It pierced him like a spear.

As far as he could discover, there were no signs of spring. The decay that covered the surface of the mottled ground was not the kind in which life generates. Last year, he remembered, May had failed to quicken these soiled fields. It had taken all the brutality of July to torture a few green spikes through the exhausted dirt.

What the little park needed, even more than he did, was a drink. Neither alcohol nor rain would do. Tomorrow, in his column, he would ask Broken-hearted, Sick-of-it-all, Desperate, Disillusioned-with-tubercular-husband and the rest of his correspondents to come here and water the soil with their tears. Flowers would then spring up, flowers that smelled of feet.

"Ah, humanity . . ." But he was heavy with shadow and the joke went into a dying fall. He tried to break its fall by laughing at himself.

Why laugh at himself, however, when Shrike was waiting at the speakeasy to do a much better job? "Miss Lonelyhearts, my friend, I advise you to give your readers stones. When they ask for bread don't give them crackers as does the Church, and don't, like the State, tell them to eat cake. Explain that man cannot live by bread alone and give them stones. Teach them to pray each morning: 'Give us this day our daily stone.' "

He had given his readers many stones; so many, in fact, that he had only one left—the stone that had formed in his gut.

Suddenly tired, he sat down on a bench. If he could only throw the stone. He searched the sky for a target. But the gray sky looked as if it had been rubbed with a soiled eraser. It held no angels, flaming crosses, olive-bearing doves, wheels within wheels. Only a newspaper struggled in the air like a kite with a broken spine. He got up and started again for the speakeasy.

Delehanty's was in the cellar of a brownstone house that differed from its more respectable neighbors by having an armored door. He pressed a concealed button and a little round window opened in its center. A blood-shot eye appeared, glowing like a ruby in an antique iron ring.

The bar was only half full. Miss Lonelyhearts looked around apprehensively for Shrike and was relieved at not finding him. However, after a third drink, just as he was settling into the warm mud of alcoholic gloom, Shrike caught his arm.

"Ah, my young friend!" he shouted ."How do I find you? Brooding again, I take it."

"For Christ's sake, shut up."

Shrike ignored the interruption. "You're morbid, my friend, morbid. Forget the crucifixion, remember the renaissance. There were no brooders then." He raised his glass, and the whole Borgia family was in his gesture. "I give you the renaissance. What a period! What pageantry! Drunken popes . . . Beautiful courtesans . . . Illegitimate children. . . ."

Although his gestures were elaborate, his face was blank. He practiced a trick used much by moving-picture comedians— the dead pan. No matter how fantastic or excited his speech, he never changed his expression. Under the shining white globe of his brow, his features huddled together in a dead, gray triangle.

"To the renaissance!" he kept shouting. "To the renaissance! To the brown Greek manuscripts and mistresses with the great smooth marbly limbs. . . . But that reminds me, I'm expecting one of my admirers—a cow-eyed girl of great intelligence." He illustrated the word *intelligence* by carving two enormous breasts in the air with his hands. "She works in a book store, but wait until you see her behind."

Miss Lonelyhearts made the mistake of showing his annoyance.

"Oh, so you don't care for women, eh? J. C. is your only

sweetheart, eh? Jesus Christ, the King of Kings, the Miss Lonelyhearts of Miss Lonelyhearts. . . ."

At this moment, fortunately for Miss Lonelyhearts, the young woman expected by Shrike came up to the bar. She had long legs, thick ankles, big hands, a powerful body, a slender neck and a childish face made tiny by a man's haircut.

"Miss Farkis," Shrike said, making her bow as a ventriloquist does his doll, "Miss Farkis, I want you to meet Miss Lonelyhearts. Show him the same respect you show me. He, too, is a comforter of the poor in spirit and a lover of God."

She acknowledged the introduction with a masculine handshake.

"Miss Farkis," Shrike said, "Miss Farkis works in a book store and writes on the side." He patted her rump.

"What were you talking about so excitedly?" she asked.

"Religion."

"Get me a drink and please continue. I'm very much interested in the new thomistic synthesis."

This was just the kind of remark for which Shrike was waiting. "St. Thomas!" he shouted. "What do you take us for— stinking intellectuals? We're not fake Europeans. We were discussing Christ, the Miss Lonelyhearts of Miss Lonelyhearts. America has her own religions. If you need a synthesis, here is the kind of material to use." He took a clipping from his wallet and slapped it on the bar.

"ADDING MACHINE USED IN RITUAL OF WESTERN SECT . . . *Figures Will Be Used for Prayers for Condemned Slayer of Aged Recluse. . . .* DENVER, COLO., Feb. 2 (A. P.) Frank H. Rice, Supreme Pontiff of the Liberal Church of America has announced he will carry out his plan for a 'goat and adding machine' ritual for William Moya, condemned slayer, despite objection to his program by a Cardinal of the sect. Rice declared the goat would be used as part of a 'sack cloth and ashes' service shortly before and after Moya's execution, set for the week of June 20. Prayers for the condemned man's soul will be offered on an adding machine. Numbers, he explained, constitute the only universal language. Moya killed Joseph Zemp, an aged recluse, in an argument over a small amount of money."

Miss Farkis laughed and Shrike raised his fist as though to strike her. His actions shocked the bartender, who hurriedly asked them to go into the back room. Miss Lonelyhearts did not want to go along, but Shrike insisted and he was too tired to argue.

They seated themselves at a table inside one of the booths. Shrike again raised his fist, but when Miss Farkis drew back, he changed the gesture to a caress. The trick worked. She gave in to his hand until he became too daring, then pushed him away.

Shrike again began to shout and this time Miss Lonelyhearts understood that he was making a seduction speech.

"I am a great saint," Shrike cried, "I can walk on my own water. Haven't you ever heard of Shrike's Passion in the Luncheonette, or the Agony in the Soda Fountain? Then I compared the wounds in Christ's body to the mouths of a miraculous purse in which we deposit the small change of our sins. It is indeed an excellent conceit. But now let us consider the holes in our own bodies and into what these congenital wounds open. Under the skin of man is a wondrous jungle where veins like lush tropical growths hang along over-ripe organs and weed-like entrails writhe in squirming tangles of red and yellow. In this jungle, flitting from rock-gray lungs to golden intestinés, from liver to lights and back to liver again, lives a bird called the soul. The Catholic hunts this bird with bread and wine, the Hebrew with a golden ruler, the Protestant on leaden feet with leaden words, the Buddhist with gestures, the Negro with blood. I spit on them all. Phooh! And I call upon you to spit. Phooh! Do you stuff birds? No, my dears, taxidermy is not religion. No! A thousand times no. Better, I say unto you, better a live bird in the jungle of the body than two stuffed birds on the library table."

His caresses kept pace with the sermon. When he had reached the end, he buried his triangular face like the blade of a hatchet in her neck.

MISS LONELYHEARTS
AND THE LAMB

Miss Lonelyhearts went home in a taxi. He lived by himself in a room that was as full of shadows as an old steel engraving. It held a bed, a table and two chairs. The walls were bare except for an ivory Christ that hung opposite the foot of the bed. He had removed the figure from the cross to which it had been fastened and had nailed it to the wall with large spikes. But the desired effect had not been obtained. Instead of writhing, the Christ remained calmly decorative.

He got undressed immediately and took a cigarette and a copy of The Brothers Karamazov to bed. The marker was in a chapter devoted to Father Zossima.

"Love a man even in his sin, for that is the semblance of Divine Love and is the highest love on earth. Love all God's creation, the whole and every grain of sand in it. Love the animals, love the plants, love everything. If you love everything, you will perceive the divine mystery in things. Once you per-

ceive it, you will begin to comprehend it better every day. And
you will come at last to love the whole world with an all-
embracing love."

It was excellent advice. If he followed it, he would be a big
success. His column would be syndicated and the whole world
would learn to love. The Kingdom of Heaven would arrive. He
would sit on the right hand of the Lamb.

But seriously, he realized, even if Shrike had not made a sane
view of this Christ business impossible, there would be little
use in his fooling himself. His vocation was of a different sort.
As a boy in his father's church, he had discovered that something stirred in him when he shouted the name of Christ,
something secret and enormously powerful. He had played
with this thing, but had never allowed it to come alive.

He knew now what this thing was—hysteria, a snake whose
scales are tiny mirrors in which the dead world takes on a
semblance of life. And how dead the world is . . . a world of
doorknobs. He wondered if hysteria were really too steep a
price to pay for bringing it to life.

For him, Christ was the most natural of excitements. Fixing
his eyes on the image that hung on the wall, he began to
chant: "Christ, Christ, Jesus Christ. Christ, Christ, Jesus
Christ." But the moment the snake started to uncoil in his
brain, he became frightened and closed his eyes.

With sleep, a dream came in which he found himself on
the stage of a crowded theater. He was a magician who did
tricks with doorknobs. At his command, they bled, flowered,
spoke. After his act was finished, he tried to lead his audience
in prayer. But no matter how hard he struggled, his prayer was
one Shrike had taught him and his voice was that of a conductor calling stations.

"Oh, Lord, we are not of those who wash in wine, water,
urine, vinegar, fire, oil, bay rum, milk, brandy, or boric acid.

Oh, Lord, we are of those who wash solely in the Blood of the Lamb."

The scene of the dream changed. He found himself in his college dormitory. With him were Steve Garvey and Jud Hume. They had been arguing the existence of God from midnight until dawn, and now, having run out of whisky, they decided to go to the market for some applejack.

Their way led through the streets of the sleeping town into the open fields beyond. It was spring. The sun and the smell of vegetable birth renewed their drunkenness and they reeled between the loaded carts. The farmers took their horseplay good-naturedly. Boys from the college on a spree.

They found the bootlegger and bought a gallon jug of applejack, then wandered to the section where livestock was sold. They stopped to fool with some lambs. Jud suggested buying one to roast over a fire in the woods. Miss Lonelyhearts agreed, but on the condition that they sacrifice it to God before barbecuing it.

Steve was sent to the cutlery stand for a butcher knife, while the other two remained to bargain for a lamb. After a long, Armenian-like argument, during which Jud exhibited his farm training, the youngest was selected, a little, stiff-legged thing, all head.

They paraded the lamb through the market. Miss Lonelyhearts went first, carrying the knife, the others followed, Steve with the jug and Jud with the animal. As they marched, they sang an obscene version of "Mary Had a Little Lamb."

Between the market and the hill on which they intended to perform the sacrifice was a meadow. While going through it, they picked daisies and buttercups. Half way up the hill, they found a rock and covered it with the flowers. They laid the lamb among the flowers. Miss Lonelyhearts was elected priest, with Steve and Jud as his attendants. While they held the lamb, Miss Lonelyhearts crouched over it and began to chant. "Christ, Christ, Jesus Christ. Christ, Christ, Jesus Christ."

When they had worked themselves into a frenzy, he brought the knife down hard. The blow was inaccurate and made a flesh wound. He raised the knife again and this time the lamb's violent struggles made him miss altogether. The knife broke on the altar. Steve and Jud pulled the animal's head back for him to saw at its throat, but only a small piece of blade remained in the handle and he was unable to cut through the matted wool.

Their hands were covered with slimy blood and the lamb slipped free. It crawled off into the underbrush.

As the bright sun outlined the altar rock with narrow shadows, the scene appeared to gather itself for some new violence. They bolted. Down the hill they fled until they reached the meadow, where they fell exhausted in the tall grass.

After some time had passed, Miss Lonelyhearts begged them to go back and put the lamb out of its misery. They refused to go. He went back alone and found it under a bush. He crushed its head with a stone and left the carcass to the flies that swarmed around the bloody altar flowers.

MISS LONELYHEARTS
AND THE FAT THUMB

Miss Lonelyhearts found himself developing an almost insane sensitiveness to order. Everything had to form a pattern: the shoes under the bed, the ties in the holder, the pencils on the table. When he looked out of a window, he composed the skyline by balancing one building against another. If a bird flew across this arrangement, he closed his eyes angrily until it was gone.

For a little while, he seemed to hold his own but one day he found himself with his back to the wall. On that day all the inanimate things over which he had tried to obtain control took the field against him. When he touched something, it spilled or rolled to the floor. The collar buttons disappeared under the bed, the point of the pencil broke, the handle of the razor fell off, the window shade refused to stay down. He fought back, but with too much violence, and was decisively defeated by the spring of the alarm clock.

He fled to the street, but there chaos was multiple. Broken groups of people hurried past, forming neither stars nor squares. The lamp-posts were badly spaced and the flagging was of different sizes. Nor could he do anything with the harsh clanging sound of street cars and the raw shouts of hucksters. No repeated group of words would fit their rhythm and no scale could give them meaning.

He stood quietly against a wall, trying not to see or hear. Then he remembered Betty. She had often made him feel that when she straightened his tie, she straightened much more. And he had once thought that if her world were larger, were *the* world, she might order it as finally as the objects on her dressing table.

He gave Betty's address to a cab driver and told him to hurry. But she lived on the other side of the city and by the time he got there, his panic had turned to irritation.

She came to the door of her apartment in a crisp, white linen dressing-robe that yellowed into brown at the edges. She held out both her hands to him and her arms showed round and smooth like wood that has been turned by the sea.

With the return of self-consciousness, he knew that only violence could make him supple. It was Betty, however, that he criticized. Her world was not the world and could never include the readers of his column. Her sureness was based on the power to limit experience arbitrarily. Moreover, his confusion was significant, while her order was not.

He tried to reply to her greeting and discovered that his

tongue had become a fat thumb. To avoid talking, he awkwardly forced a kiss, then found it necessary to apologize.

"Too much lover's return business, I know, and I . . ." He
stumbled purposely, so that she would take his confusion for
honest feeling. But the trick failed and she waited for him to
continue:

"Please eat dinner with me."

"I'm afraid I can't."

Her smile opened into a laugh.

She was laughing at him. On the defense, he examined her
laugh for "bitterness," "sour-grapes," "a-broken-heart," "the
devil-may-care." But to his confusion, he found nothing at
which to laugh back. Her smile had opened naturally, not like
an umbrella, and while he watched her laugh folded and became a smile again, a smile that was neither "wry," "ironical"
nor "mysterious."

As they moved into the living-room, his irritation increased.
She sat down on a studio couch with her bare legs under and
her back straight. Behind her a silver tree flowered in the
lemon wall-paper. He remained standing.

"Betty the Buddha," he said. "Betty the Buddha. You have
the smug smile; all you need is the pot belly."

His voice was so full of hatred that he himself was surprised.
He fidgeted for a while in silence and finally sat down beside
her on the couch to take her hand.

More than two months had passed since he had sat with her
on this same couch and had asked her to marry him. Then she
had accepted him and they had planned their life after marriage, his job and her gingham apron, his slippers beside the
fireplace and her ability to cook. He had avoided her since. He
did not feel guilty; he was merely annoyed at having been
fooled into thinking that such a solution was possible.

He soon grew tired of holding hands and began to fidget

again. He remembered that towards the end of his last visit he had put his hand inside her clothes. Unable to think of anything else to do, he now repeated the gesture. She was naked under her robe and he found her breast.

She made no sign to show that she was aware of his hand. He would have welcomed a slap, but even when he caught at her nipple, she remained silent.

"Let me pluck this rose," he said, giving a sharp tug. "I want to wear it in my buttonhole."

Betty reached for his brow. "What's the matter?" she asked. "Are you sick?"

He began to shout at her, accompanying his shouts with gestures that were too appropriate, like those of an old-fashioned actor.

"What a kind bitch you are. As soon as any one acts viciously, you say he's sick. Wife-torturers, rapers of small children, according to you they're all sick. No morality, only medicine. Well, I'm not sick. I don't need any of your damned aspirin. I've got a Christ complex. Humanity . . . I'm a humanity lover. All the broken bastards . . ." He finished with a short laugh that was like a bark.

She had left the couch for a red chair that was swollen with padding and tense with live springs. In the lap of this leather monster, all trace of the serene Buddha disappeared.

But his anger was not appeased. "What's the matter, sweetheart?" he asked, patting her shoulder threateningly. "Didn't you like the performance?"

Instead of answering, she raised her arm as though to ward off a blow. She was like a kitten whose soft helplessness makes one ache to hurt it.

"What's the matter?" he demanded over and over again. "What's the matter? What's the matter?"

Her face took on the expression of an inexperienced gam-

bler about to venture all on a last throw. He was turning for
his hat, when she spoke.

"I love you."

"You what?"

The need for repeating flustered her, yet she managed to
keep her manner undramatic.

"I love you."

"And I love you," he said. "You and your damned smiling
through tears."

"Why don't you let me alone?" She had begun to cry. "I
felt swell before you came, and now I feel lousy. Go away.
Please go away."

MISS LONELYHEARTS
AND THE CLEAN OLD MAN

In the street again, Miss Lonelyhearts wondered what to do
next. He was too excited to eat and afraid to go home. He felt
as though his heart were a bomb, a complicated bomb that
would result in a simple explosion, wrecking the world without
rocking it.

He decided to go to Delehanty's for a drink. In the speakeasy, he discovered a group of his friends at the bar. They
greeted him and went on talking. One of them was complaining about the number of female writers.

"And they've all got three names," he said. "Mary Roberts
Wilcox, Ella Wheeler Catheter, Ford Mary Rinehart. . . ."

Then some one started a train of stories by suggesting that
what they all needed was a good rape.

"I knew a gal who was regular until she fell in with a group
and went literary. She began writing for the little magazines
about how much Beauty hurt her and ditched the boy friend
who set up pins in a bowling alley. The guys on the block got

sore and took her into the lots one night. About eight of them. They ganged her proper. . . ."

"That's like the one they tell about another female writer. When this hard-boiled stuff first came in, she dropped the trick English accent and went in for scram and lam. She got to hanging around with a lot of mugs in a speak, gathering material for a novel. Well, the mugs didn't know they were picturesque and thought she was regular until the barkeep put them wise. They got her into the back room to teach her a new word and put the boots to her. They didn't let her out for three years. On the last day they sold tickets to niggers. . . ."

Miss Lonelyhearts stopped listening. His friends would go on telling these stories until they were too drunk to talk. They were aware of their childishness, but did not know how else to revenge themselves. At college, and perhaps for a year afterwards, they had believed in literature, had believed in Beauty and in personal expression as an absolute end. When they lost this belief, they lost everything. Money and fame meant nothing to them. They were not worldly men.

Miss Lonelyhearts drank steadily. He was smiling an innocent, amused smile, the smile of an anarchist sitting in the movies with a bomb in his pocket. If the people around him only knew what was in his pocket. In a little while he would leave to kill the President.

Not until he heard his own name mentioned did he stop smiling and again begin to listen.

"He's a leper licker. Shrike says he wants to lick lepers. Barkeep, a leper for the gent."

"If you haven't got a leper, give him a Hungarian."

"Well, that's the trouble with his approach to God. It's too damn literary—plain song. Latin poetry, medieval painting, Huysmans, stained-glass windows and crap like that."

"Even if he were to have a genuine religious experience, it

would be personal and so meaningless, except to a psychologist."

"The trouble with him, the trouble with all of us, is that we have no outer life, only an inner one, and that by necessity."

"He's an escapist. He wants to cultivate his interior garden. But you can't escape, and where is he going to find a market for the fruits of his personality? The Farm Board is a failure.

"What I say is, after all one has to earn a living. We can't all believe in Christ, and what does the farmer care about art? He takes his shoes off to get the warm feel of the rich earth between his toes. You can't take your shoes off in church."

Miss Lonelyhearts had again begun to smile. Like Shrike, the man they imitated, they were machines for making jokes. A button machine makes buttons, no matter what the power used, foot, steam, or electricity. They, no matter what the motivating force, death, love or God, make jokes.

"Was their nonsense the only barrier?" he asked himself. "Had he been thwarted by such a low hurdle?"

The whisky was good and he felt warm and sure. Through the light-blue tobacco smoke, the mahogany bar shone like wet gold. The glasses and bottles, their high lights exploding, rang like a battery of little bells when the bartender touched them together. He forgot that his heart was a bomb to remember an incident of his childhood. One winter evening, he had been waiting with his little sister for their father to come home from church. She was eight years old then, and he was twelve. Made sad by the pause between playing and eating, he had gone to the piano and had begun a piece by Mozart. It was the first time he had ever voluntarily gone to the piano. His sister left her picture book to dance to his music. She had never danced before. She danced gravely and carefully, a simple dance yet formal. . . . As Miss Lonelyhearts stood at the bar, swaying slightly to the remembered music, he thought of children dancing. Square replacing oblong and being replaced by circle. Every child, everywhere; in the whole world there was not one child who was not gravely, sweetly dancing.

He stepped away from the bar and accidentally collided with a man holding a glass of beer. When he turned to beg the man's pardon, he received a punch in the mouth. Later he found himself at a table in the back room, playing with a loose tooth. He wondered why his hat did not fit and discovered a lump on the back of his head. He must have fallen. The hurdle was higher than he had thought.

His anger swung in large drunken circles. What in Christ's name was this Christ business? And children gravely dancing? He would ask Shrike to be transferred to the sports department.

Ned Gates came in to see how he was getting along and suggested the fresh air. Gates was also very drunk. When they left the speakeasy together, they found that it was snowing.

Miss Lonelyhearts' anger grew cold and sodden like the snow. He and his companion staggered along with their heads down, turning corners at random, until they found themselves in front of the little park. A light was burning in the comfort station and they went in to warm up.

An old man was sitting on one of the toilets. The door of his booth was propped open and he was sitting on the turned-down toilet cover.

Gates hailed him. "Well, well, smug as a bug in a rug, eh?"

The old man jumped with fright, but finally managed to speak. "What do you want? Please let me alone." His voice was like a flute; it did not vibrate.

"If you can't get a woman, get a clean old man," Gates sang.

The old man looked as if he were going to cry, but sud-

denly laughed instead. A terrible cough started under his
laugh, and catching at the bottom of his lungs, it ripped into
his throat. He turned away to wipe his mouth.

Miss Lonelyhearts tried to get Gates to leave, but he refused
to go without the old man. They both grabbed him and pulled
him out of the stall and through the door of the comfort
station. He went soft in their arms and started to giggle. Miss
Lonelyhearts fought off a desire to hit him.

The snow had stopped falling and it had grown very cold.
The old man did not have an overcoat, but said that he found
the cold exhilarating. He carried a cane and wore gloves because, as he said, he detested red hands.

Instead of going back to Delehanty's, they went to an Italian
cellar close by the park. The old man tried to get them to
drink coffee, but they told him to mind his own business and
drank rye. The whisky burned Miss Lonelyhearts' cut lip.

Gates was annoyed by the old man's elaborate manners.
"Listen, you," he said, "cut out the gentlemanly stuff and tell
us the story of your life."

The old man drew himself up like a little girl making a
muscle.

"Aw, come off," Gates said. "We're scientists. He's Have-
lock Ellis and I'm Krafft-Ebing. When did you first discover
homosexualistic tendencies in yourself?"

"What do you mean, sir? I . . ."

"Yeh, I know, but how about your difference from other
men?"

"How dare you . . ." He gave a little scream of indignation.

"Now, now," Miss Lonelyhearts said, "he didn't mean to
insult you. Scientists have terribly bad manners. . . . But you
are a pervert, aren't you?"

The old man raised his cane to strike him. Gates grabbed it
from behind and wrenched it out of his hand. He began to

cough violently and held his black satin tie to his mouth. Still coughing he dragged himself to a chair in the back of the room.

Miss Lonelyhearts felt as he had felt years before, when he had accidentally stepped on a small frog. Its spilled guts had filled him with pity, but when its suffering had become real to his senses, his pity had turned to rage and he had beaten it frantically until it was dead.

"I'll get the bastard's life story," he shouted, and started after him. Gates followed laughing.

At their approach, the old man jumped to his feet. Miss Lonelyhearts caught him and forced him back into his chair.

"We're psychologists," he said. "We want to help you. What's your name?"

"George B. Simpson."

"What does the B stand for?"

"Bramhall."

"Your age, please, and the nature of your quest?"

"By what right do you ask?"

"Science gives me the right."

"Let's drop it," Gates said. "The old fag is going to cry."

"No, Krafft-Ebing, sentiments must never be permitted to interfere with the probings of science."

Miss Lonelyhearts put his arm around the old man. "Tell us the story of your life," he said, loading his voice with sympathy.

"I have no story."

"You must have. Every one has a life story."

The old man began to sob.

"Yes, I know, your tale is a sad one. Tell it, damn you, tell it."

When the old man still remained silent, he took his arm and twisted it. Gates tried to tear him away, but he refused to let go. He was twisting the arm of all the sick and miserable, broken and betrayed, inarticulate and impotent. He was twist-

ing the arm of Desperate, Broken-hearted, Sick-of-it-all, Disillusioned-with-tubercular-husband.

The old man began to scream. Somebody hit Miss Lonelyhearts from behind with a chair.

MISS LONELYHEARTS
AND MRS. SHRIKE

Miss Lonelyhearts lay on his bed fully dressed, just as he
had been dumped the night before. His head ached and his
thoughts revolved inside the pain like a wheel within a wheel.
When he opened his eyes, the room, like a third wheel, revolved around the pain in his head.

From where he lay he could see the alarm clock. It was half
past three. When the telephone rang, he crawled out of the
sour pile of bed clothes. Shrike wanted to know if he intended
to show up at the office. He answered that he was drunk but
would try to get there.

He undressed slowly and took a bath. The hot water made
his body feel good, but his heart remained a congealed lump of
icy fat. After drying himself, he found a little whisky in the
medicine chest and drank it. The alcohol warmed only the
lining of his stomach.

He shaved, put on a clean shirt and a freshly pressed suit
and went out to get something to eat. When he had finished
his second cup of scalding coffee, it was too late for him to go
to work. But he had nothing to worry about, for Shrike would
never fire him. He made too perfect a butt for Shrike's jokes.
Once he had tried to get fired by recommending suicide in
his column. All that Shrike had said was: "Remember, please,
that your job is to increase the circulation of our paper. Suicide,
it is only reasonable to think, must defeat this purpose."

He paid for his breakfast and left the cafeteria. Some exercise might warm him. He decided to take a brisk walk, but he soon grew tired and when he reached the little park, he slumped down on a bench opposite the Mexican War obelisk.

The stone shaft cast a long, rigid shadow on the walk in front of him. He sat staring at it without knowing why until he noticed that it was lengthening in rapid jerks, not as shadows usually lengthen. He grew frightened and looked up quickly at the monument. It seemed red and swollen in the dying sun, as though it were about to spout a load of granite seed.

He hurried away. When he had regained the street, he started to laugh. Although he had tried hot water, whisky, exercise, he had completely forgotten sex. What he really needed was a woman. He laughed again, remembering that at college all his friends had believed intercourse capable of steadying the nerves, relaxing the muscles and clearing the blood.

But he knew only two women who would tolerate him. He had spoiled his chances with Betty, so it would have to be Mary Shrike.

When he kissed Shrike's wife, he felt less like a joke. She returned his kisses because she hated Shrike. But even there Shrike had beaten him. No matter how hard he begged her to give Shrike horns, she refused to sleep with him.

Although Mary always grunted and upset her eyes, she would not associate what she felt with the sexual act. When he forced this association, she became very angry. He had been convinced that her grunts were genuine by the change that took place in her when he kissed her heavily. Then her body gave off an odor that enriched the synthetic scent she used behind her ears and in the hollows of her neck. No similar change ever took place in his own body, however. Like a dead man, only friction could make him warm or violence make him mobile.

He decided to get a few drinks and then call Mary from Delehanty's. It was quite early and the speakeasy was empty. The bartender served him and went back to his newspaper.

On the mirror behind the bar hung a poster advertising a mineral water. It showed a naked girl made modest by the mist that rose from the spring at her feet. The artist had taken a great deal of care in drawing her breasts and their nipples stuck out like tiny red hats.

He tried to excite himself into eagerness by thinking of the play Mary made with her breasts. She used them as the coquettes of long ago had used their fans. One of her tricks was to wear a medal low down on her chest. Whenever he asked to see it, instead of drawing it out she leaned over for him to look. Although he had often asked to see the medal, he had not yet found out what it represented.

But the excitement refused to come. If anything, he felt colder than before he had started to think of women. It was not his line. Nevertheless, he persisted in it, out of desperation, and went to the telephone to call Mary.

"Is that you?" she asked, then added before he could reply, "I must see you at once. I've quarreled with him. This time I'm through."

She always talked in headlines and her excitement forced him to be casual. "O. K.," he said. "When? Where?"

"Anywhere, I'm through with that skunk, I tell you, I'm through."

She had quarreled with Shrike before and he knew that in return for an ordinary number of kisses, he would have to listen to an extraordinary amount of complaining.

"Do you want to meet me here, in Delehanty's?" he asked.

"No, you come here. We'll be alone and anyway I have to bathe and get dressed."

When he arrived at her place, he would probably find Shrike

there with her on his lap. They would both be glad to see him and all three of them would go to the movies where Mary would hold his hand under the seat.

He went back to the bar for another drink, then bought a quart of Scotch and took a cab. Shrike opened the door. Although he had expected to see him, he was embarrassed and tried to cover his confusion by making believe he was extremely drunk.

"Come in, come in, homebreaker," Shrike said with a laugh. "The Mrs. will be out in a few minutes. She's in the tub."

Shrike took the bottle he was carrying and pulled its cork. Then he got some charged water and made two highballs.

"Well," Shrike said, lifting his drink, "so you're going in for this kind of stuff, eh? Whisky and the boss's wife."

Miss Lonelyhearts always found it impossible to reply to him. The answers he wanted to make were too general and began too far back in the history of their relationship.

"You're doing field work, I take it," Shrike said. "Well, don't put this whisky on your expense account. However, we like to see a young man with his heart in his work. You've been going around with yours in your mouth."

Miss Lonelyhearts made a desperate attempt to kid back. "And you," he said, "you're an old meanie who beats his wife."

Shrike laughed, but too long and too loudly, then broke off with an elaborate sigh. "Ah, my lad," he said, "you're wrong. It's Mary who does the beating."

He took a long pull at his highball and sighed again, still more elaborately. "My good friend, I want to have a heart-to-heart talk with you. I adore heart-to-heart talks and nowadays there are so few people with whom one can really talk. Everybody is so hard-boiled. I want to make a clean breast of matters, a nice clean breast. It's better to make a clean breast of matters than to let them fester in the depths of one's soul."

While talking, he kept his face alive with little nods and winks that were evidently supposed to inspire confidence and to prove him a very simple fellow.

"My good friend, your accusation hurts me to the quick. You spiritual lovers think that you alone suffer. But you are mistaken. Although my love is of the flesh flashy, I too suffer. It's suffering that drives me into the arms of the Miss Farkises of this world. Yes, I suffer."

Here the dead pan broke and pain actually crept into his voice. "She's selfish. She's a damned selfish bitch. She was a virgin when I married her and has been fighting ever since to remain one. Sleeping with her is like sleeping with a knife in one's groin."

It was Miss Lonelyhearts' turn to laugh. He put his face close to Shrike's and laughed as hard as he could.

Shrike tried to ignore him by finishing as though the whole thing were a joke.

"She claims that I raped her. Can you imagine Willie Shrike, wee Willie Shrike, raping any one? I'm like you, one of those grateful lovers."

Mary came into the room in her bathrobe. She leaned over Miss Lonelyhearts and said: "Don't talk to that pig. Come with me and bring the whisky."

As he followed her into the bedroom, he heard Shrike slam the front door. She went into a large closet to dress. He sat on the bed.

"What did that swine say to you?"

"He said you were selfish, Mary—sexually selfish."

"Of all the god-damned nerve. Do you know why he lets me go out with other men? To save money. He knows that I let them neck me and when I get home all hot and bothered, why he climbs into my bed and begs for it. The cheap bastard!"

She came out of the closet wearing a black lace slip and began to fix her hair in front of the dressing table. Miss Lonelyhearts bent down to kiss the back of her neck.

"Now, now," she said, acting kittenish, "you'll muss me."

He took a drink from the whisky bottle, then made her a highball. When he brought it to her, she gave him a kiss, a little peck of reward.

"Where'll we eat?" she asked. "Let's go where we can dance. I want to be gay."

They took a cab to a place called El Gaucho. When they entered, the orchestra was playing a Cuban rhumba. A waiter dressed as a South-American cowboy led them to a table. Mary immediately went Spanish and her movements became languorous and full of abandon.

But the romantic atmosphere only heightened his feeling of icy fatness. He tried to fight it by telling himself that it was childish. What had happened to his great understanding heart? Guitars, bright shawls, exotic foods, outlandish costumes —all these things were part of the business of dreams. He had learned not to laugh at the advertisements offering to teach writing, cartooning, engineering, to add inches to the biceps and to develop the bust. He should therefore realize that the people who came to El Gaucho were the same as those who wanted to write and live the life of an artist, wanted to be an engineer and wear leather puttees, wanted to develop a grip that would impress the boss, wanted to cushion Raoul's head on their swollen breasts. They were the same people as those who wrote to Miss Lonelyhearts for help.

But his irritation was too profound for him to soothe it in this way. For the time being, dreams left him cold, no matter how humble they were.

"I like this place," Mary said. "It's a little fakey, I know, but it's gay and I so want to be gay."

She thanked him by offering herself in a series of formal, impersonal gestures. She was wearing a tight, shiny dress that was like glass-covered steel and there was something cleanly mechanical in her pantomime.

"Why do you want to be gay?"

"Every one wants to be gay—unless they're sick."

Was he sick? In a great cold wave, the readers of his column crashed over the music, over the bright shawls and picturesque waiters, over her shining body. To save himself, he asked to see the medal. Like a little girl helping an old man to cross the street, she leaned over for him to look into the neck of her dress. But before he had a chance to see anything, a waiter came up to the table.

"The way to be gay is to make other people gay," Miss Lonelyhearts said. "Sleep with me and I'll be one gay dog."

The defeat in his voice made it easy for her to ignore his request and her mind sagged with him. "I've had a tough time," she said. "From the beginning, I've had a tough time. When I was a child, I saw my mother die. She had cancer of the breast, and the pain was terrible. She died leaning over a table."

"Sleep with me," he said.

"No, let's dance."

"I don't want to. Tell me about your mother."

"She died leaning over a table. The pain was so terrible that she climbed out of bed to die."

Mary leaned over to show how her mother had died and he made another attempt to see the medal. He saw that there was a runner on it, but was unable to read the inscription.

"My father was very cruel to her," she continued. "He was a portrait painter, a man of genius, but . . ."

He stopped listening and tried to bring his great understanding heart into action again. Parents are also part of the business of dreams. My father was a Russian prince, my father was a Piute Indian chief, my father was an Australian sheep baron, my father lost all his money in Wall Street, my father was a portrait painter. People like Mary were unable to do without such tales. They told them because they wanted to talk about something besides clothing or business or the movies, because they wanted to talk about something poetic.

When she had finished her story, he said, "You poor kid," and leaned over for another look at the medal. She bent to help him and pulled out the neck of her dress with her fingers. This time he was able to read the inscription: "Awarded by the Boston Latin School for first place in the 100 yd. dash."

It was a small victory, yet it greatly increased his fatigue and he was glad when she suggested leaving. In the cab, he again begged her to sleep with him. She refused. He kneaded her body like a sculptor grown angry with his clay, but there was too much method in his caresses and they both remained cold.

At the door of her apartment, she turned for a kiss and pressed against him. A spark flared up in his groin. He refused to let go and tried to work this spark into a flame. She pushed his mouth away from a long wet kiss.

"Listen to me," she said. "We can't stop talking. We must talk. Willie probably heard the elevator and is listening behind the door. You don't know him. If he doesn't hear us talk, he'll know you're kissing me and open the door. It's an old trick of his."

He held her close and tried desperately to keep the spark alive.

"Don't kiss my lips," she begged. "I must talk."

He kissed her throat, then opened her dress and kissed her breasts. She was afraid to resist or to stop talking.

"My mother died of cancer of the breast," she said in a

brave voice, like a little girl reciting at a party. "She died leaning over a table. My father was a portrait painter. He led a very
gay life. He mistreated my mother. She had cancer of the
breast. She . . ." He tore at her clothes and she began to
mumble and repeat herself. Her dress fell to her feet and he
tore away her underwear until she was naked under her fur
coat. He tried to drag her to the floor.

"Please, please," she begged, "he'll come out and find us."

He stopped her mouth with a long kiss.

"Let me go, honey," she pleaded, "maybe he's not home.
If he isn't, I'll let you in."

He released her. She opened the door and tiptoed in, carrying her rolled up clothes under her coat. He heard her switch
on the light in the foyer and knew that Shrike had not been
behind the door. Then he heard footsteps and limped behind
a projection of the elevator shaft. The door opened and Shrike
looked into the corridor. He had only the top of his pajamas.

5 ❧ *William H. Gass*

William H. Gass was born in Fargo, North Dakota, in 1924 and was educated at Kenyon College, Ohio Wesleyan, and Cornell. He has published a collection of stories, In the Heart of the Heart of the Country (1968), and a novel, Omensetter's Luck (1966). In attempting to redefine the nature and sensibilities of fiction, to remove it from the strictures of "reality," Gass has noted that the "so-called life one finds in novels, the worst and best of them, is nothing like actual life at all, and cannot be; it is not more real, or thrilling, or authentic; it is not truer, more complex, or pure, and its people have less spontaneity, are less intricate, less free, less full."

THE PEDERSEN KID

PART ONE
I

Big Hans yelled, so I came out. The barn was dark, but the sun burned on the snow. Hans was carrying something from the crib. I yelled, but Big Hans didn't hear. He was in the house with what he had before I reached the steps.

It was the Pedersen kid. Hans had put the kid on the kitchen table like you would a ham and started the kettle. He wasn't saying anything. I guess he figured one yell from the crib was enough noise. Ma was fumbling with the kid's clothes which were stiff with ice. She made a sound like whew from every breath. The kettle filled and Hans said,

Get some snow and call your pa.

There's coal dust in that. Get more.

A little coal won't hurt.

Get more.

Coal's warming.

It's not enough. Shut your mouth and get your pa.

Ma had rolled out some dough on the table where Hans had dropped the Pedersen kid like a filling. Most of the kid's clothes were on the floor where they were going to make a puddle. Hans began rubbing snow on the kid's face. Ma stopped trying to pull his things off and simply stood by the table with her hands held away from her as if they were wet, staring first at Big Hans and then at the kid.

Get.

Why?

I told you.

It's Pa I mean—

I know what you mean.   Get.

I found a cardboard box that condensed milk had come in and I shoveled it full of snow. It was too small as I figured it would be. I found another with rags and an old sponge I threw out.   Campbell's soup.   I filled it too, using the rest of the drift. Snow would melt through the bottom of the boxes but that was all right with me. By now the kid was naked.   I was satisfied mine was bigger.

Looks like a sick shoat.

Shut up and get your pa.

He's asleep.

Yeah.

He don't like to get waked.

I know that. Don't I know that as good as you? Get him.

What good'll he be?

We're going to need his whiskey.

He can fix that need all right. He's good for fixing the crack
in his face. If it ain't all gone.

The kettle was whistling.

What are we going to do with these? ma said.

Wait, Hed. Now I want you to get. I'm tired of talking.
Get, you hear?

What are we going to do with them? They're all wet, she
said.

I went to wake the old man. He didn't like being roused.
It was too hard and far to come, the sleep he was in. He didn't
give a damn about the Pedersen kid, any more than I did.
Pedersen's kid was just a kid. He didn't carry any weight. Not
like I did. And the old man would be mad, unable to see,
coming that way from where he was asleep. I decided I hated
Big Hans, though this was hardly something new for me. I
hated Big Hans just then because I was thinking how Pa's eyes
would blink at me—as if I were the sun off the snow and
burning to blind him. His eyes were old and they'd never seen
well, but shone on by whiskey they'd glare at my noise, growing red and raising up his rage. I decided I hated the Pedersen
kid too, dying in our kitchen while I was away where I
couldn't watch, dying just to pleasure Hans and making me
go up snapping steps and down a drafty hall, Pa lumped under
the covers at the end like dung covered with snow, snoring
and whistling. Oh he'd not care about the Pedersen kid. He'd
not care about getting waked so he could give up some of his
liquor to a slit of a kid and maybe lose one of his hiding places
in the bargain. That would make him mad enough if he was
sober. I tried not to hurry though it was cold and the Pedersen
kid was in the kitchen.

He was all shoveled up like I thought he'd be. I shoved at
his shoulder, calling his name. I think he heard his name. His
name stopped the snoring, but he didn't move except to roll a

little when I shoved him. The covers slid down his skinny neck so I saw his head, fuzzed like a dandelion gone to seed, but his face was turned to the wall—there was the pale shadow of his nose on the plaster—and I thought: well you don't look much like a pig-drunk bully now. I couldn't be sure he was still asleep. He was a cagey sonofabitch. He'd heard his name. I shook him a little harder and made some noise. Pap-pap-pap-hey, I said.

I was leaning too far over. I knew better. He always slept close to the wall so you had to lean to reach him. Oh he was smart. It put you off. I knew better but I was thinking of the Pedersen kid mother-naked in all that dough. When his arm came up I ducked away but it caught me on the side of the neck, watering my eyes, and I backed off to cough. Pa was on his side, looking at me, his eyes winking, the hand that had hit me a fist in the pillow.

Get the hell out of here.

I didn't say anything—my throat wasn't clear—but I watched him. He was a mean horse to come at from the rear. It was better, though, he'd hit me. He was bitter when he missed.

Get the hell out of here.

Big Hans sent me. He told me to wake you.

A fat turd to Big Hans. Get out of here.

He found the Pedersen kid by the crib.

Get the hell out.

Pa pulled at the covers. He was tasting his mouth.

The kid's froze like a pump. Hans is rubbing him with snow. He's got him in the kitchen.

Pedersen?

No, Pa. It's the Pedersen kid. The kid.

Nothing to steal from the crib.

Not stealing, Pa. He was just lying there. Hans found him froze. That's where he was when Hans found him.

Pa laughed.

I ain't hid nothing in the crib.

You don't understand, Pa. The Pedersen kid. The kid—

I shittin well understand.

Pa had his head up, glaring, his teeth gnawing at the place where he'd grown a mustache once.

I shittin well understand. You know I don't want to see Pedersen. That cock. Why should I? That fairy farmer. What did he come for, hey? God dammit, get. And don't come back. Find out some shittin something. You're a fool. Both you and Hans. Pedersen. That cock. That fairy farmer. Don't come back. Out. Shit. Out. Out out.

He was shouting and breathing hard and closing his fist on the pillow. He had long black hairs on his wrist. They curled around the cuff of his nightshirt.

Big Hans made me come. Big Hans said—

A fat turd to Big Hans. He's an even bigger turd than you. Fat, too, fool, hey? I taught him, dammit, and I'll teach you. Out. You want me to drop my pot?

He was about to get up so I got out, slamming the door. He was beginning to see he was too mad to sleep. Then he threw things. Once he went after Hans and dumped his pot over the banister. Pa'd been shit-sick in that pot. Hans got an ax. He didn't even bother to wipe himself off and he chopped part of Pa's door down before he stopped. He might not have gone that far if Pa hadn't been locked in laughing fit to shake the house. That pot put Pa in an awful good humor—whenever he thought of it. I always felt the thought was present in both of them, stirring in their chests like a laugh or a growl, as eager as an animal to be out. I heard Pa cursing all the way downstairs.

Hans had laid steaming towels over the kid's chest and stomach. He was rubbing snow on the kid's legs and feet. Water from the snow and water from the towels had run off the kid to the table where the dough was, and the dough was turning pasty, sticking to the kid's back and behind.

Ain't he going to wake up?

What about your pa?

He was awake when I left.

What'd he say? Did you get the whiskey?

He said a fat turd to Big Hans.

Don't be smart. Did you ask him about the whiskey?

Yeah.

Well?

He said a fat turd to Big Hans.

Don't be smart. What's he going to do?

Go back to sleep most likely.

You'd best get that whiskey.

You go. Take the ax. Pa's scared to hell of axes.

Listen to me, Jorge, I've had enough of your sassing. This kid's froze bad. If I don't get some whiskey down him he might die. You want the kid to die? Do you? Well, get your pa and get that whiskey.

Pa don't care about the kid.

Jorge.

Well he don't. He don't care at all, and I don't care to get my head busted neither. He don't care, and I don't care to have his shit flung on me. He don't care about anybody. All he cares about is his whiskey and that dry crack in his face. Get pig-drunk—that's what he wants. He don't care about nothing else at all. Nothing. Not Pedersen's kid neither. That cock. Not the kid neither.

I'll get the spirits, ma said.

I'd wound Big Hans up tight. I was ready to jump but when ma said she'd get the whiskey it surprised him like it

surprised me, and he ran down. Ma never went near the old
man when he was sleeping it off. Not any more. Not for years.
The first thing every morning when she washed her face she
could see the scar on her chin where he'd cut her with a boot
cleat, and maybe she saw him heaving it again, the dirty sock
popping out as it flew. It should have been nearly as easy for
her to remember that as it was for Big Hans to remember going
after the ax while he was still spattered with Pa's sour yellow
sick insides.

No you won't, Big Hans said.

Yes, Hans, if they're needed, ma said.

Hans shook his head but neither of us tried to stop her. If
we had, then one of us would have had to go instead. Hans
rubbed the kid with more snow . . . rubbed . . . rubbed.

I'll get more snow, I said.

I took the pail and shovel and went out on the porch. I
don't know where ma went. I thought she'd gone upstairs and
expected to hear she had. She had surprised Hans like she had
surprised me when she said she'd go, and then she surprised
him again when she came back so quick like she must have,
because when I came in with the snow she was there with a
bottle with three white feathers on its label and Hans was
holding it angrily by the throat. Oh he was being queer and
careful, pawing about in the drawer and holding the bottle like
a snake at the length of his arm. He was awful angry because
he'd thought ma was going to do something big, something
heroic even, especially for her—I know him . . . I know him
. . . we felt the same sometimes—while ma wasn't thinking
about that at all, not anything like that. There was no way of
getting even. It wasn't like getting cheated at the fair. They
were always trying, so you got to expect it. Now Hans had
given ma something of his—we both had when we thought she

was going straight to Pa—something valuable, a piece of better feeling; but since she didn't know we'd given it to her, there was no easy way of getting it back.

Hans cut the foil off finally and unscrewed the cap. He was put out too because there was only one way of understanding what she'd done. Ma had found one of Pa's hiding places. She'd found one and she hadn't said a word while Big Hans and I had hunted and hunted as we always did all winter, every winter since the spring that Hans had come and I had looked in the privy and found the first one. Pa had a knack for hiding. He know we were looking and he enjoyed it. But now ma. She'd found it by luck most likely but she hadn't said anything and we didn't know how long ago it'd been or how many other ones she'd found, saying nothing. Pa was sure to find out. Sometimes he didn't seem to because he hid them so well he couldn't find them himself or because he looked and didn't find anything and figured he hadn't hid one after all or had drunk it up. But he'd find out about this one because we were using it. A fool could see what was going on. If he found out ma found it—that'd be bad. He took pride in his hiding. It was all the pride he had. I guess fooling Hans and me took doing. But he didn't figure ma for much. He didn't figure her at all. And if he found out—a woman had—then it'd be bad.

Hans poured some in a tumbler.

You going to put more towels on him?

No.

Why not? That's what he needs, something warm to his skin, don't he?

Not where he's froze good. Heat's bad for frostbite. That's why I only put towels on his chest and belly. He's got to thaw slow. You ought to know that.

Colors on the towels had run.

Ma poked her toe in the kid's clothes.

What are we going to do with these?

Big Hans began pouring whiskey in the kid's mouth but the mouth filled without any getting down his throat and in a second it was dripping from his chin.

Here, help me prop him up. I got to hold his mouth open.

I didn't want to touch him and I hoped ma would do it but she kept looking at the kid's clothes piled on the floor and the pool of water by them and didn't make any move to.

Come on, Jorge.

All right.

Lift, don't shove . . . lift.

Okay, I'm lifting.

I took him by the shoulders. His head flopped back. His mouth fell open. The skin on his neck was tight. He was cold all right.

Hold his head up. He'll choke.

His mouth is open.

His throat's shut. He'll choke.

He'll choke anyway.

Hold his head up.

I can't.

Don't hold him like that. Put your arms around him.

Well jesus.

He was cold all right. I put my arm carefully around him. Hans had his fingers in the kid's mouth.

Now he'll choke for sure.

Shut up. Just hold him like I told you.

He was cold all right, and wet. I had my arm behind his back. He sure felt dead.

Tilt his head back a bit . . . not too much.

He felt cold and slimy. He sure was dead. We had a dead body in our kitchen. All the time he'd been dead. When Hans had brought him in, he'd been dead. I couldn't see him breathing. He was awful skinny, sunk between the ribs. We were getting him ready to bake. Hans was basting him. I had my arm around him, holding him up. He was dead and I had hold of him. I could feel my muscles jumping.

Well jesus christ.

He *is* dead. He *is*.

You dropped him.

Dead? ma said.

He's dead. I could feel. He's dead.

Dead?

Ain't you got any sense? You let his head hit the table.

Is he dead? Is he dead? ma said.

Well christ no, not yet, not yet he's not dead. Look what you done, Jorge, there's whiskey all over.

He *is* dead. He *is*.

Right now he ain't. Not yet he ain't. Now stop yelling and hold him up.

He ain't breathing.

Yes he is, he *is* breathing. Hold him up.

I ain't. I ain't holding any dead body. You can hold it if you want. You dribble whiskey on it all you want. You can do anything you want to. I ain't. I ain't holding any dead body.

If he's dead, ma said, what are we going to do with these?

Jorge, god damn you, come back here—

I went down to the crib where Big Hans had found him. There was still a hollow in the snow and some prints the wind hadn't sifted snow over. The kid must have been out on his feet, they wobbled so. I could see where he had walked smack into a drift and then backed off and lurched up beside the crib, maybe bumping into it before he fell, then lying quiet so the snow had time to curl around him, piling up until in no time it would have covered him completely. Who knows,

I thought, the way it's been snowing, we mightn't have found him till spring. Even if he was dead in our kitchen, I was glad Big Hans had found him. I could see myself coming out of the house some morning with the sun high up and strong and the eaves dripping, the snow speckled with drops and the ice on the creek slushing up; coming out and walking down by the crib on the crusts of the drift . . . coming out to play my game with the drifts . . . and I could see myself losing, breaking through the big drift that was always sleeping up against the crib and running a foot right into him, right into the Pedersen kid curled up, getting soft.

That would have been worse than holding to his body in the kitchen. The feeling would have come on quicker, and it would have been worse, happening in the middle of a game. There wouldn't have been any warning, any way of getting ready for it to happen, to know what I'd struck before I bent down, even though Old Man Pedersen would have come over between snows looking for the kid most likely and everybody would have figured that the kid was lying buried somewhere under the snow; that maybe after a high wind someday somebody would find him lying like a black stone uncovered in a field; but probably in the spring somebody would find him in some back pasture thawing out with the mud and have to bring him in and take him over to the Pedersen place and present him to Missus Pedersen. Even so, even with everyone knowing that, and hoping one of the Pedersens would find him first so they wouldn't have to pry him up out of the mud or fetch him out from a thicket and bring him in and give him to Missus Pedersen in soggy season-old clothes—even then, who would expect to stick a foot all of a sudden through the crust losing at the drift game and step on Pedersen's kid lying all crouched together right beside your own crib? It was a good thing Hans had come down this morning and found him, even if he was dead in our kitchen and I had held him up.

When Pedersen came over asking for his kid, maybe hoping
that the kid had got to our place all right and stayed, waiting
for the blizzard to quit before going home, Pa would meet
him and bring him in for a drink and tell him it was his own
fault for putting up all those snow fences. If I knew Pa, he'd
tell Pedersen to look under the drifts his snow fences had
made, and Pedersen would get so mad he'd go for Pa and
stomp out calling for the vengeance of God like he was fond
of doing. Now though, since Big Hans had found him, and he
was dead in our kitchen, Pa might not say much when Pedersen came. He might just offer Pedersen a drink and keep his
mouth shut about those snow fences. Pedersen might come
yet this morning. That would be best because Pa would be still
asleep. If Pa was asleep when Pedersen came he wouldn't have
a chance to talk about those snow fences, or offer Pedersen a
drink, or call Pedersen a bent prick or a turd machine or a
fairy farmer. Pedersen wouldn't have to refuse the drink then,
spit his chaw in the snow or call on God, and could take his
kid and go home. I hoped Pedersen would certainly come
soon. I hoped he would come and take that cold damp body
out of our kitchen. The way I felt I didn't think that today
I'd be able to eat. I knew every bite I'd see the Pedersen kid
in the kitchen being fixed for the table.

The wind had dropped. The sun lay burning on the snow.
I got cold just the same. I didn't want to go in but I could
feel the cold crawling over me like it must have crawled over
him while he was coming. It had slipped over him like a sheet,
icy at first, especially around the feet, and he'd likely wiggled
his toes in his boots and wanted to wrap his legs around each
other like you do when you first come to bed. But then things
would begin to warm up some, the sheet feeling warmer all
the time until it felt real cozy and you went to sleep. Only
when the kid went to sleep by our crib it wasn't like going to

sleep in bed because the sheet never really got warm and he never really got warm either. Now he was just as cold in our kitchen with the kettle whistling and ma getting ready to bake as I was out by the crib jigging my feet in our snow.   I had to go in.   I looked but I couldn't see anyone trying to come down where the road was. All I could see was a set of half-filled prints jiggling crazily away into the snow until they sank under a drift. There wasn't anything around. There wasn't anything: a tree or a stick or a rock whipped bare or a bush hugged by snow sticking up to mark the place where those prints came up out of the drift like somebody had come up from underground.

I decided to go around by the front though I wasn't sup-posed to track through the parlor. The snow came to my thighs, but I was thinking of where the kid lay on the kitchen table in all that dough, pasty with whiskey and water, like spring had come all at once to our kitchen, and our all the time not knowing he was there, had thawed the top of his grave off and left him for us to find, stretched out cold and stiff and bare; and who was it that was going to have to take him to the Pedersen place and give him to Missus Pedersen, naked, and flour on his bare behind?

I I

Just his back.   The green mackinaw. The black stocking cap. The yellow gloves. The gun.

Big Hans kept repeating it. He was letting the meaning have a chance to change. He'd look at me and shake his head and say it over.

"He put them down the cellar so I ran."

Hans filled the tumbler. It was spotted with whiskey and flecks of flour.

"He didn't say nothing the whole time."

He put the bottle on the table and the bottom sank unevenly in the paste, tilting heavily and queerly to one side—
acting crazy, like everything else.

That's all he says he saw, Hans said, staring at the mark of
the kid's behind in the dough. Just his back. The green mackinaw. The black stocking cap. The yellow gloves. The gun.

That's all?

He waited and waited.

That's all.

He tossed the whiskey off and peered at the bottom of the
glass.

Now why should he remember all them colors?

He leaned over, his legs apart, his elbows on his knees; and
held the glass between them with both hands, tilting it to
watch the liquor that was left roll back and forth across the
bottom.

How does he know? I mean, for sure.

He thinks he knows, Hans said in a tired voice. He thinks
he knows.

He picked up the bottle and a hunk of dough was stuck
to it.

Christ. That's all. It's how he feels. It's enough, ain't it?
Hans said.

What a mess, ma said.

He was raving, Hans said. He couldn't think of anything
else. He had to talk. He had to get it out. You should have
heard him grunt.

Poor poor Stevie, ma said.

He was raving?

All right, is it something you dream? Hans said.

He must have been dreaming. Look—how could he have
got there? Where'd he come from? Fall from the sky?

He came through the storm.

That's just it, Hans, he'd have had to. It was blizzarding all day. It didn't let up—did it?—till late afternoon. He'd have had to. Now what chance is there of that? What?

Enough a chance it happened, Hans said.

But listen. Jesus. He's a stranger. If he's a stranger he's come a ways. He'd never make it in a blizzard, not even knowing the country.

He came through the storm. He came out of the ground like a grub. Hans shrugged. He came.

Hans poured himself a drink, not me.

He came through the storm, he said. He came through just like the kid came through. The kid had no chance neither, but he came. He's here, ain't he? He's right upstairs, right now. You got to believe that.

It wasn't blizzarding when the kid came.

It was starting.

That ain't the same.

All right. The kid had forty-five minutes, maybe an hour before it started to come on good. That isn't enough. You need the whole time, not a start. In a blizzard you got to be where you're going if you're going to get there.

That's what I mean. See, Hans? See? The kid had a chance. He knew the way. He had a head start. Besides, he was scared. He ain't going to be lazying. And he's lucky. He had a chance to be lucky. Now yellow gloves ain't got that chance. He has to come farther. He has to come through the storm all the way. But he don't know the way, and he ain't scared proper, except maybe by the storm. He hasn't got a chance to be lucky.

The kid was scared, you said. Right. Now why? You tell me that.

Hans kept his eyes on the whiskey that was shining in his glass. He was holding on hard.

And yellow gloves—he ain't scared? he said. How do you know he ain't scared, by something else besides wind and snow and cold and howling, I mean?

All right, I don't know, but it's likely, ain't it? Anyway, the kid, well maybe he ain't scared at all, starting out. Maybe his pa was just looking to tan him and he lit out. Then first thing he knows it's blizzarding again and he's lost, and when he gets to our crib he don't know where he is.

Hans slowly shook his head.

Yes yes, hell Hans, the kid's scared of having run away. He don't want to say he done a fool stunt like that. So he makes the whole thing up. He's just a little kid. He made the whole thing up.

Hans didn't like that. He didn't want to believe the kid any more than I did, but if he didn't then the kid had fooled him sure. He didn't want to believe that either.

No, he said. Is it something you make up? Is it something you come to—raving with frostbite and fever and not knowing who's there or where you are or anything—and make up?

Yeah.

No it ain't. Green, black, yellow: you don't make up them colors neither. You don't make up putting your folks down cellar where they'll freeze. You don't make up his not saying anything the whole time or only seeing his back or exactly what he was wearing. It's more than a make-up; it's more than a dream. It's like something you see once and it hits you so hard you never forget it even if you want to; lies, dreams, pass—this has you; it's like something that sticks to you like burrs, burrs and you try to brush off while you're doing some-thing else, but they never brush off, they just roll a little, and the first thing you know you ain't doing what you set out to, you're just trying to get them burrs off.   I know.   I got things stuck to me like that. Everybody has.   Pretty soon you get tired trying to pick them off. If they was just burrs, it wouldn't matter, but they ain't. They never is. The kid saw something that hit him hard like that; hit him so hard that probably all the time he was running over here he didn't see anything else but what hit him. Not really. It hit him so hard he couldn't do anything but spit it out raving when he come to. It hit him. You don't make things like that up, Jorge.

No.   He came through the storm, just like the kid. He had no business coming, but he came. I don't know how or why or when exactly, except it must have been during the blizzard yesterday. He got to the Pedersen place just before or just after it stopped snowing. He got there and he shoved them all in the fruit cellar to freeze and I'll bet he had his reasons.

You got dough stuck to the bottom of Pa's bottle.

I couldn't think of anything else to say. What Hans said sounded right. It sounded right but it couldn't be right. It just couldn't be. Whatever was right, the Pedersen kid had run off from his pa's place probably late yesterday afternoon when the storm let up, and had turned up at our crib this morning. I knew he was here. I knew that much. I'd held him. I'd felt him dead in my hands, only I guess he wasn't dead now. Hans had put him to bed upstairs but I could still see him in the kitchen, so skinny naked, two towels steaming on him, whiskey drooling from the corners of his mouth, lines of dirt between his toes, squeezing ma's dough in the shape of his behind.

I reached for the bottle. Hans held it away.

He didn't see him do it though, I said.

Hans shrugged.

Then he ain't sure.

He's sure, I told you. Do you run out in a blizzard unless you're sure?

It wasn't blizzarding.

It was starting.

I don't run out in blizzards.

Crap.

Hans pointed the doughy end of the bottle at me.

Crap.

He shook it.

You come in from the barn—like this morning. As far as you know there ain't a gun in yellow gloves in a thousand miles. You come in from the barn not thinking anything special. You just get inside—you just get inside when you see a guy you never saw before, the guy that wasn't in a thousand miles, that wasn't in your mind even, he was so far away, and he's wearing them yellow gloves and that green mackinaw, and he's got me and your ma and pa lined up with our hands back of our necks like this—

Hans hung the bottle and the glass behind his head.

He's got me and your ma and your pa lined up with our hands here back of our necks, and he's got a rifle in between them yellow gloves and he's waving the point of it up and down in front of your ma's face real slow and quiet.

Hans got up and waved the bottle violently in ma's face. She shivered and shooed it away. Hans stopped to come to me. He stood over me, his black eyes buttons on his big face, and I tried to look like I wasn't hunching down any in my chair.

What do you do? Hans roared. You drop a little kid's cold head on the table.

Like hell—

Hans had the bottle in front of him again, smack in my face.

Hans Esbyorn, ma said, don't pester the boy.

Like hell—

Jorge.

I wouldn't run, ma.

Ma sighed. I don't know. But don't yell.

Well christ almighty, ma.

Don't swear neither. Please. You been swearing too much— you and Hans both.

But I wouldn't run.

Yes, Jorge, yes. I'm sure you wouldn't run, she said.

Hans went back and sat down and finished his drink and poured another. He could relax now he'd got me all strung up. He was a fancy bastard.

You'd run all right, he said, running his tongue across his lips. Maybe you'd be right to run. Maybe anybody would. With no gun, with nothing to stop him.

Poor child.   Wheweee.   And what are we going to do with these?

Hang them up, Hed, for christ's sake.

Where?

Well, where do you, mostly?

Oh no, she said, I wouldn't feel right doing that.

Then jesus, Hed, I don't know. Jesus.

Please Hans, please. Those words are hard for me to bear. She stared at the ceiling.

Dear.   The kitchen's such a mess.   I can't bear to see it.   And the baking's not done.

That's all she could think of. That's all she had to say. She didn't care about me. I didn't count. Not like her kitchen. I wouldn't have run.

Stick the baking, I said.

Shut your face.

He could look as mean as he liked, I didn't care. What was his meanness to me? A blister on my heel, another discomfort, a cold bed. Yet when he took his eyes off me to drink, I felt better. I was going to twist his balls.

All right, I said. All right. All right.

He was lost in his glass, thinking it out.

They're awful cold in that cellar, I said.

There was a little liquor burning in the bottom. I was going to twist his balls like the neck of a sack.

What are you going to do about it?

He was putting his mean look back but it lacked enthusiasm. He was seeing things in his glass.

I saved the kid, didn't I? he finally said.

Maybe you did.

You didn't.

No. I didn't.

It's time you did something then, ain't it?

Why should I? I don't think they're freezing. You're the one who thinks that. You're the one who thinks he ran for help. You're the one. You saved him. All right. You didn't let his head hit the table. I did that. You didn't. No. It was you who rubbed him. All right. You saved him. That wasn't the kid's idea though. He came for help. According to you, that is. He didn't come to be saved. You saved him, but what are you going to do now to help him? You've been feeling mighty, ain't you? thinking how you did it. Still feel like a savior, Hans? How's it feel?

You little bastard.

All right. Little or big. Never mind. You did it all. You found him. You raised the rumpus, ordering everybody around. He was as good as dead. I held him and I felt him. Maybe in your way he was alive, but it was a way that don't count. No—but you couldn't leave him alone. Rubbing. Well I felt him . . . cold . . . christ!   Ain't you proud? He was dead, right here, dead. And there weren't no yellow gloves. Now, though, there is. That's what comes of rubbing. Rubbing . . . ain't you proud? You can't believe the kid was lying good enough to fool you. So he was dead. But now he ain't. Not for you. He ain't for you.

He's alive for you too. You're crazy. He's alive for everybody.

No he ain't. He ain't alive for me. He never was. I never seen him except he was dead. Cold . . . I felt him . . . christ! Ain't you proud? He's in your bed. All right. You took him up there. It's your bed he's in, Hans. It was you he babbled to. You believe him too, so he's alive for you then. Not for me. Not for me he ain't.

You can't say that.

I am saying it though. Hear me saying?   Rubbing . . . You didn't know what you was bringing to, did you? Something besides the kid came through the storm, Hans. I ain't saying yellow gloves did neither. He didn't. He couldn't. But something else did. While you was rubbing you didn't think of that.

You little bastard.

Hans, Hans, please, ma said.

Never mind that. Little or big, like I said. I'm asking what you're going to do. You believe it. You made it. What are you going to do about it? It'd be funny if right now while we're sitting here the kid's dying upstairs.

Jorge, ma said, what an awful thing—in Hans's bed.

All right. But suppose. Suppose you didn't rub enough—not long and hard enough, Hans. And suppose he dies up there in your bed. He might. He was cold, I know. That'd be funny because that yellow gloves—he won't die. It ain't going to be so easy, killing him.

Hans didn't move or say anything.

I ain't no judge. I ain't no hand at saving, like you said. It don't make no difference to me. But why'd you start rubbing if you was going to stop? Seems like it'd be terrible if the Pedersen kid was to have come all that way through the

storm, scared and freezizng, and you was to have done all that
rubbing and saving so he could come to and tell you his
fancy tale and have you believe it, if you ain't going to do
nothing now but sit and hold hands with that bottle. That
ain't a burr so easy picked off.

Still he didn't say anything.

Fruit cellars get mighty cold. Of course they ain't supposed
to freeze.

I leaned back easy in my chair. Hans just sat.

They ain't supposed to freeze so it's all right.

The top of the kitchen table looked muddy where it
showed. Patches of dough and pools of water were scattered
all over it. There were rusty streaks through the paste and the
towels had run. Everywhere there were little sandy puddles of
whiskey and water. Something, it looked like whiskey, dripped
slowly to the floor and with the water trickled to the puddle
by the pile of clothes. The boxes sagged. There were thick
black tracks around the table and the stove. I thought it was
funny the boxes had gone so fast. The bottle and the glass
were posts around which Big Hans had his hands.

Ma began picking up the kid's clothes. She picked them up
one at a time, delicately, by their ends and corners, lifting a
sleeve like you would the flat, burned, crooked leg of a frog
dead of summer to toss it from the road. They didn't seem
human things, the way her hands pinched together on them,
but animal—dead and rotting things out of the ground. She
took them away and when she came back I wanted to tell her
to bury them—to hide them somehow quick under the snow—
but she scared me, the way she came with her arms out,
trembling, fingers coming open and closed, moving like a
combine between rows.

I heard the dripping clearly, and I heard Hans swallow, I
heard the water and the whiskey fall. I heard the frost on the

window melt to the sill and drop into the sink. Hans poured whiskey in his glass. I looked past Hans and Pa was watching from the doorway. His nose and eyes were red, his feet in red slippers.

What's this about the Pedersen kid? he said.

Ma stood behind him with a mop.

I I I

Ever think of a horse? Pa said.

A horse? Where'd he get a horse?

Anywhere—on the way—anyplace.

Could he make it on a horse?

He made it on something.

Not on a horse though.

Not on his feet.

I ain't saying he made it on anything.

Horses can't get lost.

Yes they can.

They got a sense.

That's a lot of manure about horses.

In a blizzard a horse'll go home.

That's so.

You let them go and they go home.

That's so.

If you steal a horse, and let him go, he'll take you to the barn you stole him from.

Couldn't give him his head then.

Must have really rode him then.

And known where he was going.

Yeah, and gone there.

If he had a horse.

Yeah, if he had a horse.

If he stole a horse before the storm and rode it a ways, then when the snow came, the horse would be too far off and wouldn't know how to head for home.

They got an awful good sense.

Manure.

What difference does it make? He made it. What difference does it make how? Hans said.

I'm considering if he could have, Pa said.

And I'm telling you he did, Hans said.

And I've been telling you he didn't. The kid made the whole thing up, I said.

The horse'd stop. He'd put his head into the wind and stop.

I've seen them put their rears in.

They always put their heads in.

He could jockey him.

If he was gentle and not too scared.

A plower is gentle.

Some are.

Some don't like to be rid.

Some don't like strangers neither.

Some.

What the hell, Hans said.

Pa laughed. I'm just considering, he said. Just considering, Hans, that's all.

Pa'd seen the bottle. Right away. He'd been blinking. But he hadn't missed it. He'd seen it and the glass in Hans's hand. I'd expected him to say something. So had Hans. He'd held on to the glass long enough so no one would get the idea he was afraid to, then he'd set it down casual, like he hadn't any reason to hold it or any reason to put it down, but was putting it down anyway, without thinking. I'd grinned but he hadn't seen me, or else he made out he hadn't. Pa'd kept his mouth shut about the bottle though he'd seen it right away. I guess we had the Pedersen kid to thank for that, though we had him to thank for the bottle too.

It's his own fault for putting out all them snow fences, Pa said. You'd think, being here the time he has, he'd know the forces better.

Pedersen just likes to be ready, Pa, that's all.

Hell he does. He likes to *get* ready, that cock. Get, get, get, get. He's always getting ready, but he ain't never *got* ready. Not yet, he ain't. Last summer, instead of minding his crops, he got ready for hoppers. Christ. Who wants hoppers? Well that's the way to get hoppers—that's the sure way—get ready for hoppers.

Bull.

Bull? You say bull, Hans, hey?

I say bull, yeah.

You're one to get ready, ain't you? Like Pedersen, ain't you? Oh what a wrinkled scrotum you got, with all that thinking. You'd put out poison for a million, hey? You know what you'd get? Two million. Wise, oh these wise men, yeah. Pedersen *asked* for hoppers. He *begged* for hoppers. He went on his knees for hoppers. So me? I got hoppers too. Now he's gone and asked for snow, gone on his knees for snow, wrung his fingers off for snow. Is he ready, tell me? Hey? Snow? For real snow? Anybody ever ready for real snow? Oh jesus, that fool. He should have kept his kid behind them fences. What business —what—what business—to send him here. By god, a man's got to keep his stock up.   Look—Pa pointed out the window. See—see—what did I tell you—snowing . . . always snowing.

You seen a winter it didn't snow?

You were ready, I guess.

It always snows.

You were ready for the Pedersen kid too, I guess. You was just out there waiting for him, cooling your cod.

Pa laughed and Hans got red.

Pedersen's a fool. Wise men can't be taught. Oh no, not old holy Pete. He never learned all the things that can fall out the sky and happen to wheat. His neck's bent all the time too, studying clouds—hah, that shit. He don't even keep an eye on his kid in a blizzard. A man by god's got to keep his stock up. But you'll keep an eye out for him, hey, Hans? You're a bigger fool because you're fatter.

Hans's face was red and swollen like the skin around a splinter. He reached out and picked up the glass. Pa was sitting on a corner of the kitchen table, swinging a leg. The glass was near his knee. Hans reached by Pa and took it. Pa watched and swung his leg, laughing. The bottle was on the counter and Pa watched closely while Hans took it.

Ah, you plan to drink some of my whiskey, Hans?

Yeah.

It'd be polite to ask.

I ain't asking, Hans said, tilting the bottle.

I suppose I'd better make some biscuits, ma said.

Hans looked up at her, keeping the bottle tilted. He didn't pour.

Biscuits, ma? I said.

I ought to have something for Mr. Pedersen and I haven't a thing.

Hans straightened the bottle.

There's a thing to consider, he said, beginning to smile. Why ain't Pedersen here looking for his kid?

Why should he be?

Hans winked at me through his glass. No wink would make me a friend of his.

Why not? We're nearest. If the kid ain't here he can ask us to help him hunt.

Fat chance.

He ain't come through. How do you consider that?

I ain't considering it, Pa said.

Why ain't you? Seems to me like something worth real long and fancy considering.

No it ain't.

Pedersen's a fool.

So you like to say. I've heard you often enough. All right, maybe he is. How long do you expect he'll wander around looking before he comes over this way?

A long time. A long time maybe.

The kid's been gone a long time.

Pa arranged his nightshirt over his knee. He had on the striped one.

How long's a long time? Hans said.

The kid's been gone.

Oh Pedersen'll be here before too long now, Pa said.

And if he don't?

What do you mean, if he don't? Then he don't. By god, he don't. It ain't no skin off my ass. If he don't he don't. I don't care what he does.

Yeah, Big Hans said. Yeah.

Pa folded his arms, looking like a judge. He swung his leg. Where'd you find the bottle?

Hans jiggled it.

You're pretty good at hiding, ain't you?

I'm asking the questions. Where'd you find it?

Hans was enjoying himself too much.

I didn't.

Jorge, hey. Pa chewed his lip. So you're the nosy bastard.

He didn't look at me and it didn't seem like he was talking to me at all. He said it like I wasn't there and he was thinking out loud. Awake, asleep—it didn't fool me.

It wasn't me, Pa, I said.

I tried to get Hans's attention so he'd shut up but he was enjoying himself.

Little Hans ain't no fool, Big Hans said.

No.

Now Pa wasn't paying attention.

He ain't no kin to you, Pa said.

Why ain't he here then? He'd be looking too. Why ain't he here?

Gracious, I'd forgot all about Little Hans, ma said, quickly taking a bowl from the cupboard.

Hed, what are you up to? Pa said.

Oh, biscuits.

Biscuits? What in hell for? Biscuits. I don't want any biscuits. Make some coffee. All this time you been just standing around.

For Pedersen and little Hans. They'll be coming and they'll want some biscuits and coffee, and I'll put out some elderberry jelly. The coffee needed reminding, Magnus, thank you.

Who found the bottle?

She scooped some flour from the bin.

Pa'd been sitting, swinging. Now he stopped and stood up.

Who found it? Who found it? God dammit, who found it? Which one of them was it?

Ma was trying to measure the flour but her hands shook. The flour ran off the scoop and fell across the rim of the cup, and I thought, Yeah, You'd have run, Yeah, Your hands shake.

Why don't you ask Jorge? Big Hans said.

How I hated him, putting it on me, the coward. And he had thick arms.

That snivel, Pa said.

Hans laughed so his chest shook.

He couldn't find nothing I hid.

You're right there, Hans said.

I could, I said. I have.

A liar, Hans, hey? You found it.

Pa was somehow pleased and sat on the corner of the table again. Was it Hans he hated most, or me?

I never said Jorge found it.

I've got a liar working for me. A thief and a liar. Why should I keep a liar? I'm just soft on him, I guess, and he's got such a sweet face. But why should I keep a thief . . . little movey eyes like traveling specks . . . why?

I ain't like you. I don't spend every day drinking just to sleep the night and then sleep half the day too, fouling your bed and your room and half the house.

You been doing your share of lying down. Little Hans is half your size and worth twice. You—you got a small dick.

Pa's words didn't come out clear.

How about Little Hans? Little Hans ain't showed up. Folks must be getting pretty worried at the Pedersens'. They'd like some news maybe. But Pedersen don't come. Little Hans don't come. There's a thousand drifts out there. The kid might be under any one. If anybody's seen him, we have, and if we haven't, nobody's going to till spring, or maybe if the wind shifts, which ain't likely. But nobody comes to ask. That's pretty funny, I'd say.

You're an awful full-up bastard, Pa said.

I'm just considering, that's all.

Where'd you find it?

I forgot. It needed reminding. I was going to have a drink.

Where?

You're pretty good at hiding, Hans said.

I'm asking. Where?

I didn't, I told you, I didn't find it. Jorge didn't find it neither.

You bastard, Hans, I said.

It hatched, Hans said. Like the fellow, you know, who blew in. He hatched. Or maybe the kid found it—had it hid under his coat.

Who? Pa roared, standing up quick.

Oh Hed found it. You don't hide worth a damn and Hed found it easy. She knew right away where to look.

Shut up, Hans, I said.

Hans tilted the bottle.

She must have known where it was a long time now. Maybe she knows where they're all hid. You ain't very smart. Or maybe she's took it up herself, eh? And it ain't yours at all, maybe that.

Big Hans poured himself a drink. Then Pa kicked the glass out of Hans's hand. Pa's slipper flew off and sailed by Hans's head and bounced off the wall. The glass didn't break. It fell by the sink and rolled slow by ma's feet, leaving a thin line. The scoop flew a light white cloud. There was whiskey on Hans's shirt and on the wall and cupboards, and a splash on the floor where the glass had hit.

Ma had her arms wrapped around her chest. She looked faint and she was whewing and moaning.

Okay, Pa said, we'll go. We'll go right now, Hans. I hope to god you you get a bullet in your belly. Jorge, go upstairs and see if the little sonofabitch is still alive.

Hans was rubbing the spots on his shirt and licking his lips when I hunched past Pa and went out.

PART TWO
I

There wasn't any wind. The harness creaked, the wood creaked, the runners made a sound like a saw working easy,

and everything was white about Horse Simon's feet. Pa had
the reins between his knees and he and Hans and I kept ourselves close together. We bent our heads and clenched our
feet and wished we could huddle both hands in one pocket.
Only Hans was breathing through his nose. We didn't speak.
I wished my lips could warm my teeth. The blanket we had
wasn't worth a damn. It was just as cold underneath and Pa
drank from a bottle by him on the seat.

I tried to hold the feeling I'd had starting out when we'd
hitched up Horse Simon when I was warm and decided to
risk the North Corn Road to the Pedersen place. It catty-
cornered and came up near the grove behind his barn. We
figured we could look at things from there. I tried to hold the
feeling but it was warm as new bath water and just as hard to
hold. It was like I was setting out to do something special and
big—like a knight setting out—worth remembering. I dreamed
coming in from the barn and finding his back to me in the
kitchen and wrestling with him and pulling him down and
beating the stocking cap off his head with the barrel of the
gun. I dreamed coming in from the barn still blinking with
the light and seeing him there and picking the shovel up and
taking him on. That had been then, when I was warm, when
I was doing something big, heroic even, and well worth remembering. I couldn't put the feeling down in Pedersen's back
yard or Pedersen's porch or barn. I couldn't see myself, or him,
there. I could only see him back where I wasn't any more—
standing quiet in our kitchen with his gun going slowly up and
down in ma's face and ma shooing it away and at the same
time trying not to move an inch for getting shot.

When I got good and cold the feeling slipped away. I
couldn't imagine him with his gun or cap or yellow gloves. I
couldn't imagine me coming on to him. We weren't any-place
and I didn't care. Pa drove by staring down the sloping white

road and drank from his bottle. Hans rattled his heels on the
back of the seat. I just tried to keep my mouth shut and
breathe and not think why in the name of the good jesus
christ I had to.

It wasn't like a sleigh ride on an early winter evening when
the air is still, the earth is warm, and the stars are flakes being
born that will not fall. The air was still all right, the sun
straight up and cold. Behind us on the trough that marked
the road I saw our runners and the holes that Simon tore.
Ahead of us it melted into drifts. Pa squinted like he saw
where he knew it really went. Horse Simon steamed. Ice hung
from his harness. Snow caked his belly. I was afraid the crust
might cut his knees and I wanted a drink out of Pa's bottle.
Big Hans seemed asleep and shivered in his dreams. My rear
was god almighty sore.

We reached a drift across the road and Pa eased Simon
round her where he knew there wasn't any fence. Pa figured to
go back to the road but after we got round the bank I could
see there wasn't any point in that. There were rows of high
drifts across it.

They ain't got no reason to do that, Pa said.

It was the first thing Pa'd said since he told me to go upstairs and see if the Pedersen kid was still alive. He hadn't
looked alive to me but I'd said I guessed he was. Pa'd gone and
got his gun first, without dressing, one foot still bare so he
favored it, and took the gun upstairs cradled in his arm, broke,
and pointing down. He had a dark speckled spot on the rump
of his nightshirt where he'd sat on the table. Hans had his
shotgun and the forty-five he'd stolen from the Navy. He made
me load it and when I'd stuck it in my belt he'd said it'd likely
go off and keep me from ever getting out to stud. Then gun
felt like a chunk of ice against my belly and the barrel dug.

Ma'd put some sandwiches and a Thermos of coffee in a

sack. The coffee'd be cold. My hands would be cold when I ate mine even if I kept my gloves on. Chewing would be painful. The lip of the Thermos would be cold if I drank out of that, and I'd spill some on my chin which would dry to ice; or if I used the cup, the tin would stick to my lip like lousy liquor you didn't want to taste by licking off, and it would burn and then tear my skin coming away.

Simon went into a hole. He couldn't pull out so he panicked and the sleigh skidded. We'd had crust but now the front right runner broke through and we braked in the soft snow underneath. Pa made quiet impatient noises and calmed Simon down.

That was damn fool, Hans said.

He lost his footing. Jesus, I ain't the horse.

I don't know. Simon's a turd binder, Hans said.

Pa took a careful drink.

Go round and lead him out.

Jorge is on the outside.

Go round and lead him out.

You. You go round. You led him in.

Go round and lead him out.

Sometimes the snow seemed as blue as the sky. I don't know which seemed colder.

Oh god I'll go, I said. I'm on the outside.

Your old man's on the outside, Hans said.

I guess I know where I am, Pa said. I guess I know where I'm staying.

Can't you let up, for christ's sake? I'm going, I said.

I threw off the blanket and stood up but I was awful stiff. The snow dazzle struck me and the pain of the space around us. Getting out I rammed my ankle against the sideboard's iron brace. The pain shot up my leg and shook me like an ax handle will when you strike wrong. I cursed, taking my time jumping off. The snow looked as stiff and hard as cement and I could only think of the jar.

You've known where that brace was for ten years, Pa said.

The snow went to my crotch. The gun bit. I waded round the hole trying to keep on tiptoe and the snow away from my crotch but it wasn't any use.

You practicing to be a bird? Hans said.

I got hold of Horse Simon and tried to coax him out. Pa swore at me from his seat. Simon kicked and thrashed and lunged ahead. The front right runner dug in. The sleigh swung around on it and the left side hit Simon's back legs hard behind the knees. Simon reared and kicked a piece out of the side of the sleigh and then pulled straight ahead tangling the reins. The sleigh swung back again and the right runner pulled loose with a jerk. Pa's bottle rolled. From where I sat in the snow I saw him grab him for it. Simon went on ahead. The seigh slid sideways into Simon's hole and the left runner went clear of the snow. Simon pulled up short though Pa had lost the reins and was holding on and yelling about his bottle. I had snow in my eyes and down my neck.

Simon didn't have no call to do that, Hans said, mimicking Pa.

Where's my bottle? Pa said, looking over the side of the sleigh at the torn snow. Jorge, go find my bottle. It fell in the snow here somewheres.

I tried to brush the snow off without getting more in my pockets and up my sleeves and down my neck.

You get out and find it. It's your bottle.

Pa leaned way over.

If you hadn't been so god damn dumb it wouldn't have fell out. Where'd you learn to lead a horse? You never learned that dumb trick from me. Of all the god damn dumb tricks I never seen any dumber.

Pa waved his arms in a circle.

That bottle fell out about here. It couldn't have got far. It was corked, thank god. I won't lose none.

Snow was slipping down the hollow of my back. The forty-five had slipped through my belt. I was afraid it would go off like Big Hans said. I kept my right forearm pressed against it. I didn't want it slipping off down my pants. I didn't like it. Pa shouted directions.

You hid it, I said. You're such a hand at hiding. You find it then. I ain't good at finding. You said so yourself.

Jorge, you know I got to have that bottle.

Then get off your ass and find it.

You know I got to have it.

Then get off.

If I get down off here, it ain't the bottle I'm coming after. I'll hold you under till you drown, you little smart-talking snot.

I started kicking around in the snow.

Hans giggled.

There's a trace broke, he said.

What's so damn funny?

I told you that trace was worn.

I kicked about. Pa followed my feet.

Hell. Not that way. He pointed. You know about everything there is, Hans, I guess, he said, still watching me. First little thing you figure out you tell somebody about. Then somebody else knows. So then they can do what needs to be done, and you don't have to—jesus, not there, *there*. Don't it, Hans? don't it always let you out?   You ain't going deep enough.   I never figured that out. How come somebody else's knowing always lets you out? You're just a pimp for jobs, I guess. You ain't going deep enough, I said.

It ain't my job to fix traces.

Hey, get your hands in it, *your hands*. It's clean. You always

was that way about manure. Why ain't it your job? Too busy
screwing sheep?   Try over there. You ought to have hit it.
No, there, not there.

I never fixed traces.

Christ, they never needed fixing while you been here hardly.
Jorge, will you stop nursing that fool gun with your cock and
use both hands.

I'm cold, Pa.

So'm I. That's why you got to find that bottle.

If I find it do I get a drink?

Ain't you growed up—a man—since yesterday!

I've had a few, Pa.

Ha. Of what, hey? Hear that, Hans? He's had a few. For
medicine maybe, like your ma says. The spirits, the spirits,
Jorgen Segren . . . ha.   He's had a few he says. He's had a
few.

Pa.

He's had a few. He's had a few. He's had a few.

Pa. I'm cold, Pa.

Maybe. Only look, for god's sake, don't just thrash about like
a fool chicken.

Well, we're finished anyway, Hans said.

We're finished if we don't find that bottle.

You're finished, maybe. You're the only one who needs that
bottle. Jorge and I don't need it, but there you are, old man,
eh? Lost in the snow.

My gloves were wet. Snow had jammed under my sleeves.
It was working down into my boots. I stopped to pick some out
with a finger if I could.

Maybe some of ma's coffee is still hot, I said.

Say.   Yeah.   Maybe.   But that's my coffee, boy. I
never got none. I ain't even had breakfast. What are you
stopping for? Come on. Hell, Jorge, it's cold.

I know that better than you. You're sitting there all nice and
dry, bossing; but I'm doing all the work and getting the snow
inside me.

Say.   Yeah.   That's right.

Pa leaned back and grinned. He clutched the blanket to him
and Hans pulled it back.

It's easier to keep warm moving around, anybody knows
that. Ain't that right, Hans? It's easier to keep warm moving,
ain't it?

Yeah, Hans said. If you ain't got a blanket.

See there, Jorge, hey? You just keep good and warm . . .
stirring. It'd be a pity if your pee should freeze. And moving
around good prevents calluses on the bottom. Don't it Hans?

Yeah.

Hans here knows. He's nothing but calluses.

You'll wear out your mouth.

I can't find it, Pa. Maybe some of ma's coffee is still warm.

You damn snivel—you ain't looking. Get tramping proper
like I told you and find it. Find it fast, you hear. You ain't
getting back up on this sleigh until you do.

I started jumping up and down, not too fast, and Pa blew
his nose with his fingers.

Cold makes the snot run, he says, real wise.

If I found the bottle I'd kick it deep under the snow. I'd
kick it and keep kicking it until it sank under a drift. Pa
wouldn't know where it was. I wouldn't come back to the
sleigh either. They weren't going anywhere anyway. I'd go
home though it was a long walk. Looking back I could see our
tracks in the trough of the road. They came together before I
lost them. It would be warm at home and worth the walk. It
was frightening—the endless white space. I'd have to keep my
head down. Winded slopes and rises all around me. I'd never
wanted to go to Pedersen's. That was Hans's fight, and Pa's.

I was just cold . . . cold . . . and scared and sick of snow. That's
what I'd do if I found it—kick it under a drift. Then later, a
lot later in the spring one day I'd come out here and find the
old bottle sticking out of the rotting snow and stuck in the
mud like dough, and I'd hide it back of the barn and have a
drink whenever I wanted. I'd get some real cigarettes, maybe a
carton, and hide them too. Then someday I'd come in and
Pa'd smell whiskey on me and think I'd found one of his
hiding places. He'd be mad as hell and not know what to say.
It'd be spring and he'd think he'd taken them all in like he
always did, harvesting the crop like he said.

I looked to see if there was something to mark the place by
but it was all gone under snow. There was only the drifts and
the deep holes of snow and the long runnered trough of the
road. It might be a mudhole we was stuck in. In the spring
cattails grow up in it and the blackbirds come. Or it might be
low and slimy at first and then caked dry and cracked. Pa'd
never find out how I came by the bottle. Someday he'd act too
big and I'd stick his head under the pump or slap his skinny
rump with the backside of a fork full of manure. Hans would
act smart and then someday—

Jee-suss, will you move?

I'm cold, Pa.

You're going to be a pig's size colder.

Well, we're finished anyway, Hans said. We ain't going
nowhere. The trace is broke.

Pa stopped watching me thrash the snow. He frowned at
Horse Simon. Simon was standing quiet with his head down.

Simon's shivering, he said. I should have remembered he'd
be heated up. It's so cold I forgot.

Pa yanked the blanket off of Hans like Hans was a bed he
was stripping, and jumped down, Hans yelled but Pa didn't
pay attention. He threw the blanket over Simon.

We got to get Simon moving. He'll stiffen up.

Pa ran his hand tenderly down Simon's legs.

The sleigh don't seem to have hurt him none.

The trace is broke.

Then Hans stood up. He beat his arms aginst his body and jigged.

We'll have to walk him home, he said.

Home, hey, Pa said, giving Hans a funny sidewise look. It's a long walk.

You can ride him then, Hans said.

Pa looked real surprised and even funnier. It wasn't like Hans to say that. It was too cold. It made Hans generous. There was some good in cold.

Why?

Pa waded, patting Simon, but he kept his eye on Hans like it was Hans might kick.

Hans let out a long impatient streamer.

Jesus—the trace.

Hans was being real cautious. Hans was awful cold. His nose was red. Pa's was white but it didn't look froze. It just looked white like it usually did—like it was part of him had died long ago. I wondered what color my nose was. Mine was bigger and sharper at the end. It was ma's nose, ma said. I was bigger all over than Pa. I was taller than Hans too. I pinched my nose but my gloves were wet so I couldn't feel anything except how my nose hurt when I pinched it. It couldn't be too cold. Hans was pointing at the ends of the trace which were trailing in the snow.

Tie a knot in it, Pa was saying.

It won't hold, Hans said, shaking his head.

Tie a good one, it will.

It's too cold to get a good knot. Leather's too stiff.

Hell no, it ain't too stiff.

Well, it's too thick. Can't knot something like that.

You can do it.

She'll pull crooked.

Let her pull crooked.

Simon won't work well pulling her crooked.

He'll have to do the best he can. I ain't going to leave this sleigh out here. Hell, it might snow again before I got back with a new trace.   Or you got back, hey?   When I get home I'm going to stay there and I'm going to eat my breakfast if it's suppertime. I ain't coming back out here trying to beat another blizzard and wind up like the Pedersen kid.

Yeah, Hans said, nodding. Let's get this damn thing out of here and get Simon home before he stiffens. I'll tie the trace.

Hans got down and I stopped kicking. Pa watched Hans real careful from his side of Horse Simon and I could see him smiling like he'd thought of something dirty. I started to get on the sleigh but Pa shouted and made me hunt some more.

Maybe we'll find it when we move the sleigh, I said.

Pa laughed but not at what I said. He opened his mouth wide, looking at Hans, and laughed hard, though his laugh was quiet.

Yeah, maybe we will, he said, and gave Simon an extra hard pat. Maybe we will, hey, at that.

I didn't find the bottle and Big Hans tied the trace. He had to take his gloves off to do it but he did it quick and I had to admire him for it. Pa coaxed Simon while Hans, boosting, heaved. She got clear and suddenly was going—skidding out. I heard a noise like a light bulb busting. A brown stain spread over the sleigh track. Pa peered over his shoulder at the stain, his hands on the halter, his legs wide in the snow.

Oh no, he said.   Oh no.

But Big Hans broke up. He lifted a leg clear of the snow.

He hit himself. His shoulders shook. He hugged his belly. He rocked back and forth. Oh—oh—oh, he screamed, and he held his sides. Tears streamed down his cheeks. You—you—you, he howled. Hans's cheeks, his nose, his head was red. Found—found—found, he choked.

Everything about Pa was frozen. The white hair that stuck out from his hat looked hard and sharp and seemed to shine like snow. Big Hans went on laughing. I never saw him so humored. He staggered, weakening—Pa as still as a stake. Hans began to heave and gasp, running down. In a minute he'd be cold again, worn out, and then he'd wish he could drink out of that bottle. Its breaking had made him drunk. The stain had stopped spreading and was fading, the snow bubbling and sagging. We could melt and drink the snow, I thought. I wanted that bottle back bad. I hated Hans. I'd hate Hans forever—as long as there was snow.

Hans was puffing quietly when Pa told me to get in the sleigh. Then Hans climbed awkwardly on. Pa took the blanket off Horse Simon and threw it in the sleigh. Then he got Simon started. I pulled the blanket over me and tried to stop shivering. Our stove, I though, was black . . . god . . . black . . . lovely sooty black . . . and glowed rich as cherry through its holes. I thought of the kettle steaming on it, the steam alive, hissing white and warm, not like my breath coming slow and cloudy and hanging heavy and dead in the still air.

Hans jumped.

Where we going? he said. Where we going?

Pa didn't say nothing.

This ain't the way, Hans said. Where we going?

The gun was an ache in my stomach. Pa squinted at the snow.

For christ's sake, Hans said. I'm sorry about the bottle.

But Pa drove.

II

Barberry had got in the grove and lay about the bottom of the trees and hid in snow. The mossycups went high, their branches put straight out, the trunk bark black and wrinkled. There were spots where I could see the frosted curls of dead grass frozen to the ground and high hard-driven piles of snow the barberry stuck its black barbs from. The wind had thrown some branches in the drifts. The sun made shadows of more branches on their sides and bent them over ridges. The ground rose up behind the grove. The snow rose. Pa and Hans had their shotguns. We followed along the drifts and kept down low. I could hear us breathing and the snow, earth, and our boots squeaking. We went slow and all of us was cold.

Above the snow, through the branches, I could see the peak of Pedersen's house, and nearer by, the roof of Pedersen's barn. We were making for the barn. Once in a while Pa would stop and watch for smoke but there was nothing in the sky. Big Hans bumped into a bush and got a barb through his woolen glove. Pa motioned Hans to hush. I could feel my gun through my glove—heavy and cold. Where we went the ground was driven nearly bare. Mostly I kept my eyes on Big Hans's heels because it hurt my neck so to look up. When I did, for smoke, the faint breeze caught my cheek and drew the skin across the bone. I didn't think of much except how to follow Hans's heels and how, even underneath my cap, my ears burned, and how my lips hurt and how just moving made me ache. Pa followed where a crazy wind had got in among the oaks and blown the snow bare from the ground in flat patches against their trunks. Sometimes we had to break through a small drift or we'd have gone in circles. The roof of Pedersen's house grew above the banks as we went until finally we passed across one corner of it and I saw the chimney very black in the sun stick up from the steep bright pitch like a dead cigar rough-ashed with snow.

I thought: the fire's dead, they must be froze.

Pa stopped and nodded at the chimney.

You see, Hans said unhappily.

Just then I saw a cloud of snow float from the crest of a drift and felt my eyes smart. Pa looked quick at the sky but it was clear. Hans stomped his feet, hung his head, swore in a whisper.

Well, Pa said, it looks we made this trip for nothing. Nobody's to home.

The Pedersens are all dead, Hans said, still looking down.

Shut up. I saw Pa's lips were chapped . . . a dry dry hole now. A muscle jumped along his jaw.   Shut up, he said.

A faint ribbon of snow suddenly shot from the top of the chimney and disappeared. I stood as still as I could in the tubes of my clothes, the snow shifting strangely in my eyes, alone, frightened by the space that was bowling up inside me, a white blank glittering waste like the waste outside, coldly burning, roughed with waves, and I wanted to curl up, face to my thighs, but I knew my tears would freeze my lashes together. My stomach began to growl.

What's the matter with you, Jorge? Pa said.

Nothing. I giggled. I'm cold, Pa, I guess, I said. I belched.

Jesus, Hans said loudly.

Shut up.

I poked at the snow with the toe of my boot. I wanted to sit down and if there'd been anything to sit on I would have. All I wanted was to go home or sit down. Hans had stopped stomping and was staring back through the trees toward the way we'd come.

Anybody in that house, Pa said, would have a fire.

He sniffed and rubbed his sleeve across his nose.

Anybody—see? He began raising his voice. Anybody who was in that house now would have a fire. The Pedersens is all most likely out hunting that fool kid. They probably tore ass off without minding the furnace. Now it's out. His voice got braver. Anybody who might have come along while they was gone, and gone in, would have started a fire someplace first thing, and we'd see the smoke. It's too damn cold not to.

Pa took the shotgun he'd carried broken over his left arm and turned the barrel over, slow and deliberate. Two shells fell out and he stuffed them in his coat pocket.

That means there ain't anybody to home. There ain't no smoke, he said with emphasis, and that means there ain't nobody.

I wanted to sit down. Here was the sofa, here the bed—mine —white and billowy. And the stairs, cold and snapping. And I had the dry cold toothaching mouth I always had at home, and the cold storm in my belly, and my pinched eyes. There was the print of the kid's rear in the dough. I wanted to sit down. I wanted to go back where we'd tied up Horse Simon and sit numb in the sleigh.

Yes yes yes, let's, I said.

Pa smiled—oh the bastard—the *bastard*—and he didn't know half what I knew now, numb in the heart the way I felt, and with my burned-off ears.

We could at least leave a note saying Big Hans saved their kid. Seems to me like the only neighborly thing to do. And after all the way we come. Don't it you?

What the hell do you know about what's neighborly? Hans shouted.

With a jerk he dumped his shotgun shells into the snow and kicked at them until one skidded into a drift and only the brass showed. The other sank in the snow before it broke. Black powder spilled out under his feet.

Pa laughed.

Come on, Pa, I'm cold, I said. Look, I ain't brave. I ain't.
I don't care. All I am is cold.

Quit whimpering, we're all cold. Big Hans here is awful cold.
Sure, ain't you?

Hans was grinding the black grains under.

Yeah, Pa said, grinning. Some.   I'm some. He turned
around. Think you can find your way back, Jorge?

I got going and he laughed again, loud and ugly, damn his
soul. I hated him. Jesus, how I did. But no more like a father.
Like the burning space.

I never did like that bastard Pedersen anyway, he said as we
started. Pedersen's one of them that's always asking for trouble.
On his knees for it all the time. Let him find out about his
kid himself. He knows where we live. It ain't neighborly but
I never said I wanted him a neighbor.

Yeah, Hans said. Let the old bastard find out himself.

He should have kept his kid behind them fences. What
business did he have, sending his kid to us to take care of? He
went and asked for snow. He went on his knees for snow. Was
he ready? Hey? Was he? For *snow?* Nobody's ever ready for
snow.

The old bastard wouldn't have come to tell you if it'd been
me who'd been lost, I said, but I wasn't minding my words
at all, I was just talking. Neighbor all over him, I said, he has
it coming. I was feeling the sleigh moving under me.

Can't tell about holy Pete, Hans said.

I was going fast. I didn't care about keeping low. I had my
eyes on the spaces between trees. I was looking for the place
where we'd left Simon and the sleigh. I thought I'd see Simon
first, maybe his breath above a bank or beside the trunk of a
tree. I slipped on a little snow the wind hadn't blown from
the path we'd took. I still had the gun in my right hand so I
lost my balance. When I put out my left for support, it went

into a drift to my elbow and into the barberry thorns. I jerked
back and fell hard. Hans and Pa found it funny. But the legs
that lay in front of me weren't mine. I'd gone out in the
blazing air. It was queer. Out of the snow I'd kicked away with
my foot stuck a horse's hoof and I didn't feel the least terror
or surprise.

Looks like a hoof, I said.

Hans and Pa were silent. I looked up at them far away.
Nothing now. Three men in the snow. A red scarf and some
mittens . . . somebody's ice and coal . . . the picture for January.
But behind them on the blank hills? Then it rushed over me
and I thought: this is as far as he rid him. I looked at the hoof
and the shoe which didn't belong in the picture. No dead
horses for January. And on the snowhills there would be wild
sled tracks and green trees and falling toboggans. This is as
far. Or a glazed lake and rowdy skaters. Three men. On his ass:
one. Dead horse and gun. And the question came to me very
clearly, as if out of the calendar a girl had shouted: are you
going to get up and walk on? Maybe it was the Christmas picture. The big log and the warm orange wood I was sprawled on
in my flannel pajamas. I'd just been given a pistol that shot
BBs. And the question was: was I going to get up and walk
on? Hans's shoes, and Pa's, were as steady as the horse's. Were
they hammered on? Their bodies stolen? Who'd left them
standing here? And Christmas cookies cut in the shape of the
kid's dead wet behind . . . with maybe a cherry to liven the
pale dough . . . a coal from the stove. But I couldn't just say
that looks like a hoof or that looks like a shoe and go right on
because Hans and Pa were waiting behind me in their wool
hats and pounding mittens . . . like a picture for January.
Smiling. I was learning to skate.

Looks like this is as far as he rid him.

Finally Pa said in a flat voice: what are you talking about?

You said he had a horse, Pa.

What are you talking about?

This here horse.

Ain't you never seen a shoe before?

It's just a horse's hoof, Hans said. Let's get on.

What are you talking about? Pa said again.

The man who scared the Pedersen kid. The man he saw.

Manure, Pa said. It's one of Pedersen's horses. I recognize the shoe.

That's right, Big Hans said.

Pedersen only has one horse.

This here's it, Big Hans said.

This horse's brown, ain't it?

Pedersen's horse has got two brown hind feet. I remember, Big Hans said.

His is black.

It's got two brown hind feet.

I started to brush away some snow. I knew Pedersen's horse was black.

What the hell, Hans said. Come on. It's too cold to stand here and argue about the color of Pedersen's god damn horse.

Pedersen's horse is black, Pa said. He don't have any brown on him at all.

Big Hans turned angrily on Pa. You said you recognized his shoe.

I thought I did.   It ain't.

I kept scraping snow away. Hans leaned down and pushed me. The horse was white where frozen snow clung to his hide.

He's brown, Hans. Pedersen's horse is black. This one's brown.

Hans kept pushing at me. God damn you, he was saying over and over in a funny high voice.

You knew all along it wasn't Pedersen's horse.

It went on like singing. I got up carefully, taking the safety off. Later in the winter maybe somebody would stumble on his shoes sticking out of the snow. Shooting Hans seemed like something I'd done already. I knew where he kept his gun— under those magazines in his drawer—and though I'd really never thought of it before, the whole thing moved before me now so naturally it must have happened that way. Of course I shot them all—Pa in his bed, ma in her kitchen, Hans when he came in from his rounds. They wouldn't look much different dead than alive only they wouldn't be so loud.

Jorge, now—look out with that thing, Jorge.   Jorge.

His shotgun had fallen in the snow. He was holding both hands in front of him. Afterwards I stood alone in every room.

You're yellow, Hans.

He was backing slowly, fending me off—fending—fending— Jorge . . . Jorge . . . hey now . . . Jorge . . . Like singing.

Afterwards I looked through his magazines, my hand on my pecker, hot from head to foot.

I've shot you, yellow Hans. You can't shout or push no more or goose me in the barn.

Hey now wait, Jorge—listen—What?   Jorge . . . wait . . . Like singing.

Afterwards only the wind and the warm stove. Shivering I rose on my toes. Pa came up and I moved the gun to take him in. I kept it moving back and forth . . . Hans and Pa . . . Pa and Hans. Gone. Snow piling in the window corners. In the spring I'd shit with the door open, watching the blackbirds.

Don't be a damn fool, Jorge, Pa said. I know you're cold. We'll be going home.

. . . yellow yellow yellow yellow . . . Like singing.

Now Jorge, I ain't yellow, Pa said, smiling pleasantly.

I've shot you both with bullets.

Don't be a fool.

The whole house with bullets. You too.

Funny I don't feel it.

They never does, do they? Do rabbits?

He's crazy, jesus, Mag, he's crazy—

I never did want to. I never hid it like you did, I said. I never believed him. I ain't the yellow one but you you made me made me come but you're the yellow yellow ones; you were all along the yellow ones.

You're cold is all.

Cold or crazy—jesus—it's the same.

He's cold is all.

Then Pa took the gun away, putting it in his pocket. He had his shotgun hanging easy over his left arm but he slapped me and I bit my tongue. Pa was spitting. I turned and ran down the path we'd come, putting one arm over my face to ease the stinging.

You little shit, Big Hans called after me.

III

Pa came back to the sleigh where I was sitting hunched up under the blanket and got a shovel out of the back.

Feeling better?

Some.

Why don't you drink some of that coffee?

It's cold by now. I don't want to anyhow.

How about them sandwiches?

I ain't hungry. I don't want anything.

Pa started back with the shovel.

What are you going to do with that? I said.

Dig a tunnel, he said, and he went around a drift out of sight, the sun flashing from the blade.

I almost called him back but I remembered the grin in his

face so I didn't. Simon stamped. I pulled the blanket closer. I
didn't believe him. Just for a second, when he said it, I had.
It was a joke. Well I was too cold for jokes. What did he want
a shovel for? There's be no point in digging for the horse. They
could see it wasn't Pedersen's.

Poor Simon. He was better than they were. They'd left us
in the cold.

Pa'd forgot about the shovel in the sleigh. I could have used
it hunting for his bottle. That had been a joke too. Pa'd sat
there thinking how funny Jorge is out there beating away at
the snow, I'll just wait and see if he remembers about that
shovel. It'd be funny if Jorge forgot, he'd thought, sitting there
in the blanket and bobbing his head here and there like a
chicken. I'd hear about it when we got home till I was sick.
I put my head down and closed my eyes. All right. I didn't
care. I'd put up with it to be warm. But that couldn't be
right. Pa must have forget the same as me. He wanted that
bottle too bad. Now it was all gone. It was colder with my eyes
closed. I tried to think about all that underwear and the girls
in the pictures. I had a crick in my neck.

Whose horse was it then?

I decided to keep my eyes closed a while longer, to see if I
could do it. Then I decided not to. There was a stream of
light in my eyes. It was brighter than snow, and as white. I
opened them and straightened up. Keeping my head down
made me dizzy. Everything was blurry. There were a lot of
blue lines that moved.

Did they know the horse even so? Maybe it was Carlson's
horse, or even Schmidt's. Maybe he was Carlson in yellow
gloves, or Schmidt, and the kid, because he came in sudden
from the barn and didn't know Carlson had come, saw him
in the kitchen holding a gun like he might of if it'd been
Schmidt, and the kid got scared and run, because he didn't
understand and it's been snowing lots, and how did Schmidt

get there, or Carlson get there, if it was one of them, so the kid got scared and run and came to our crib where the snow grew around him and then in the morning Hans found him.

And we'd been god damn fools. Especially Hans. I shivered. The cold had settled in my belly. The sun had bent around to the west. Near it the sky was hazy. The troughs of some of the drifts were turning blue.

He wouldn't have been that scared. Why'd Carlson or Schmidt be out in a storm like that? If somebody was sick, they were closer to town than either the Pedersens or us. It was a long way for them in this weather. They wouldn't get caught out. But if the horse was stole, who was there but Carlson and Schmidt or maybe Hansen to steal it from?

He goes to the barn before the snow, most likely in the night, and knows horses. Oats or hay lead it out. He's running away. The blizzard sets down. He drives himself and the horse hard, bending in the wind, leaning over far to see fences, any marks, a road. He makes the grove. He might not know it. The horse runs into the barberry, rears, goes to its knees; or a low branch of a mossycup he doesn't see knocks him into a drift; or he slides off when the horse rears as the barbs go in. The horse wanders a little way, not far. Then it stops—finished. And he—he's stunned, windburned, worn like a stone in a dream. He's frozen and tired, for snow's cold water. The wind's howling. He's blind. He's hungry, frozen, and scared. The snow is stinging his face, wearing him smooth. Standing still, all alone, it blows by him. Then the snow hides him. The wind blows a crust over him. Only a shovel poking in the drifts or a warm rain will find him lying by the horse.

I threw off the blanket and jumped down and ran up the path we'd made between the drifts and trees, slipping, cutting sharply back and forth, working against my stiffness, but all the time keeping my head up, looking out carefully ahead.

They weren't by the horse. A hoof and part of the leg I'd

uncovered lay by the path like nothing more went with them. Seeing them like that, like they might have blown down from one of the trees in a good wind, gave me a fright. Now there was a slight breeze and I discovered my tongue was sore. Hans's and Pa's tracks went farther on—toward Pedersen's barn. I wasn't excited any more. I remembered I'd left the blanket on the seat instead of putting it on Simon. I thought about going back. Pa'd said a tunnel. That had to be a joke. But what were they doing with the shovel? Maybe they'd found him by the barn. What if it really was Schmidt or Carlson? I thought about which I wanted it to be. I went more slowly in Pa's tracks. Now I kept down. The roof of Pedersen's barn got bigger; the sky was hazier; here and there little clouds of snow leaped up from the top of a drift like they'd been pinched off, and sailed swiftly away.

They were digging a tunnel. They didn't hear me come up. They were really digging a tunnel.

Hans was digging in the great drift. It ran from the grove in a high curve against the barn. It met the roof where it went lowest and flowed onto it like there wasn't a barn underneath. It seemed like the whole snow of winter was gathered there. If the drift hadn't ended in the grove it would have been swell for sledding. You could put a ladder on the edge of the roof and go off from there. The crust looked hard enough.

Hans and Pa had put about a ten-foot hole in the bank. Hans dug and Pa put what Hans dug in small piles behind him. I figured it was near a hundred feet to the barn. If we'd been home and not so cold, it would have been fun. But it would take all day. They were great damn fools.

I been thinking, I started out, and Hans stopped in the tunnel with a shovel of snow in the air.

Pa didn't turn around or stop.

You can help dig, he said.

I been thinking, I said, and Hans dropped the shovel, spilling the snow, and came out. I been thinking, I said, that you're digging in the wrong place.

Hans pointed to the shovel. Get digging.

We need something to carry snow with, Pa said. It's getting too damn far.

Pa kicked at the snow and flailed with his arms. He was sweating and so was Hans. It was terrible foolish.

I said you was digging in the wrong place.

Tell Hans. It's his idea. He's the hot digger.

You thought it was a good idea, Hans said.

I never did.

Well, I said, it ain't likely you'll find him clear in there.

Pa chuckled. He ain't going to find us neither.

He ain't going to find anybody if he's where I think.

Oh yeah—*think.* Hans moved nearer. Where?

As far as he got. It really didn't make much difference to me what Hans did. He could come as close as he liked. In the snow near that horse.

Hans started but Pa chewed on his lip and shook his head.

Probably Schmidt or Carlson, I said.

Probably Schmidt or Carlson, shit, Pa said.

Of course, Hans shouted.

Hans scooped up the shovel, furious, and carried it by me like an ax.

Hans has been working like a thrasher, Pa said.

You'll never finish it.

No.

It's higher than it needs to be.

Sure.

Why are you digging it then?

Hans.   Hans wants to.

Why, for christ's sake?

So we can get to the barn without being seen.

Why not cross behind the drift?

Hans.   Hans says no.   Hans says that from an upstairs window he could see over the bank.

What the hell.

He's got a rifle.

But who knows he's upstairs?

Nobody. We don't know he's even there. But that horse is. He's back where I said.

No he ain't. You only wish he was. So does Hans, hey? But he ain't. What did the kid see if he is—his ghost?

I walked into the tunnel to the end. Everything seemed blue. The air was dead and wet. It could have been fun, snow over me, hard and grainy, the excitement of a tunnel, the games. The face of a mine, everything muffled, the marks of the blade in the snow. Well I knew how Hans felt. It would have been wonderful to burrow down, disappear under the snow, sleep out of the wind in soft sheets, safe. I backed out. We went to get Hans and go home. Pa gave me the gun with a smile.

We heard the shovel cutting the crust and Hans puffing. He was using the shovel like a fork. He'd cut up the snow in clods around the horse. He grunted when he drove the shovel in. Next he began to beat the shovel against the snow, packing it down, then ripping the crust with the side of the blade.

Hans.   It ain't no use, Pa said.

But Hans went right on pounding with the shovel, spearing and pounding, striking out here and there like he was trying to kill a snake.

You're just wasting your time. It ain't no use, Hans. Jorge was wrong. He ain't by the horse.

But Hans went right on, faster and faster.

Hans. Pa had to make his voice hard and loud.

The shovel speared through the snow. It struck a stone and rang. Hans went to his knees and pawed at the snow with his hands. When he saw the stone he stopped. On his knees in the snow he simply stared at it.

Hans.

The bastard.   I'd have killed him.

He ain't here, Hans. How could he be? The kid didn't see him here, he saw him in the ktichen.

Hans didn't seem to be listening.

Jorge was wrong. He ain't here at all. He sure ain't here. He couldn't be.

Hans grabbed up the shovel like he was going to swing it and jumped up. He looked at me so awful I forgot how indifferent I was.

We got to think of what to do, Pa said. The tunnel won't work.

Hans didn't look at Pa. He would only look at me.

We can go home, Pa said. We can go home or we can chance crossing behind the bank.

Hans slowly put the shovel down. He started dragging up the narrow track to the barn.

Let's go home, Hans, I said. Come on, let's go home.

I can't go home, he said in a low flat voice as he passed us. Pa sighed and I felt like I was dead.

PART THREE
I

Pedersen's horse was in the barn. Pa kept her quiet. He rubbed his hand along her flank. He laid his head upon her neck and whispered in her ear. She shook herself and nickered. Big Hans opened the door a crack and peeked out. He motioned to Pa to hush the horse but Pa was in the stall. I asked

Hans if he saw anything and Hans shook his head. I warned
Pa about the bucket. He had the horse settled down. There
was something that looked like sponges in the bucket. If they
was sponges, they was hard. Hans turned from the door to
rub his eyes. He leaned back against the wall.

Then Pa came and looked out the crack.

Don't look like anybody's to home.

Big Hans had the hiccups. Under his breath he swore and
hiccuped.

Pa grunted.

Now the horse was quiet and we were breathing careful and
if the wind had picked up we couldn't hear it or any snow it
drove. It was warmer in the barn and the little light there was
was soft on hay and wood. We were safe from the sun and it
felt good to use the eyes on quiet tools and leather. I leaned
like Hans against the wall and put my gun in my belt. It felt
good to have emptied that hand. My face burned and I was
very drowsy.   I could dig a hole in the hay. Even if there
were rats, I would sleep with them in it.   Everything was
still in the barn. Tools and harness hung from the walls, and
pails and bags and burlap rested on the floor. Nothing shifted
in the straw or moved in hay. The horse stood easy. And Hans
and I rested up against the wall, Hans sucking in his breath
and holding it, and we waited for Pa, who didn't make a
sound. Only the line of sun that snuck under him and lay
along the floor and came up white and dangerous to the pail
seemed a living thing.

Don't look like it, Pa said finally. Never can tell.

Now who will go, I thought.   It isn't fair.   Then it'll
be over.   It's just across the yard.   It isn't any farther
than the walk behind the drift.   There's only windows
watching.   If he's been, he's gone, and nothing's there to
hurt.

He's gone.

Maybe, Jorge. But if he came on that brown horse you stumbled on, why didn't he take his mare of Pedersen's when he left?

Jesus, Hans whispered. He's here.

Could be in the barn, we'd never see him.

Hans hiccuped. Pa laughed softly.

Damn you, said Big Hans.

Thought I'd rid you of them hics.

Let me look, I said.

He must be gone, I thought. It's such a little way.   He must be gone.   He never came.   It isn't far but who will go across?   I saw the house by squinting hard. The nearer part, the dining room, came toward us. The porch was on the left and farther off. You could cross to the nearer wall and under the windows edge around. He might see you from the porch window. But he'd gone. Yet I didn't want to go across that little winded space of snow to find it out.

I wished Big Hans would stop. I was counting the spaces. It was comfortable behind my back except for that. There was a long silence while he held his breath and afterwards we waited.

The wind was rising by the snowman. There were long blue shadows by the snowman now. The eastern sky was clear. Snow sifted slowly to the porch past the snowman. An icicle hung from the nose of the pump. There were no tracks anywhere. I asked did they see the snowman and I heard Pa grunt. Snow went waist-high to the snowman. The wind had blown from his face his eyes. A silent chimney was an empty house.

There ain't nobody there, I said.

Hans had hiccups again so I ran out.

I ran to the dining room wall and put my back flat against it, pushing hard. Now I saw clouds in the western sky. The

wind was rising. It was okay for Hans and Pa to come. I would
walk around the corner. I would walk around the wall. The
porch was there. The snowman was alone beside it.

All clear, I shouted, walking easily away.

Pa came carefully from the barn with his arms around his
gun. He walked slow to be brave but I was standing in the
open and I smiled.

Pa sat hugging his knees as I heard the gun, and Hans
screamed. Pa's gun stood up. I backed against the house. My
god, I thought, he's real.

I want a drink.

I held the house. The snow'd been driven up against it.

I want a drink. He motioned with his hand to me.

Shut up. Shut up.   I shook my head.   Shut up. Shut
up and die, I thought.

I want a drink, I'm dry, Pa said.

Pa bumped when I heard the gun again. He seemed to point
his hand at me. My fingers slipped along the boards. I tried to
dig them in but my back slipped down. Hopelessly I closed
my eyes. I knew I'd hear the gun again though rabbits don't.
Silently he'd come.   My back slipped.   Rabbits, though,
are hard to hit the way they jump around. But prairie dogs,
like pa, they sit.   I felt snowflakes against my face, crumbling as they struck. He'd shoot me, by god.   Was pa's head
tipped? Don't look.   I felt snowflakes falling softly against
my face, breaking. The glare was painful, closing the slit in
my eyes. That crack in pa's face must be awful dry. Don't
look.   Yes . . . the wind was rising . . . faster flakes.

I I

When I was so cold I didn't care I crawled to the south
side of the house and broke a casement window with the gun

I had forgot I had and climbed down into the basement ripping my jacket on the glass. My ankles hurt so I huddled there in the dark corner places and in the cold moldy places by boxes. Immediately I went to sleep.

I thought it was right away I woke though the light through the window was red. He put them down the cellar, I remembered. But I stayed where I was, so cold I seemed apart from myself, and wondered if everything had been working to get me in this cellar as a trade for the kid he'd missed. Well, he was sudden. The Pedersen kid—maybe he'd been a message of some sort. No, I liked better the idea that we'd been prisoners exchanged. I was back in my own country. No, it was more like I'd been given a country. A new blank land. More and more, while we'd been coming, I'd been slipping out of myself, pushed out by the cold maybe. Anyway I had a queer head, sear-eyed and bleary, everywhere ribboned. Well, he was quick and quiet. The rabbit simply stumbled. Tomatoes were unfeeling when they froze. I thought of the softness of the tunnel, the mark of the blade in the snow. Suppose the snow was a hundred feet deep. Down and down. A blue-white cave, the blue darkening. Then tunnels off of it like the branches of trees. And fine rooms. Was it February by now? I remembered a movie where the months had blown from the calendar like leaves. Girls in red peek-a-boo BVDs were skiing out of sight. Silence of the tunnel. In and in. Stairs. Wide tall stairs. And balconies. Windows of ice and sweet green light. Ah. There would still be snow in February. Here I go off of the barn, the runners hissing. I am tilting dangerously but I coast on anyway. Now to the trough, the swift snow trough, and the Pedersen kid floating chest down. They were all drowned in the snow now, weren't they? Well more or less, weren't they? The kid for killing his family.   But what about me?   Must freeze.   But I would leave ahead of that, that was the nice

thing, I was already going. Yes. Funny. I was something to run
my hands over, feeling for its hurts, like there were worn
places in leather, rust and rot in screws and boards I had to
find, and the places were hard to reach and the fingers in my
gloves were stiff and their ends were sore. My nose was running. Mostly interesting. Funny. There was a cramp in my leg
that must have made me wake. Distantly I felt the soft points
of my shoulders in my jacket, the heavy line of my cap around
my forehead, and on the hard floor my harder feet, and to my
chest my hugged-tight knees. I felt them but I felt them differently . . . like the pressure of a bolt through steel or the
cinch of leather harness or the squeeze of wood by wood in
floors . . . like the twist and pinch, the painful yield of tender
tight together wheels, and swollen bars, and in deep winter
springs.

I couldn't see the furnace but it was dead. Its coals were
cold, I knew. The broken window held a rainbow and put a
colored pattern on the floor. Once the wind ran through it and
a snowflake turned. The stairs went into darkness. If a crack
of light came down the steps, I guessed I had to shoot. I
fumbled for my gun. Then I noticed the fruit cellar and the
closed door where the Pedersens were.

Would they be dead already? Sure they'd be. Everybody was
but me. More or less. Big Hans, of course, wasn't really, unless
the fellow had caught up with him, howling and running. But
Big Hans had gone away a coward. I knew that. It was almost
better he was alive and the snow had him. I didn't have his
magazines but I remembered how they looked, puffed in their
bras.

The door was wood with a wooden bar. I slipped the bar off
easily but the door itself was stuck. It shouldn't have stuck but
it was stuck—stuck at the top. I tried to see the top by standing on tiptoe, but I couldn't bend my toes well and kept

toppling to the side. Got no business sticking, I thought. There's no reason for that. I pulled again, very hard. A chip fell as it shuddered open. Wedged. Why? It had a bar.   It was even darker in the fruit cellar and the air had a musty earthen smell.

Maybe they were curled up like the kid was when he dropped. Maybe they had frost on their clothes, and stiff hair. What color would their noses be? Would I dare to tweak them? Say. If the old lady was dead I'd peek at her crotch.   I wasn't any Hans to rub them. Big Hans had run. The snow had him. There wasn't any kettle, any stove, down here.   Before you did a thing like that you'd want to be sure. I thought of how the sponges in the bucket had got hard.

I went back behind the boxes and hid and watched the stairs. The chip was orange in the pattern of light. He'd heard me when I broke the glass or when the door shook free or when the wedge fell down. He was waiting behind the door at the top of the stairs. All I had to do was come up. He was waiting. All this time. He waited while we stood in the barn. He waited for pa with his arms full of gun to come out. He took no chances and he waited.

I knew I couldn't wait. I knew I'd have to try to get back out. There he'd be waiting too. I'd sit slowly in the snow like pa. That'd be a shame, a special shame after all I'd gone through, because I was on the edge of something wonderful, I felt it trembling in me strangely, in the part of me that flew high and calmly looked down on my stiff heap of clothing. Oh what pa'd forgot. We could have used the shovel. I'd have found the bottle with it. With it we'd have gone on home. By the stove I'd come to myself again. By it I'd be warm again. But as I thought about it, it didn't appeal to me any more. I didn't want to come to myself that way again. No. I was glad he'd forgot the shovel.   But he was . . . he was wait-

ing.   Pa always said that he could wait; that Pedersen never
could. But pa and me, we couldn't—only Hans stayed back
while we came out, while all the time the real waiter waited.
He knew I couldn't wait. He knew I'd freeze.

Maybe the Pedersens were just asleep.   Have to be sure
the old man wasn't watching. What a thing. Pa pretended
sleep. Could he pretend death too? She wasn't much. Fat.
Gray. But a crotch is a crotch. The light in the window paled.
The sky I could see was smoky. The bits of broken glass had
glimmered out. I heard the wind. Snow by the window rose.
From a beam a cobweb swung stiffly like a net of wire. Flakes
followed one another in and disappeared. I counted desperately
three, eleven, twenty-five. One lit beside me.   Maybe the
Pedersens were just asleep. I went to the door again and looked
in. Little rows of lights lay on the glasses and the jars. I felt
the floor with my foot. I thought suddenly of snakes. I pushed
my feet along. I got to every corner but the floor was empty.
Really it was a relief. I went back and hid behind the boxes.
The wind was coming now, with snow, the glass glinting in
unexpected places. The dead tops of roofing nails in an open
keg glowed white. Oh for the love of god.   Above me in
the house I heard a door slam sharply. He was finished with
waiting.

The kid for killing his family must freeze.

The stair was railless and steep. It seemed to stagger in the
air. Thank god the treads were tight, and didn't creak. Darkness swept under me. Terror of height. But I was only climbing with my sled under my arm. In a minute I'd shoot from
the roof edge and rush down the steep drift, snow smoke
behind me. I clung to the stair, stretched out. Fallen into
space I'd float around a dark star. Not the calendar for March.
Maybe they would find me in the spring, hanging from this
stairway like a wintering cocoon.

I crawled up slowly and pushed the door open. The kitchen wallpaper had flowerpots on it, green and very big. Out of every one a great red flower grew. I began laughing. I liked the wallpaper. I loved it; it was mine; I felt the green pots and traced the huge flower that stuck out of it, laughing. To the left of the door at the head of the stair was a window that looked out on the back porch. I saw the wind hurrying snow off toward the snowman. Down the length of it the sky and all its light was lead and all the snow was ashy. Across the porch were footprints, deep and precise.

I was on the edge of celebration but I remembered in time and scooted in a closet, hunkering down between brooms, throwing my arms across my eyes. Down a long green hill there was a line of sheep. It had been my favorite picture in a book I'd had when I was eight. There were no people in it.

I'd been mad and pa had laughed. I'd had it since my birthday in the spring. Then he'd hid it. It was when we had the privy in the back. God, it was cold in there, dark beneath. I found it in the privy torn apart and on the freezing soggy floor in leaves. And down the hole I saw floating curly sheep. There was even ice. I'd been seized, and was rolling and kicking. Pa had struck himself and laughed. I only saved a red-cheeked fat-faced boy in blue I didn't like. The cow was torn. Ma'd said I'd get another one someday. For a while, every day, even though the snow was piled and the sky dead and the winter wind was blowing, I watched for my aunt to come again and bring me a book like my ma'd said she would. She never came.

And I almost had Hans's magazines.

But he might come again. Yet he'd not chase me home, not now, no.   By god, the calendar was clean, the lines sharp and clear, the colors bright and gay, and there were eights on the ice and red mouths singing and the snow belonged to me and the high sky too, burningly handsome, fiercely blue.   But he might. He was quick.

If it was warmer I couldn't tell but it wasn't as damp as by the boxes and I could smell soap. There was light in the kitchen. It came through the crack I'd left in the closet door to comfort me. But the light was fading. Through the crack I could see the sink, now milky. Flakes began to slide out of the sky and rub their corners off on the pane before they were caught by the wind again and blown away. In the gray I couldn't see them. Then they would come—suddenly—from it, like chaff from grain, and brush the window while the wind eddied. Something black was bobbing. It was deep in the gray where the snow was. It bounced queerly and then it went. The black stocking cap, I thought.

I kicked a pail coming out and when I ran to the window my left leg gave way, banging me against the sink. The light was going. The snow was coming. It was coming almost even with the ground, my snow. Puffs were rising. Then, in a lull when the snow sank and it was light enough to see the snow-bank shadows growing, I saw his back upon a horse. I saw the tail flick. And the snow came back. Great sheets flapped. He was gone.

III

Once, when dust rolled up from the road and the fields were high with heavy-handled wheat and the leaves of every tree were gray and curled up and hung head down, I went in the meadow with an old broom like a gun, where the dandelions had begun to seed and the low ground was cracked, and I flushed grasshoppers from the goldenrod in whirring clouds like quail and shot them down. I smelled wheat in the warm wind and every weed. I tasted dust in my mouth, and the

house and barn and all the pails burned my eyes to look at. I
rode the broom over the brown rocks. I hunted Horse Simon
in the shade of a tree. I rode the broom over the brown
meadow grass and with a fist like pistol butt and trigger shot
the Indian on Horse Simon down. I rode across the dry plain.
I rode into the dry creek. Dust rose up behind me. I went fast
and shouted. The tractor was bright orange. It shimmered.
Dust rolled behind it. I hid in the creek and followed as it
came. I waited as its path curved toward me. I watched and
waited. My eyes were tiny. I sprang out with a whoop and rode
across the dry plain. My horse had a golden tail. Dust rolled up
behind me. Pa was on the tractor in a broad-brimmed hat.
With a fist like a pistol butt and trigger, going fast, I shot him
down.

Pa would stop the tractor and get off and we'd walk across
the creek to the little tree Simon stood his bowed head under.
We'd sit by the tree and pa would pull a water bottle out
from between its roots and drink. He'd swish it around in his
mouth good before he swallowed. He'd wipe off the top and
offer it to me. I'd take a pull like it was fiery and hand it back.
Pa'd take another drink and sigh and get on up. Then he'd say:
you feed the chickens like I told you? and I'd say I had, and
then he'd say: how's the hunting? and I'd say pretty good.
He'd nod like he agreed and clap Simon on the behind and
go on off, but he'd always say I'd best not play in the sun too
long. I'd watch him go over the creek, waving his hat before
his face before he put it on. Then I'd take a secret drink out
of the bottle and wipe my lips and the lip of it. After that I'd
go and let the ragweed brush against my knees, and then,
sometimes, go home.

The fire had begun to feel warm. I rubbed my hands. I ate
a stale biscuit.

Pa had taken the wagon to town. The sun was shining. Pa

had gone to meet Big Hans at the station. There was snow
around but mud was flowing and the fields had green in them
again. Mud rode up on the wagon wheels. There was sweet
air sometimes and the creek had water with the winter going.
Through a crack in the privy door I saw him take the wagon
to the train. I'd a habit, when I was twelve, of looking down.
Something sparkled on the water. It was then I found the first
one. The sun was shining. Mud was climbing the wagon
wheels and pa was going to the train and down the tight creek
snow was flowing. He had a ledge beneath the seat. You could
reach right down. Already he had a knack for hiding. So I
found it and poured it out in the hole. That was the last year
we had the privy because when Big Hans came we tore it
down.

I ate an apple I'd found. The skin was shriveled but the
meat was sweet.

Big Hans was stronger than Simon, I thought. He let me
help him with his chores, and we talked, and later he showed
me some of the pictures in his magazines. See anything like
that around here? he'd say, shaking his head. Only teats like
that round here is on a cow. And he would tease, laughing
while he spun the pages, giving me only a glimpse. Or he
would come up and spank me on the rump. We tore the privy
down together. Big Hans hated it. He said it was a dirty job
fit only for soldiers. But I helped him a lot, he said. He told
me that Jap girls had their slice on sideways and no hair. He
promised to show me a picture of one of them and though I
badgered him, he never did. We burned the boards in a big
pile back of the barn and the flames were a deep orange like
the sun going down and the smoke rolled darkly. It's piss wet,
Hans said. We stood by the fire and talked until it sank down
and the stars were out and the coals glowed and he told me
about the war in whispers and the firing of big guns.

Pa liked the summer. He wished it was summer all year long. He said once whiskey made it summer for him. But Hans liked the spring like me, though I liked summer too. Hans talked and showed me this and that. He measured his pecker once when he had a hard one. We watched how the larks ran across the weeds and winked with their tails taking off. We watched the brown spring water foam by the rocks in the creek, and heard Horse Simon blow and the pump squeak.

Then pa took a dislike to Hans and said I shouldn't go with Hans so much. And then in the winter Hans took a dislike to pa as he almost had to, and Hans said fierce things to ma about pa's drinking, and one day pa heard him. Pa was furious and terrible to ma all day. It was a night like this one. The wind was blowing hard and the snow was coming hard and I'd built a fire and was sitting by it, dreaming. Ma came and sat near me, and then pa came, burning inside himself, while Hans stayed in the kitchen. All I heard was the fire, and in the fire I saw ma's sad quiet face the whole evening without turning, and I heard pa drinking, and nobody not even me said anything the whole long long evening. The next morning Hans went to wake pa and pa threw the pot and Hans got the ax and pa laughed fit to shake the house. It wasn't long before Hans and I took to hating one another and hunting pa's bottles alone.

The fire was burning down. There was some blue but mostly it was orange. For all Pedersen's preparing like pa said he always did, he hadn't got much wood in the house. It was good to be warm but I didn't feel so set against the weather as I had been. I thought I'd like winter pretty well from now on. I sat as close as I could and stretched and yawned.   Even if his cock was thicker . . . I was here and he was in the snow.   I was satisfied.

He was in the wind now and in the cold now and sleepy

now like me. His head was bent down low like the horse's head must be and he was rocking in the saddle very tired of holding on and only rocking sleepy with his eyes shut and with snow on his heavy lids and on his lashes and snow in his hair and up his sleeves and down inside his collar and his boots. It was good I was glad he was there it wasn't me was there sticking up bare in the wind on a horse like a stick with the horse most likely stopped by this time with his bowed head bent into the storm, and I wouldn't like lying all by myself out there in the cold white dark, dying all alone out there, being buried out there while I was still trying to breathe, knowing I'd only come slowly to the surface in the spring and would soon be soft in the new sun and worried by curious dogs.

The horse must have stopped though he made the other one go on. Maybe he'd manage to drive this one too until it dropped, or he fell off, or something broke. He might make the next place. He just might. Carlson's or Schmidt's. He had once before though he never had a right or any chance to. Still he had. He was in the thick snow now. More was coming. More was blowing down. He was in it now and he could go on and he could come through it because he had before. Maybe he belonged in the snow. Maybe he lived there, like a fish does in a lake. Spring didn't have anything like him. I surprised myself when I laughed the house was so empty and the wind so steady it didn't count for noise.

I saw him coming up beside our crib, the horse going down to its knees in the drift there. I saw him going to the kitchen and coming in unheard because of all the wind. I saw Hans sitting in the kitchen. He was drinking like pa drank—lifting the bottle. Ma was there, her hands like a trap on the table. The Pedersen kid was there too, naked in the flour, towels lapping his middle, whiskey and water steadily dripping. Hans was watching, watching the kid's dirty toes, watching him like

he watched me with his pin-black eyes and his tongue sliding
in his mouth. Then he'd see the cap, the mackinaw, the gloves
wrapped thick around the gun, and it would be the same as
when pa kicked the glass from Big Hans's hand, only the
bottle this time would roll on the floor, squirting. Ma would
worry about her kitchen getting tracked and get up and mix
biscuits with a shaky spoon and put the coffee on.

They'd disappear like the Pedersens had. He'd put them
away somewhere out of sight for at least as long as the winter.
But he'd leave the kid, for we'd been exchanged, and we were
both in our own new lands. Then why did he stand there so
pale I could see through? Shoot. Go on. Hurry up. Shoot.

The horse had circled round in it. He hadn't known the
way. He hadn't known the horse had circled round. His hands
were loose upon the reins and so the horse had circled round.
Everything was black and white and everything the same. There
wasn't any road to go. There wasn't any track. The horse had
circled round in it. He hadn't known the way. There was only
snow to the horse's thighs. There was only cold to the bone
and driving snow in his eyes. He hadn't known. How could
he know the horse had circled round in it? How could he really
ride and urge the horse with his heels when there wasn't any-
place to go and everything was black and white and all the
same? Of course the horse had circled round, of course he'd
come around in it. Horses have a sense. That's all manure
about horses. No it ain't, pa, no it ain't. They do, Hans said.
They do. Hans knows. He's right. He was right about the
wheat that time. He said the rust was in it and it was. He was
right about the rats, they do eat shoes, they eat anything, so
the horse has circled round in it. That was a long time ago.
Yes, pa, but Hans was right even though that was a long time
ago, and how would you know anyway, you was always drinking . . . not in summer . . . no, pa . . . not in spring or fall

either . . . no, pa, but in the winter, and it's winter now and
you're in bed where you belong—don't speak to me, be quiet.
The bottle made it spring for me just like that fellow's made
it warm for you.   Shut up.   Shut up.   I wanted a cat
or a dog awful bad since I was a little kid.   You know those
pictures of Hans's, the girls with big brown nipples like bottle
ends . . .   Shut up.   Shut up.   I'm not going to grieve.
You're no man now. Your bottle's broken in the snow. The
sled rode over it, remember? I'm not going to grieve. You were
always after killing me, yourself, pa, oh yes you were. I was
cold in your house always, pa.   Jorge—so was I.   No. I
was. I was the one wrapped in the snow. Even in the
summer I'd shiver sometimes in the shade of a tree. And pa
—I didn't touch you, remember—there's no point in haunting
me. *He* did. He's even come round maybe.   Oh no jesus
please.   Round.   He wakes.   He sees the horse has
stopped. He sits and rocks and thinks the horse is going on
and then he sees it's not. He tries his heels but the horse has
finally stopped. He gets off and leads him on smack into the
barn, and there it is, the barn, the barn he took the horse
from. Then in the barn he begins to see better and he makes
out something solid in the yard where he knows the house is
and there are certain to be little letups in the storm and
through one of them he sees a flicker of something almost
orange, a flicker of the fire and a sign of me by it all stretched
out my head on my arm and near asleep.   If they'd given
me a dog, I'd have called him Shep.

   I jumped up and ran to the kitchen only stopping and going
back for the gun and then running to the closet for the pail
which I dropped with a terrible clatter. The tap gasped. The
dipper in the pail beneath the sink rattled. So I ran to the
fire and began to poke at it, the logs tumbling, and then I beat

the logs with the poker so that sparks flew and then I beat the
logs with the poker so that sparks flew in my hair.

I crouched down behind a big chair in a corner away from
the fire. Then I remembered I'd left the gun in the kitchen.
My feet were sore and bare. The room was full of orange light
and blackened shadows, moving. The wind whooped and the
house creaked like steps do. I was alone with all that could
happen. I began to wonder if the Pedersens had a dog, if the
Pedersen kid had a dog or cat maybe and where it was if they
did and if I'd known its name and whether it'd come if I
called. I tried to think of its name as if it was something I'd
forgot. I knew I was all muddled up and scared and crazy and
I tried to think god damn over and over or what the hell or
jesus christ, instead, but it didn't work. All that could happen
was alone with me and I was alone with it.

The wagon had a great big wheel.   Papa had a paper
sack.   Mama held my hand.   High horse waved his tail.
Papa had a paper sack. We both ran to hide.   Mama
held my hand.   The wagon had a great big wheel.   High
horse waved his tail. We both ran to hide.   Papa had a
paper sack.   The wagon had a great big wheel.   Mama
held my hand.   Papa had a paper sack.   High horse
waved his tail.   The wagon had a great big wheel. We both
ran to hide.   High horse waved his tail.   Mama held my
hand. We both ran to hide.   The wagon had a great big
wheel.   Papa had a paper sack.   Mama held my hand.
     High horse waved his tail.   Papa had a paper sack. We
both ran to hide.   Papa had a paper sack. We both ran to
hide.

The wind was still. The snow was still. The sun burned on
the snow. The fireplace was cold and all the logs were ashy.
I lay stiffly on the floor, my legs drawn up, my arms around

me. The fire had gone steadily into gray while I slept, and the night away, and I saw the dust float and glitter and settle down. The walls, the rug, the furniture, all that I could see from my elbow looked pale and tired and drawn up tight and cramped with cold. I felt I'd never seen these things before. I'd never seen a wasted morning, the sick drawn look of a winter dawn or how things were in a room where things were stored away and no one ever came, and how the dust came gently down.

I put my socks on. I didn't remember at all coming from behind the chair, but I must have. I got some matches from the kitchen and some paper twists out of a box beside the fireplace and I put them down, raking the ashes aside. Then I put some light kindling on top. Pieces of orange crate I think they were. And then a log. I lit the paper and it flared up and flakes of the kindling curled and got red and black and dropped off and finally the kindling caught when I blew on it. It didn't warm my hands any, though I kept them close, so I rubbed my arms and legs and jigged, but my feet still hurt. Then the fire growled. Another log.   I found I couldn't whistle.   I warmed my back some.   Outside snow.   Steep. There were long hard shadows in the hollows of the drifts but the eastern crests were bright.   After I'd warmed up a little I walked about the house in my stocking feet; and snagged my socks on the stairs. I looked under all the beds and in all the closets and behind most of the furniture. I remembered the pipes were froze. I got the pail from under the sink and opened the door to the back porch against a drift and scooped snow in the pail with a dipper. Snow had risen to the shoulders of the snowman. The pump was banked. There were no tracks anywhere.

I started the stove and put snow in a kettle. It always took so much snow to make a little water. The stove was black as

char. I went back to the fireplace and put more logs on. It was
beginning to roar and the room was turning cheerful, but it
always took so much fire. I wriggled into my boots. Somehow
I had a hunch I'd see a horse.

The front door was unlocked. All the doors were, likely. He
could have walked right in. I'd forgot about that. But now I
knew he wasn't meant to. I laughed to see how a laugh would
sound.   Again.   Good.

The road was gone. Fences, bushes, old machinery: what
there might be in any yard was all gone under snow. All I
could see was the steep snow and the long shadow lines and
the hard bright crest about to break but not quite breaking
and the hazy sun rising, throwing down slats of orange like a
snow fence had fallen down. He'd gone off this way yet there
was nothing now to show he'd gone; nothing like a bump of
black in a trough or an arm or leg sticking out of the side of
a bank like a branch had blown down or a horse's head uncovered like a rock; nowhere Pedersen's fences had kept bare
he might by lying huddled with the horse on its haunches by
him; nothing even in the shadows shrinking while I watched
to take for something hard and not of snow and once alive.

I saw the window I'd broke. The door of the barn hung
ajar, banked steeply with snow. The house threw a narrow
shadow clear to one end of the barn where it ran into the high
drift that Hans had tunneled in. Higher now. Later I'd cut a
path out to it. Make the tunnel deeper maybe. Hollow the
whole bank like a hollow tree. There was time. I saw the oaks
too, blown clean, their twigs about their branches stiff as quills.
The path I'd taken from the barn to the house was filled and
the sun was burning brightly on it. The wind had curled in
and driven a steep slope of snow against the house where I'd
stood. As I turned my head the sun flashed from the barrel
of pa's gun. The snow had risen steeply around him. Only the

top of the barrel was clear to take the sun and it flashed
squarely in my eye when I turned my head just right. There
was nothing to do about that till spring. Another snowman,
he'd melt. I picked my way back to the front of the house, a
dark spot dancing in the snow ahead of me. Today there was
a fine large sky.

It was pleasant not to have to stamp the snow off my boots,
and the fire was speaking pleasantly and the kettle was sounding softly. There was no need for me to grieve. I had been the
brave one and now I was free. The snow would keep me. I
would bury pa and the Pedersens and Hans and even ma if
I wanted to bother. I hadn't wanted to come but now I didn't
mind. The kid and me, we'd done brave things well worth
remembering. The way that fellow had come so mysteriously
through the snow and done us such a glorious turn—well it
made me think how I was told to feel in church. The winter
time had finally got them all, and I really did hope that the
kid was as warm as I was now, warm inside and out, burning
up, inside and out, with joy.

6 ֍ *Leonard Cohen*

Poet, novelist, songwriter, and singer Leonard Cohen was born in Mon-
treal in 1934. He has published five books of poetry and two novels, The
Favorite Game (1963) and Beautiful Losers (1966). Leslie Fiedler has
called Beautiful Losers "an honest-to-God pop art novel."

"F."

(FROM *BEAUTIFUL LOSERS*)

Catherine Tekakwitha, who are you? Are you (1656–1680)? Is
that enough? Are you the Iroquois Virgin? Are you the Lily of
the Shores of the Mohawk River? Can I love you in my own
way? I am an old scholar, better-looking now than when I was
young. That's what sitting on your ass does to your face. I've
come after you, Catherine Tekakwitha. I want to know what
goes on under that rosy blanket. Do I have any right? I fell
in love with a religious picture of you. You were standing
among birch trees, my favorite trees. God knows how far up
your moccasins were laced. There was a river behind you, no
doubt the Mohawk River. Two birds in the left foreground
would be delighted if you tickled their white throats or even
if you used them as an example of something or other in a
parable. Do I have any right to come after you with my dusty

mind full of the junk of maybe five thousand books? I hardly
even get out to the country very often. Could you teach me
about leaves? Do you know anything about narcotic mushrooms? Lady Marilyn just died a few years ago. May I say that
some old scholar four hundred years from now, maybe of my
own blood, will come after her in the way I come after you?
But right now you must know more about heaven. Does it
look like one of these little plastic altars that glow in the dark?
I swear I won't mind if it does. Are the stars tiny, after all?
Can an old scholar find love at last and stop having to pull
himself off every night so he can get to sleep? I don't even
hate books any more. I've forgotten most of what I've read
and, frankly, it never seemed very important to me or to the
world. My friend F. used to say in his hopped-up fashion:
We've got to learn to stop bravely at the surface. We've got
to learn to love appearances. F. died in a padded cell, his brain
rotted from too much dirty sex. His face turned black, this I
saw with my own eyes, and they say there wasn't much left of
his prick. A nurse told me it looked like the inside of a worm.
Salut F., old and loud friend! I wonder if your memory will
persist. And you, Catherine Tekakwitha, if you must know, I
am so human as to suffer from constipation, the rewards of
a sedentary life. Is it any wonder I have sent my heart out into
the birch trees? Is it any wonder that an old scholar who never
made much money wants to climb into your Technicolor postcard?

2

I am a well-known folklorist, an authority on the A——s, a
tribe I have no intention of disgracing by my interest. There
are, perhaps, ten full-blooded A——s left, four of them teen-age
girls. I will add that F. took full advantage of my anthro-

pological status to fuck all four of them. Old friend, you paid
your dues. The A——s seem to have made their appearance in
the fifteenth century, or rather, a sizable remnant of the tribe.
Their brief history is characterized by incessant defeat. The
very name of the tribe, A——s, is the word for corpse in the
language of all the neighboring tribes. There is no record that
this unfortunate people ever won a single battle, while the
songs and legends of its enemies are virtually nothing but a
sustained howl of triumph. My interest in this pack of failures
betrays my character. Borrowing money from me, F. often said:
Thanks, you old A——! Catherine Tekakwitha, do you listen?

3

Catherine Tekakwitha, I have come to rescue you from the
Jesuits. Yes, an old scholar dares to think big. I don't know
what they are saying about you these days because my Latin
is almost defunct. "Que le succès couronne nos espérances, et
nous verrons sur les autels, auprès des Martyrs canadiens, une
Vierge iroquoise—près des roses du martyre le lis de la vir-
ginité." A note by one Ed. L., S.J., written in August 1926.
But what does it matter? I don't want to carry my old belligerent life on my journey up the Mohawk River. Pace, Company
of Jesus! F. said: A strong man cannot but love the Church.
Catherine Tekakwitha, what care we if they cast you in plaster?
I am at present studying the plans of a birch-bark canoe. Your
brethren have forgotten how to build them. And what if there
is a plastic reproduction of your little body on the dashboard
of every Montréal taxi? It can't be a bad thing. Love cannot
be hoarded. Is there a part of Jesus in every stamped-out
crucifix? I think there is. Desire changes the world! What
makes the mountainside of maple turn red? Peace, you manu-
facturers of religious trinkets! You handle sacred material!

Catherine Tekakwitha, do you see how I get carried away?
How I want the world to be mystical and good? Are the stars
tiny, after all? Who will put us to sleep? Should I save my
fingernails? Is matter holy? I want the barber to bury my hair.
Catherine Tekakwitha, are you at work on me already?

4

Marie de l'Incarnation, Marguerite Bourgeoys, Marie-Mar-
guerite d'Youville, maybe you could arouse me if I could move
out of myself. I want to get as much as I can. F. said that he'd
never once heard of a female saint he wouldn't like to have
screwed. What did he mean? F., don't tell me that at last you
are becoming profound. F. once said: At sixteen I stopped
fucking faces. I had occasioned the remark by expressing disgust at his latest conquest, a young hunchback he had met
while touring an orphanage. F. spoke to me that day as if I
were truly one of the underprivileged; or perhaps he was not
speaking to me at all when he muttered: Who am I to refuse
the universe?

5

The French gave the Iroquois their name. Naming food is
one thing, naming a people is another, not that the people in
question seem to care today. If they never cared, so much the
worse for me: I'm far too willing to shoulder the alleged humil-
iations of harmless peoples, as evidenced by my life work with
the A——s. Why do I feel so lousy when I wake up every
morning? Wondering if I'm going to be able to shit or not. Is
my body going to work? Will my bowels churn? Has the old
machine turned the food brown? Is it surprising that I've
tunneled through libraries after news about victims? Fictional

victims! All the victims we ourselves do not murder or im-
prison are fictional victims. I live in a small apartment building.
The bottom of the elevator shaft is accessible through the sub-
basement. While I sat downtown preparing a paper on lem-
mings she crawled into the elevator shaft and sat there with
her arms around her drawn-up knees (or so the police determined from the mess). I came home every night at twenty to
eleven, regular as Kant. She was going to teach me a lesson,
my old wife. You and your fictional victims, she used to say.
Her life had become gray by imperceptible degrees, for I swear,
that very night, probably at the exact moment when she was
squeezing into the shaft, I looked up from the lemming research and closed my eyes, remembering her as young and
bright, the sun dancing in her hair and she sucked me off in a
canoe on Lake Orford. We were the only ones who lived in
the sub-basement, we were the only ones who commanded the
little elevator into those depths. But she taught no one a
lesson, not the kind of lesson she meant. A delivery boy from
the Bar-B-Q did the dirty work by misreading the numbers on
a warm brown paper bag. Edith! F. spent the night with me.
He confessed at 4 a.m. that he'd slept with Edith five or six
times in the twenty years he'd known her. Irony! We ordered
chicken from the same place and we talked about my poor
squashed wife, our fingers greasy, barbecue-sauce drops on the
linoleum. Five or six times, a mere friendship. Could I stand
on some holy mountain of experience, a long way off, and
sweetly nod my Chinese head over their little love? What harm
had been done to the stars? You lousy fucker, I said, how
many times, five or six? Ah, F. smiled, grief makes us precise!
So let it be known that the Iroquois, the brethren of Catherine
Tekakwitha, were given the name Iroquois by the French.
They called themselves Hodenosaunee, which means People
of the Long House. They had developed a new dimension to

conversation. They ended every speech with the word *hiro*, which means: like I said. Thus each man took full responsibility for intruding into the inarticulate murmur of the spheres. To *hiro* they added the word *koué*, a cry of joy or distress, according to whether it was sung or howled. Thus they essayed to pierce the mysterious curtain which hangs between all talking men: at the end of every utterance a man stepped back, so to speak, and attempted to interpret his words to the listener, attempted to subvert the beguiling intellect with the noise of true emotion. Catherine Tekakwitha, speak to me in *Hiro-Koué*. I have no right to mind what the Jesuits say to the slaves, but on that cool Laurentian night which I work toward, when we are wrapped in our birch-bark rocket, joined in the ancient enduring way, flesh to spirit, and I ask you my old question: are the stars tiny, after all, O Catherine Tekakwitha, answer me in *Hiro-Koué*. That other night F. and I quarreled for hours. We didn't know when morning arrived because the only window of that miserable apartment faced into the ventilation shaft.

—You lousy fucker, how many times, five or six?

—Ah, grief makes us precise!

—Five or six, five or six, five or six?

—Listen, my friend, the elevator is working again.

—Listen, F., don't give me any of your mystical shit.

—Seven.

—Seven times with Edith?

—Correct.

—You were trying to protect me with an optional lie?

—Correct.

—And seven itself might just be another option.

—Correct.

—But you were trying to protect me, weren't you? Oh, F.,

do you think I can learn to perceive the diamonds of good amongst all the shit?

—It is all diamond.

—Damn you, rotten wife-fucker, that answer is no comfort. You ruin everything with your saintly pretensions. This is a bad morning. My wife's in no shape to be buried. They're going to straighten her out in some stinking doll hospital. How am I going to feel in the elevator on my way to the library? Don't give me this all diamond shit, shove it up your occult hole. Help a fellow out. Don't fuck his wife for him.

Thus the conversation ran into the morning we could not perceive. He kept to his diamond line. Catherine Tekakwitha, I wanted to believe him. We talked until we exhausted ourselves, and we pulled each other off, as we did when we were boys in what is now downtown but what was once the woods.

6

F. talked a great deal about Indians, and in an irritating facile manner. As far as I know he had no scholarship on the subject beyond a contemptuous and minor acquaintance with my own books, his sexual exploitation of my four teen-age A——s, and about a thousand Hollywood Westerns. He compared the Indians to the ancient Greeks, suggesting a similarity of character, a common belief that every talent must unfold itself in fighting, a love of wrestling, an inherent incapacity to unite for any length of time, an absolute dedication to the idea of the contest and the virtue of ambition. None of the four teen-age A——s achieved orgasm, which, he said, must be characteristic of the sexual pessimism of the entire tribe, and he concluded, therefore, that every other Indian woman could. I couldn't argue. It is true that the A——s seem to present a

very accurate negative of the whole Indian picture. I was
slightly jealous of him for his deduction. His knowledge of
ancient Greece was based entirely on a poem by Edgar Allan
Poe, a few homosexual encounters with restaurateurs (he ate
free at almost every soda fountain in the city), and a plaster
reproduction of the Akropolis which, for some reason, he had
coated with red nail polish. He had meant to use colorless nail
polish merely as a preservative, but naturally he succumbed to
his flamboyant disposition at the drug-store counter when confronted with that fortress of bright samples which ranged the
cardboard ramparts like so many Canadian Mounties. He chose
a color named Tibetan Desire, which amused him since it
was, he claimed, such a contradiction in terms. The entire
night he consecrated to the staining of his plaster model. I
sat beside him as he worked. He was humming snatches from
"The Great Pretender," a song which was to change the
popular music of our day. I could not take my eyes from the
tiny brush which he wielded so happily. White to viscous red,
one column after another, a transfusion of blood into the
powdery ruined fingers of the little monument. F. saying: I'm
wearing my heart like a crown. So they disappeared, the leprous
metopes and triglyphs and other wiggly names signifying
purity, pale temple and destroyed altar disappeared under the
scarlet glaze. F. said: Here, my friend, you finish the caryatids.
So I took the brush, thus Cliton after Themistocles. F. sang:
Ohohohoho, I'm the great pretender, my need is such I pretend too much, and so on—an obvious song under the circumstances but not inappropriate. F. often said: Never overlook
the obvious. We were happy! Why should I resist the exclama-
tion? I had not been so happy since before puberty. How close
I came, earlier in this paragraph, to betraying that happy night!
No, I will not! When we had covered every inch of the old
plaster bone F. placed it on a card table in front of a window.

The sun was just coming up over the sawtooth roof of the
factory next door. The window was rosy and our handicraft,
not yet dry, gleamed like a huge ruby, a fantastic jewel! It
seemed the intricate cradle of all the few noble perishable
sentiments I had managed to preserve, and somewhere safe I
could leave them. F. had stretched out on the carpet, stomach
down, chin in hands supported by wrists and elbows, gazing up
at the red akropolis and the soft morning beyond. He beckoned to me to lie beside him. Look at it from here, he said,
squint your eyes a bit. I did as he suggested, narrowed my eyes,
and—it burst into a cool lovely fire, sending out rays in all
directions (except downward, since that was where the card
table was). Don't weep, F. said, and we began to talk.

—That's the way it must have looked to them, some early
morning when they looked up at it.

—The ancient Athenians, I whispered.

—No, F. said, the old Indians, the Red Men.

—Did they have such a thing, did they build an akropolis?
I asked him, for I seemed to have forgotten everything I knew,
lost it in stroke after stroke of the small brush, and I was
ready to believe anything. Tell me, F., did the Indians have
such a thing?

—I don't know.

—Then what are you talking about? Are you trying to make
a damn fool of me?

—Lie down, take it easy. Discipline yourself. Aren't you
happy?

—No.

—Why have you allowed yourself to be robbed?

—F., you spoil everything. We were having such a nice
morning.

—Why have you allowed yourself to be robbed?

—Why do you always try to humiliate me? I asked him so

solemnly that I scared myself. He stood up, covered the model
with a plastic Remington typewriter cover. He did this so
gently, with a kind of pain, that for the first time I saw that
F. suffered, but from what I could not tell.

—We almost began a perfect conversation, F. said as he
turned on the six o'clock news. He turned the radio very loud
and began to shout wildly against the voice of the commentator, who was reciting a list of disasters. Sail on, sail on, O Ship
of State, auto accidents, births, Berlin, cures for cancer! Listen,
my friend, listen to the present, the right now, it's all around
us, painted like a target, red, white, and blue. Sail into the
target like a dart, a fluke bull's eye in a dirty pub. Empty your
memory and listen to the fire around you. Don't forget your
memory, let it exist somewhere precious in all the colors that
it needs but somewhere else, hoist your memory on the Ship
of State like a pirate's sail, and aim yourself at the tinkly
present. Do you know how to do this? Do you know how to
see the akropolis like the Indians did who never even had one?
Fuck a saint, that's how, find a little saint and fuck her over
and over in some pleasant part of heaven, get right into her
plastic altar, dwell in her silver medal, fuck her until she
tinkles like a souvenir music box, until the memorial lights
go on for free, find a little saintly faker like Teresa or Catherine
Tekakwitha or Lesbia, whom prick never knew but who lay
around all day in a chocolate poem, find one of these quaint
impossible cunts and fuck her for your life, coming all over
the sky, fuck her on the moon with a steel hourglass up your
hole, get tangled in her airy robes, suck her nothing juices,
lap, lap, lap, a dog in the ether, then climb down to this fat
earth and slouch around the fat earth in your stone shoes, get
clobbered by a runaway target, take the senseless blows again
and again, a right to the mind, piledriver on the heart, kick in
the scrotum, help! help! it's time, my second, my splinter of

the shit glory tree, police, firemen! look at the traffic of happiness and crime, it's burning in crayon like the akropolis rose!

And so on. I couldn't hope to write down half the things
he said. He raved like a lunatic, spit flying with every second
word. I guess the disease was already nibbling at his brain, for
he died like that, years later, raving. What a night! And from
this distance, how sweet our argument now seems, two grown
men lying on the floor! What a perfect night! I swear I can
still feel the warmth of it, and what he did with Edith matters
not at all, indeed, I marry them in their unlawful bed, with an
open heart I affirm the true right of any man and woman to
their dark slobbering nights which are rare enough, and against
which too many laws conspire. If only I could live in this
perspective. How quickly they come and go, the memories of
F., the nights of comradeship, the ladders we climbed and the
happy views of simple human clockwork. How quickly pettiness returns, and that most ignoble form of real estate, the
possessive occupation and tyranny over two square inches of
human flesh, the wife's cunt.

7

The Iroquois almost won. Their three major enemies were
the Hurons, the Algonquins, and the French. "La Nouvelle-
France se va perdre si elle n'est fortement et promptement
secourue." So wrote Le P. Vimont, Supérieur de Québec, in
1641. Whoop! Remember the movies. The Iroquois was a
confederation of five tribes situated between the Hudson River
and Lake Erie. Going from east to west we have the Agniers
(whom the English called Mohawks), the Onneyouts, the
Onnontagués, the Goyoqouins (or Goyogouins), and the
Tsonnontouans. The Mohawks (whom the French called
Agniers) occupied a territory between the upper reaches of

the Hudson River, Lake George, Lake Champlain, and the
Richelieu River (first called the Iroquois River). Catherine
Tekakwitha was a Mohawk, born in 1656. Twenty-one years
of her life she spent among the Mohawks, on the banks of the
Mohawk River, a veritable Mohawk lady. The Iroquois were
composed of twenty-five thousand souls. They could put two
thousand five hundred warriors in the field, or ten per cent of
the confederation. Of these only five or six hundred were
Mohawks, but they were especially ferocious, and not only
that, they possessed firearms which they got from the Dutch
at Fort Orange (Albany) in exchange for furs. I am proud that
Catherine Tekakwitha was or is a Mohawk. Her brethren must
be right out of those uncompromising black and white movies
before the Western became psychological. Right now I feel
about her as many of my readers must feel about pretty
Negresses who sit across from them in the subway, their thin
hard legs shooting down from what pink secrets. Many of my
readers will never find out. Is this fair? And what about the
lily cocks unbeknownst to so many female American citizens?
Undress, undress, I want to cry out, let's look at each other.
Let's have education! F. said: At twenty-eight (yes, my friend,
it took that long) I stopped fucking colors. Catherine Tekakwitha, I hope you are very dark. I want to detect a little whiff
of raw meat and white blood on your thick black hair. I hope
there is a little grease left in your thick black hair. Or is it all
buried in the Vatican, vaults of hidden combs? One night in
our seventh year of marriage Edith coated herself with deep
red greasy stuff she had bought in some theatrical supply store.
She applied it from a tube. Twenty to eleven, back from the
library, and there she was, stark naked in the middle of the
room, sexual surprise for her old man. She handed me the
tube, saying: Let's be other people. Meaning, I suppose, new
ways to kiss, chew, suck, bounce. It's stupid, she said, her

voice cracking, but let's be other people. Why should I diminish her intention? Perhaps she meant: Come on a new journey with me, a journey only strangers can take, and we can remember it when we are ourselves again, and therefore never be merely ourselves again. Perhaps she had some landscape in mind where she always meant to travel, just as I envisage a northern river, a night as clean and bright as river pebbles, for my supreme trip with Catherine Tekakwitha. I should have gone with Edith. I should have stepped out of my clothes and into the greasy disguise. Why is it that only now, years past, my prick rises up at the vision of her standing there so absurdly painted, her breasts dark as eggplants, her face resembling Al Jolson? Why does the blood rush now so uselessly? I disdained her tube. Take a bath, I said. I listened to her splashing, looking forward to our midnight snack. My mean little triumph had made me hungry.

8

Lots of priests got killed and eaten and so forth. Micmacs, Abénaquis, Montagnais, Attikamègues, Hurons: the Company of Jesus had their way with them. Lots of semen in the forest, I'll bet. Not the Iroquois, they ate priests' hearts. Wonder what it was like. F. said he once ate a raw sheep's heart. Edith liked brains. René Goupil got it on September 29, 1642, first victim in black robes of the Mohawks. Yum, yummy. Le P. Jogues fell under the "hatchet of the barbarian" on October 18, 1646. It's all down there in black and white. The Church loves such details. I love such details. Here come the little fat angels with their queer bums. Here come the Indians. Here comes Catherine Tekakwitha ten years later, lily out of the soil watered by the Gardener with the blood of martyrs. F., you ruined my life with your experiments. You ate a raw sheep's heart, you ate bark, once you ate shit. How can I live in the world beside all your damn adventures? F. once said: There is nothing so depressing as the eccentricity of a contemporary. She was a Tortoise, best clan of the Mohawks. Our journey will be slow, but we'll win. Her father was an Iroquois, an asshole, as it turns out. Her mother was an Algonquin Christian, baptized and educated at Three-Rivers, which happens to be a lousy town for an Indian girl (I was told recently by a young Abénaqui who went to school there). She was taken captive in an Iroquois raid, which was probably the best lay she ever had. Help me, someone, help my crude tongue. Where is my silver tongue? Aren't I meant to speak of God? She was the slave of an Iroquois brave, and she had a wild tongue or something because he married her when he could have just pushed her around. She was accepted by the tribe and enjoyed all the rights of the Tortoises from that day on. It is recorded that she prayed incessantly. Glog, glog, dear God, hump, fart push, sweet Almighty, slurp, flark, glamph, hiccup, jerk, zzzzzz, snort, Jesus, she must have made his life hell.

9

F. said: Connect nothing. He screamed that remark at me while overlooking my wet cock about twenty years ago. I don't know what he saw in my swooning eyes. maybe some glimmering of a fake universal comprehension. Sometimes after I have come or just before I fall asleep, my mind seems to go out on a path the width of a thread and of endless length, a thread that is the same color as the night. Out, out along the narrow highway sails my mind, driven by curiosity, luminous with acceptance, far and out, like a feathered hook whipped deep into the light above the stream by a magnificent cast.

Somewhere, out of my reach, my control, the hook unbends into a spear, the spear shears itself into a needle, and the needle sews the world together. It sews skin onto the skeleton and lipstick on a lip, it sews Edith to her greasepaint, crouching (for as long as I, this book, or an eternal eye remembers) in our lightless sub-basement, it sews scarves to mountain, it goes through everything like a relentless bloodstream, and the tunnel is filled with a comforting message, a beautiful knowledge of unity. All the disparates of the world, the different wings of the paradox, coin-faces of problem, petal-pulling questions, scissors-shaped conscience, all the polarities, things and their images and things which cast no shadow, and just the everyday explosions on a street, this face and that, a house and a toothache, explosions which merely have different letters in their names, my needle pierces it all, and I myself, my greedy fantasies, everything which has existed and does exist, we are part of a necklace of incomparable beauty and unmeaning. Connect nothing: F. shouted. Place things side by side on your arborite table, if you must, but connect nothing! Come back, F. shouted, pulling my limp cock like a bell rope, shaking it like a dinner bell in the hands of a grand hostess who wants the next course served. Don't be fooled, he cried. Twenty years ago, as I say. I am just speculating now what it was that occasioned his outburst, that is, some kind of smirk of universal acceptance, which is very disagreeable on the face of a young man. It was that same afternoon that F. told me one of his most remarkable lies.

—My friend, F. said, you mustn't feel guilty about any of this.

—Any of what?

—Oh, you know, sucking each other, watching the movies, Vaseline, fooling around with the dog, sneaking off during government hours, under the armpits.

—I don't feel in the least guilty.

—You do. But don't. You see, F. said, this isn't homo-sexuality at all.

—Oh, F., come off it. Homosexuality is a name.

—That's why I'm telling you this, my friend. You live in a world of names. That's why I have the charity to tell you this.

—Are you trying to ruin another evening?

—Listen to me, you poor A——!

—It's you who feel guilty, F. Guilty as hell. You're the guilty party.

—Ha. Ha. Ha. Ha. Ha.

—I know what you want to do, F. You want to destroy the evening. You're not satisfied with a couple of simple comes and a nice poke in the hole.

—All right, my friend, you've convinced me. I'm perishing with guilt. I'll keep quiet.

—What were you going to say?

—Some fabrication of my guilty guilt.

—Well, tell me, now that you started the whole thing.

—No.

—Tell me, F., for Christ's sake, it's just conversation now.

—No.

—God damn you, F., you are trying to destroy the evening.

—You're pathetic. That's why you must not try to connect anything, your connection would be pathetic. The Jews didn't let young men study the Cabala. Connections should be for-bidden citizens under seventy.

—Please tell me.

—You mustn't feel guilty about any of this because it isn't strictly homesexual.

—I know it isn't, I—

—Shut up. It isn't strictly homosexual because I am not

strictly male. The truth is, I had a Swedish operation, I used to be a girl.

—Nobody's perfect.

—Shut up, shut up. A man tires in his works of charity. I was born a girl, I went to school as a girl in a blue tunic, with a little embroidered crest on the front of it.

—F., you're not talking to one of your shoeshine boys. I happen to know you very well. We lived on the same street, we went to school together, we were in the same class, I saw you a million times in the shower after gym. You were a boy when you went to school. We played doctor in the woods. What's the point of all this?

—Thus do the starving refuse sustenance.

—I hate the way you try to end everything off.

But I broke off the argument just then because I noticed that it was almost eight, and we were in danger of missing the entire double feature. How I enjoyed the movies that night. Why did I feel so light? Why did I have so deep a sense of comradeship with F.? Walking home through the snow my future seemed to open me: I resolved to give up work on the A——s, whose disastrous history was not yet clear to me. I didn't know what I wanted to do, but it didn't bother me, I knew that the future would be strewn with invitations, like a President's calendar. The cold, which hitherto froze my balls off every winter, braced me that night, and my brain, for which I have always had little respect, seemed constructed of arrangements of crystal, like a storm of snowflakes, filling my life with rainbow pictures. However, it didn't work out that way. The A——s found their mouthpiece and the future dried up like an old dug. What was F.'s. part in that lovely night? Had he done something which opened doors, doors which I slammed back in their frames? He tried to tell me something.

I still don't understand. Is it fair that I don't understand? Why did I have to be stuck with such an obtuse friend? My life might have been so gloriously different. I might never have married Edith, who, I now confess, was an A——!

10

I always wanted to be loved by the Communist Party and the Mother Church. I wanted to live in a folk song like Joe Hill. I wanted to weep for the innocent people my bomb would have to maim. I wanted to thank the peasant father who fed us on the run. I wanted to wear my sleeve pinned in half, people smiling while I salute with the wrong hand. I wanted to be against the rich, even though some of them knew Dante: just before his destruction one of them would learn that I knew Dante, too. I wanted my face carried in Peking, a poem written down my shoulder. I wanted to smile at dogma, yet ruin my ego against it. I wanted to confront the machines of Broadway. I wanted Fifth Avenue to remember its Indian trails. I wanted to come out of a mining town with rude manners and convictions given to me by an atheist uncle, barfly disgrace of the family. I wanted to rush across America in a sealed train, the only white man whom the Negroes will accept at the treaty convention. I wanted to attend cocktail parties wearing a machine gun. I wanted to tell an old girl friend who is appalled at my methods that revolutions do not happen on buffet tables, you can't pick and choose, and watch her silver evening gown dampen at the crotch. I wanted to fight against the Secret Police takeover, but from *within* the Party. I wanted an old lady who had lost her sons to mention me in her prayers in a mud church, taking her sons' word for it. I wanted to cross myself at dirty words. I wanted to tolerate pagan remnants in village ritual, arguing against the Curia. I

wanted to deal in secret real estate, agent of ageless, anonymous billionaire. I wanted to write well about the Jews. I
wanted to be shot among the Basques for carrying the Body
into the battlefield against Franco. I wanted to preach about
marriage from the unassailable pulpit of virginity, watching
the black hairs on the legs of brides. I wanted to write a tract
against birth control in very simple English, a pamphlet to be
sold in the foyer, illustrated with two-color drawings of shooting stars and eternity. I wanted to suppress dancing for a time.
I wanted to be a junkie priest who makes a record for Folk-
ways. I wanted to be transferred for political reasons. I have
just discovered that Cardinal —— has taken a huge bribe
from a ladies' magazine, have suffered a fairy attack from my
confessor, have seen the peasants betrayed for a necessary reason, but the bells are ringing this evening, it is another evening
in God's world, and there are many to be fed, many knees
yearning to be bent, I mount the worn steps in my tattered
ermine.

11

The long house of the Iroquois must be clear. Length:
varied from one hundred to one hundred fifty feet. Height
and width: twenty-five feet. Lateral beams supporting a roof
made from large pieces of bark, cedar, ash, elm, or pine.
Neither window nor chimney, but a door at each extremity.
Light got in and smoke got out through holes in the roof.
Several fires in the cabin, four families to each fire. Families
arranged so that there was a corridor running down the length
of the cabin. "La manière dont les familles se groupent dans
les cabanes n'est pas pour entraver le libertinage." Thus Le P.
Edouard Lecompte, S.J., wrote in 1930, whetting our sexual
appetite in his expert Company manner. The long-house setup

did little to "hinder licentiousness." What went on in the
dark tunnel? Catherine Tekakwitha, what did you see with
your swollen eyes? What juices mixing on the bearskin? Was
it worse than a movie theater? F. said: The atmsophere of a
movie theater is a nighttime marriage of a man's prison and a
woman's prison; the prisoners know nothing about it—only
the bricks and gates have combined; in the ventilation system
the mystic union is consummated: the smells absorb each
other. F's extravagant observation coincides with something a
clergyman told me. He said that on Sunday morning the odor
of semen hangs like a damp cloud above the men gathered for
chapel at Bordeaux Jail. The modern art-cinema house, made
of concrete and velvet, is a joke, which, as F. said, is nothing
but the death of an emotion. No marriage in these stark con-
fines, everybody sitting on their genitals because: silver genitals
on the screen. Bring back hidden sex! Let cocks again rise and
twine like ivy round the gold projector beam, and cunts yawn
under gloves and white paper bags of candy, and no naked
flashing breasts lure the dirty laundry of our daily lives into the
movie palace, deadly as a radar signal, no neorealist patent
fucking hang the impenetrable curtains of possibility between
each member of the audience! In the gloomy long house of
my mind let me trade wives, let me stumble upon you,
Catherine Tekakwitha, three hundred years old, fragrant as a
birch sapling, no matter what the priests or plague have done
to you.

12

The Plague! The Plague! It invaded my pages of research.
My desk is suddenly contagious. My erection topples like a
futuristic Walt Disney film of the leaning Tower of Pisa, to
the music of timpani and creaking doors. I speed down my

zipper and out falls dust and rubble. Hard cock alone leads to
Thee, this I know because I've lost everything in this dust.
Plague among the Mohawks! In 1660 it broke out, raging
along the Mohawk River, assaulting the Indian villages, Gandaouagué, Gandagoron, Tionnontoguen, like a forest fire powered by the wind, and it came to Ossernenon, where lived
Catherine Tekakwitha, four years old. Down goes her warrior
father and her Christian mother, croaking out her final confession, down goes her little brother, his little prick useless as
an appendix forever. Of this doomed, intermarried family, only
Catherine Tekakwitha survived, the price of admission gouged
in her face. Catherine Tekakwitha is not pretty! Now I want
to run from my books and dreams. I don't want to fuck a pig.
Can I yearn after pimples and pock marks? I want to go outside and walk in the park and look at the long legs of American
children. What keeps me here while lilacs grow outside for
everybody? Can F. teach me something? He said that at the
age of sixteen he stopped fucking faces. Edith was lovely when
I first met her in the hotel, where she sold manicures. Her
hair was black, long and smooth, the softness of cotton rather
than silk. Her eyes were black, a solid depthless black that gave
nothing away (except once or twice), like those sunglasses
made of mirrors. In fact, she often wore that kind of sunglasses. Her lips were not full but very soft. Her kisses were
loose, somehow unspecific, as if her mouth couldn't choose
where to stay. It slipped over my body like a novice on roller
skates. I always hoped it would fasten somewhere perfect and
find its home in my ecstasy, but off it slipped after too brief a
perch, in search of nothing but balance, driven not by passion
but by a banana peel. God knows what F. has to say about all
this, damn him. I couldn't bear to discover that she lingered
for him. Stay, stay, I wanted to shout at her in the thick air
of the sub-basement, come back, come back, don't you see

where all my skin is pointing? But off she skidded, up the piggy
steps of my toes, a leap into my ear while my manhood ached
like a frantic radio tower, come back, come back, a plunge into
my eye where she sucked too hard (remembering her taste for
brains), not there, not there, now grazing the hair of my chest
like a seagull over spray, come back to Capistrano sang the
knob, up to my kneecap, a desert of sensation, exploring the
kneecap so very carefully as if it hid a locket clasp her tongue
could spring, infuriating waste of tongue, now descending like
laundry down the washboard of my ribs, her mouth wants me
to turn over so that it can roller-coast down my spine or some
foolish thing, no I won't turn over and bury my hope, down,
down, come back, come back, no I won't fold it against my
stomach like a hideaway bed, Edith, Edith, let some things
happen in heaven, don't make me tell you! . . . I didn't think
this would force itself into my preparations. It is very hard to
court you, Catherine Tekakwitha, with your pock-marked face
and your insatiable curiosity. One lick, now and then, brief
warm coronations promising glory, an occasional collar of
ermine teeth, then a swift disgrace, as if the archbishop suddenly learned he'd crowned the wrong son, her saliva cold as
an icicle as it dried down the length of her exit, and this member of mine rigid as a goal post, hopeless as a pillar of salt in
the destruction, ready at last to settle for a lonely night with
my own hands, Edith! I broke my problem to F.

—I listen in envy, F. said. Don't you know you're being
loved?

—I want her to love me in my way.

—You've got to learn—

—No lessons, I'm not going to settle for lessons this time.
This is my bed and my wife, I have some rights.

—Then ask her.

—What do you mean "ask her"?

—Please make me come with your mouth, Edith.

—You're disgusting, F. How dare you use that language in connection with Edith? I didn't tell you this so that you could soil our intimacy.

—I'm sorry.

—Of course, I could ask her, that's obvious. But then she'd be under duress, or worse, it would become a matter of duty. I don't want to hold a strap over her.

—Yes you do.

—I warn you, F., I'm not going to take your cowardly guru shit.

—You are being loved, you are being invited into a great love, and I envy you.

—And stay away from Edith. I don't like the way she sits between us at the movies. That is just courtesy on our part.

—I'm grateful to you both. I assure you, she could love no other man as she loves you.

—Do you think that's true, F.?

—I know it's true. Great love is not a partnership, for a partnership can be dissolved by law or parting, and you're stuck with a great love, as a matter of fact, you are stuck with two great loves, Edith's and mine. Great love needs a servant, but you don't know how to use your servants.

—How should I ask her?

—With whips, with imperial commands, with a leap into her mouth and a lesson in choking.

I see F. standing there, the window behind him, his paper-thin ears almost transparent. I remember the expensively appointed slum room, the view of the factory he was trying to buy, his collection of soap arranged like a model town on the green felt of an elaborately carved billiard table. The light came through his ears as if they were made of a bar of Pears Soap. I hear his phony voice, the slight Eskimo accent which he affected after a student summer in the Arctic. You are stuck with two great loves, F. said. What a poor custodian I have been of those two loves, an ignorant custodian who walked his days in a dream museum of self-pity. F. and Edith loved me! But I didn't hear his declaration that morning or didn't believe it. You don't know how to use your servants, F. said, his ears beaming like Jap lanterns. I was loved in 1950! But I didn't speak to Edith, I couldn't. Night after night I lay in the dark listening to the sounds of the elevator, my silent commands buried in my brain, like those urgent proud inscriptions on Egyptian monuments dumb under tons of sand. So her mouth sailed crazily over my body like a flock of Bikini birds, their migratory instincts destroyed by radiation.

—But I warn you, F. continued, a time will come when you'll want nothing in the world but those aimless kisses.

Talking about transparent skin, Edith's throat was like that, the thinnest, softest cover. You thought a heavy shell necklace would draw blood. To kiss her there was to intrude into something private and skeletal, like a turtle's shoulder. Her shoulders were bony but not meager. She wasn't thin but no matter how full the flesh her bones were always in command. From the age of thirteen she had the kind of skin which was called ripe, and the men who pursued her then (she was finally raped in a stone quarry) said that she was the kind of girl who would age quickly, which is the way that men on corners comfort themselves about an unattainable child. She grew up in a small town on the north shore of the St. Lawrence, where she infuriated a number of men who thought that they should be able to rub her small breasts and round bum simply because she was an Indian, an A—— at that! At sixteen, when I married her, I myself believed that her skin couldn't last. It had that fragile juicy quality we associate with growing things just about to decline. At twenty-four, the year of her death, nothing had altered but her buttocks. At sixteen they had been two half spheres suspended in midair, later they came to rest on two deep curved creases, and this was the extent of her body's decay until she was squashed all at once. Let me think about her. She liked me to rub her skin with olive oil. I complied even though I really didn't like playing around with food. Sometimes she filled her belly-button hole with oil and using her little finger she drew the spokes of Asoka's wheel, then she smeared it, skin darkening. Her breasts were small, somewhat muscular, fruit with fiber. Her freakish nipples make me want to tear up my desk when I remember them, which I do at this very instant, miserable paper memory while my cock soars hopelessly into her mangled coffin, and my arms wave my duties away, even you, Catherine Tekakwitha, whom I court with this confession. Her wondrous nipples were dark as mud and very long when stiffened by desire, over an inch high, wrinkled with wisdom and sucking. I stuffed them into my nostrils (one at a time). I stuffed them in my ears. I believed continually that if anatomy permitted and I could have stuffed a nipple into each of my ears at the same time—shock treatment! What is the use of reviving this fantasy, impossible then as now? But I want those leathery electrodes in my head! I want to hear the mystery explained, I want to hear the conversations between those stiff wrinkled sages. There were such messages going between them that even Edith could not hear, signals, warnings, conceits. Revelations! Mathematics! I told F. about this the night of her death.

—You could have had everything you wanted.

—Why do you torment me, F.?

—You lost yourself in particulars. All parts of the body are erotogenic, or at least have the possibility of so becoming. If she had stuck her index fingers in your ears you would have got the same results.

—Are you sure?

—Yes.

—Have you tried it?

—Yes.

—I have to ask you this. With Edith?

—Yes.

—F.!

—Listen, my friend, the elevators, the buzzers, the fan: the world is waking up in the heads of a few million.

—Stop. Did you do that with her? Did you go that far? Did you do that together? You're going to sit right there and tell me every detail. I hate you, F.

—Well, she stuck her index fingers—

—Was she wearing nail polish?

—No.

—She was, damn you, she was! Stop trying to protect me.

—All right, she was. She stuck her red nails in my ears—

—You enjoy this, don't you?

—She stuck her fingers in my ears and I stuck my fingers in her ears and we kissed.

—You did it to each other? With your bare fingers? You touched ears and fingers?

—You begin to learn.

—Shut up. What did her ears feel like?

—Tight.

—Tight!

—Edith had very tight ears, nearly virgin, I'd say.

—Get out, F.! Get off our bed! Take your hands off me!

—Listen, or I'll break your neck, chicken voyeur. We were fully dressed except for our fingers. Yes! We sucked each other's fingers, and then we stuck them in each other's ears—

—The ring, did she take the ring off?

—I don't think so. I was worried about my eardrums because

of her long red nails, she was digging so hard. We shut our eyes and we kissed like friends, without opening our mouths. Suddenly the sounds of the lobby were gone and I was listening to Edith.

—To her body! Where did this happen? When did you do this to me?

—So those are your questions. It happened in a telephone booth in the lobby of a movie theater downtown.

—What theater?

—The System Theatre.

—You're lying! There is no telephone booth in the System. There's only one or two telephones on the wall separated by glass partitions, I think. You did it out in the open! I know that dirty basement lobby! There's always some fairy hanging around there, drawing cocks and telephone numbers on the green wall. Out in the open! Was anyone watching? How could you do this to me?

—You were in the men's room. We were waiting for you beside the telephones, eating chocolate-covered ice-cream bars. I don't know what was keeping you so long. We finished our ice cream. Edith spotted a flake of chocolate sticking to my little finger. In a very charming fashion she leaned over and flicked it into her mouth with her tongue, like an anteater. She had overlooked a flake of chocolate on her own wrist. I swooped in and got that, clumsily, I confess. Then it turned into a game. Games are nature's most beautiful creation. All animals play games, and the truly Messianic vision of the brotherhood of creatures must be based on the idea of the game, indeed—

—So Edith began it! And who touched whose ear first? I have to know everything now. You saw her tongue stretched out, you probably stared. Who started it with the ears?

—I don't remember. Maybe we were under the influence of

the telephones. If you remember, one of the fluorescent lights was flickering, and the corner where we were standing jumped in and out of shadows as though great wings were passing over us or the huge blades of an immense electric fan. The telephones kept their steady black, the only stable shape in the shifting gloom. They hung there like carved masks, black, gleaming, smooth as the toes of kissed stone R.C. saints. We were sucking each other's fingers, slightly frightened now, like children pulling at lollipops during the car chase. And then one of the telephones rang! It rang just once. I am always startled when a pay phone rings. It is so imperial and forlorn, like the best poem of a minor poet, like King Michael saying good-by to Communist Romania, like a message in a floating bottle which begins: If anyone finds this, know that—

—Damn you, F.! You're torturing me. Please.

—You asked me for the whole picture. I forgot to mention that the lights were buzzing, unevenly, like the snores of a sinus victim. I was sucking her narrow finger, careful of the sharp nail, thinking of the wolves who bleed to death from licking the blood-baited knife. When the light was healthy our skin was yellow, the merest pimple exaggerated, and when it failed we fell into a purple pallor, our skin like old wet mushrooms. And when it rang we were so startled that we actually bit each other! Children in a scary cave. Yes, there was someone watching us, not that we cared. He was watching us in the mirror of the fortune-telling scale which he was climbing off and on, dropping in nickel after nickel, dialing various questions, or the same one for all I know. And where the hell were you? The basement of the System is a horrible place if you do not stick with the people you came with. It smells like a desperate clearing in a siege of rats—

—You lie. Edith's skin was perfect. And it smells of piss, nothing else, just piss. And never mind what I was doing.

—I know what you were doing, but never mind. When the

telephone rang this fellow wheeled around and stepped off the scale, quite gracefully, I must say, and in that moment the whole eerie place seemed like his personal office. We were standing between him and his telephone, and I feared (it sounds ridiculous) that he would do some violence, pull a knife or expose himself, for his whole weary life among the water pipes and urinals seemed to hang on this telephone message—

—I remember him! He was wearing one of those Western string neckties.

—Right. I remember thinking in that instant of terror that he had conjured up the ring himself with his incessant dialing, that he had been performing a ritual, like rain-making. He was looking right through us as he stepped forward. He stopped, waiting. I suppose, for the second ring, which never came. He snapped his fingers, turned, climbed back on the scale, and returned to his combinations. We felt delivered, Edith and I! The telephone, hitherto so foreboding and powerful, was our friend! It was the agent of some benign electronic deity, and we wanted to praise it. I suppose that certain primitive bird and snake dances began the same way, a need to imitate the fearful and the beautiful, yes an imitative procedure to acquire some of the qualities of the adored awesome beast.

—What are you trying to tell me, F.?

—We invented the Telephone Dance. Spontaneously. I don't know who made the first move. Suddenly our index fingers were in each other's ears. We became telephones!

—I don't know whether to laugh or cry.

—Why are you crying?

—I think you have ruined my life, F. For years I've been telling secrets to an enemy.

—You're wrong, my friend. I have loved you, we've both loved you, and you're very close to understanding this.

—No, F., no. Maybe it's true, but it's been too hard, too

much crazy education, and God knows for what. Every second day I've had to learn something, some lesson, some lousy parable, and what am I this morning, a Doctor of Shit.

—That's it. That's love!

—Please go away.

—Don't you want to hear what happened when I was a telephone?

—I do, but I don't want to beg. I have to beg you for every scrap of information about the world.

—But that's the only way you value it. When it falls on you from out of the trees you think it's rotten fruit.

—Tell me about Edith when you were telephones.

—No.

—Arrwk! Sob! Ahahah! Sob!

—Contain yourself. Discipline!

—You're killing me, you're killing me, you're killing me!

—Now you're ready. We dug our index fingers in each other's ears. I won't deny the sexual implications. You are ready to face them now. All parts of the body are erotogenic. Assholes can be trained with whips and kisses, that's elementary. Pricks and cunts have become monstrous! Down with genital imperialism! All flesh can come! Don't you see what we have lost? Why have we abdicated so much pleasure to that which lives in our underwear? Orgasms in the shoulder! Knees going off like firecrackers! Hair in motion! And not only caresses leading us into the nourishing anonymity of the climax, not only sucking and wet tubes, but wind and conversation and a beautiful pair of gloves, fingers blushing! Lost! Lost!

—You're insane. I've told my secrets to an insane person.

—There we were, locked in the Telephone Dance. Edith's ears began to wrap around my fingers, at least so it seemed. She was very highly developed, perhaps the most highly developed woman I ever knew. Her ear folded around my throbbing fingers—

—I don't want the details! I see the two of you a lot clearer than you could ever describe. That's a picture I'll never be able to get out of my mind.

—Jealousy is the education you have chosen.

—Fuck you. What did you hear?

—Hear is not the right word. I *became* a telephone. Edith was the electrical conversation that went through me.

—Well, what was it, what was it?

—Machinery.

—Machinery?

—Ordinary eternal machinery.

—And?

—Ordinary eternal machinery.

—Is that all you're going to say?

—Ordinary eternal machinery like the grinding of the stars.

—That's better.

—That was a distortion of the truth, which, I see, suits you very well. I distorted the truth to make it easy for you. The truth is: ordinary eternal machinery.

—Was it nice?

—It was the most beautiful thing I have ever felt.

—Did she like it?

—No.

—Really?

—Yes, she liked it. How anxious you are to be deceived!

—F., I could kill you for what you've done. Courts would forgive me.

—You've done enough killing for one night.

—Get off our bed! Our bed! This was our bed!

I don't want to think too much about what F. said. Why must I? Who was he after all but a madman who lost control of his bowels, a fucker of one's wife, a collector of soap, a politician? Ordinary eternal machinery. Do I have to understand that? This morning is another morning, flowers have

opened up again, men turn on their sides to see whom they
have married, everything is ready to begin anew. Why must I
be lashed to the past by the words of a dead man? Why must
I reproduce these conversations so painstakingly, letting not
one lost comma alter the beat of our voices? I want to talk
to men in taverns and buses and remember nothing. And you,
Catherine Tekakwitha, burning in your stall of time, does it
please you that I strip myself so cruelly? I fear you smell of
the Plague. The long house where you crouch day after day
smells of the Plague. Why is my research so hard? Why can't
I memorize baseball statistics like the Prime Minister? Why
do baseball statistics smell like the Plague? What has happened
to the morning? My desk smells! 1660 smells! The Indians are
dying! The trails smell! They are pouring roads over the trails,
it doesn't help. Save the Indians! Serve them the hearts of
Jesuits! I caught the Plague in my butterfly net. I merely
wanted to fuck a saint, as F. advised. I don't know why it
seemed like such a good idea. I barely understand it but it
seemed like the only thing left to me. Here I am courting with
research, the only juggling I can do, waiting for the statues to
move—and what happens? I've poisoned the air, I've lost my
erection. Is it because I've stumbled on the truth about
Canada? I don't want to stumble on the truth about Canada.
Have the Jews paid for the destruction of Jericho? Will the
French learn how to hunt? Are wigwam souvenirs enough?
City Fathers, kill me, for I have talked too much about the
Plague. I thought the Indians died of bullet wounds and
broken treaties. More roads! The forest stinks! Catherine Te-
kakwitha, is there something sinister in your escape from the
Plague? Do I have to love a mutant? Look at me, Catherine
Tekakwitha, a man with a stack of contagious papers, limp in
the groin. Look at you, Catherine Tekakwitha, your face half
eaten, unable to go outside in the sun because of the damage

to your eyes. Shouldn't I be chasing someone earlier than you?
Discipline, as F said. This must not be easy. And if I knew
where my research led, where would the danger be? I confess
that I don't know the point of anything. Take one step to the
side and it's all absurd. What is this fucking of a dead saint?
It's impossible. We all know that. I'll publish a paper on
Catherine Tekakwitha, that's all. I'll get married again. The
National Museum needs me. I've been through a lot, I'll make
a marvelous lecturer. I'll pass off F.'s sayings as my own, become a wit, a mystic wit. He owes me that much. I'll give
away his soap collection to female students, a bar at a time,
lemon cunts, pine cunts, I'll be a master of mixed juices. I'll
run for Parliament, just like F. I'll get the Eskimo accent. I'll
have the wives of other men. Edith! Her lovely body comes
stalking back, the balanced walk, the selfish eyes (or are they?).
Oh, she does not stink of the Plague. Please don't make me
think about your parts. Her belly button was a tiny swirl,
almost hidden. If all the breeze it took to ruffle a tea rose
suddenly became flesh, it would be like her belly button. On
different occasions she covered it with oil, semen, thirty-five
dollars' worth of perfume, a burr, rice, urine, the parings of a
man's fingernails, another man's tears, spit, a thimbleful of rain
water. I've got to recall the occasions.

OIL: Countless times. She kept a bottle of olive oil beside the
bed. I always thought flies would come.

SEMEN: F.'s too? I couldn't bear that. She made me deposit it
there myself. She wanted to see me masturbate for the last
time. How could I tell her that it was the most intense
climax of my life?

RICE: Raw rice. She kept one grain in there for a week, claiming that she could cook it.

URINE: Don't be ashamed, she said.

FINGERNAILS: She said that Orthodox Jews buried their fingernail parings. I'm uneasy as I remember this. It's just the kind of observation that F. would make. Did she get the idea from him?

MAN'S TEARS: A curious incident. We were sunbathing on the beach at Old Orchard, Maine. A complete stranger in a blue bathing suit threw himself on her stomach, weeping. I grabbed his hair to pull him away. She struck my hand sharply. I looked around, nobody had noticed so I felt a little better about it. I timed the man: he cried for five minutes. There were thousands stretched on the beach. Why did he have to pick us? I smiled stupidly at people passing, as if this loony were my bereaved brother-in-law. Nobody seemed to notice. He had on one of those cheap wool bathing suits that do nothing for the balls. He cried quietly, Edith's right hand on the nape of his neck. This isn't happening, I tried to think, Edith's not a sandy whore. Abruptly and clumsily, he rose on one knee, stood up, ran away. Edith looked after him for a while, then turned to comfort me. He was an A——, she whispered. Impossible! I shouted furiously. I've documented every living A——! You're lying, Edith! You loved him slobbering on your navel. Admit it! Perhaps you're right, she said, perhaps he wasn't an A——. That was a chance I couldn't take. I spent the rest of the day patrolling miles of beach, but he'd gone somewhere with his snotty nose.

SPIT: I don't know why. In fact, I can't remember when exactly. Have I imagined this one?

RAIN WATER: She got the idea it was raining at two in the morning. We couldn't tell because of the window situation. I took a thimble and went upstairs. She appreciated the favor.

There is no doubt that she believed her belly button to be a sensory organ, better than that, a purse which guaranteed possession in her personal voodoo system. Many times she held me hard and soft against her there, telling stories through the night. Why was I never quite comfortable? Why did I listen to the fan and the elevator?

13

Days without work. Why did that list depress me? I should never have made the list. I've done something bad to your belly, Edith. I tried to use it. I tried to use your belly against the Plague. I tried to be a man in a padded locker room telling a beautiful smutty story to eternity. I tried to be an emcee in tuxedo arousing a lodge of honeymooners, my bed full of golf widows. I forgot that I was desperate. I forgot that I began this research in desperation. My briefcase fooled me. My tidy notes led me astray. I thought I was doing a job. The old books on Catherine Tekakwitha by P. Cholenec, the manuscripts of M. Remy, Miracles faits en sa paroisse par l'intercession de la B. Cath. Tekakwith, 1696, from the archives of Collège Sainte-Marie—the evidence tricked me into mastery. I started making plans like a graduating class. I forgot who I was. I forgot that I never learned to play the harmonica. I forgot that I gave up the guitar because F chord made my fingers bleed. I forgot about the socks I've stiffened with semen. I tried to sail past the Plague in a gondola, young tenor about to be discovered by talent-scout tourist. I forgot about jars Edith handed me that I couldn't open. I forgot the way Edith died, the way F. died, wiping his ass with a curtain. I forgot that I only have one more chance. I thought Edith would rest in a catalogue. I thought I was a citizen, private, user of public facilities. I forgot about constipation! Constipation didn't let me forget. Constipation ever since I compiled the list. Five days ruined in their first half-hours. Why me?—the great complaint of the constipated. Why doesn't the world work for me? The lonely sitting man in the porcelain machine. What did I do wrong yesterday? What unassailable bank in my psyche needs shit? How can I begin anything new with all of yesterday in me? The hater of history crouched over the immaculate bowl. How can I prove the body is on my side? Is my stomach an enemy? The chronic loser at morning roulette plans his suicide: a leap into the St. Lawrence weighted with a sealed bowel. What good are movies? I am too heavy for music. I am invisible if I leave no daily evidence. Old food is poison, and the sacks leak. Unlock me! Exhausted Houdini! Lost ordinary magic! The squatting man bargains with God, submitting list after list of New Year's Resolutions. I will eat only lettuce. Give me diarrhea if I've got to have something. Let me into the world club. I am not enjoying sunsets, then for whom do they burn? I'll miss my train. My portion of the world's work will not be done, I warn you. If sphincter must be coin let it be Chinese coin. Why me? I'll use science against you. I'll drop in pills like depth charges. I'm sorry, I'm sorry, don't make it tighter. Nothing helps, is that what you want me to learn? The straining man perched on a circle prepares to abandon all systems. Take hope, take cathedrals, take the radio, take my research. These are hard to give up, but a load of shit is harder still. Yes, yes, I abandon even the system of renunciation. In the tiled dawn courtroom a folded man tries a thousand oaths. Let me testify! Let me prove Order! Let me cast a shadow! Please make me empty, if I'm empty then I can receive, if I can receive it means it comes from somewhere outside of me, if it comes from outside of me I'm not alone! I cannot bear this loneliness. Above all it is loneliness. I don't want to be a star, merely dying. Please let me be hungry, then I am not the dead center, then I can single out the trees in their particular lives, then I can be curious

about the names of rivers, the altitude of mountains, the
different spellings of Tekakwitha, Tegahouita, Tegahkouita,
Tehgakwita, Tekakouita, oh, I want to be fascinated by
phenomena! I don't want to live inside! Renew my life. How
can I exist as the vessel of yesterday's slaughter? Is the meat
punishing me? Are there wild herds who think poorly of me?
Murder in the kitchen! Dachau farmyards! We are grooming
beings to eat! Does God love the world? What a monstrous
system of nourishment! All of us animal tribes at eternal war!
What have we won? Humans, the dietary Nazis! Death at the
center of nourishment! Who will apologize to the cows? It's
not our fault, we didn't think this whole thing up. These kidneys are kidneys. This is not chicken, this is a chicken. Think
of the death camps in the basement of a hotel. Blood on the
pillows! Matter impaled on toothbrushes! All animals eating,
not for pleasure, not for gold, not for power, but merely to be.
For whose eternal Pleasure? Tomorrow I begin my fast. I resign. But I can't resign with a full stomach. And does fasting
please or offend Thee? You might construe it as pride or
cowardice. I have memorized my bathroom forever. Edith kept
it very clean, but I have been less fastidious. Is it fair to ask
the intended to scrub the electric chair? I'm using old newspapers, I'll buy rolls when I deserve them. I've promised the
toilet much attention if it will be good to me, I'll unblock it.
But why should I humiliate myself? You don't polish windows
in a car wreck. When my body starts, the old routines will
start, I promise. Help! Give me a hint. For five days, except
for that first half-hour of failure, I cannot enter the bathroom.
My teeth and hair are dirty. I can't begin to shave, to mock
myself with a little deposit of hair. I would stink at an autopsy.
Nobody wants to eat me, I'm sure. What's it like outside?
Is there an outside? I am the sealed, dead, impervious museum
of my appetite. This is the brutal solitude of constipation, this

is the way the world is lost. One is ready to stake everything on a river, a nude bath before Catherine Tekakwitha, and no promises.

14

Into the world of names with us. F. said: Of all the laws which bind us to the past, the names of things are the most severe. If what I sit in is my grandfather's chair, and what I look out of is my grandfather's window—then I'm deep in his world. F. said: Names preserve the dignity of Appearance. F. said: Science begins in coarse naming, a willingness to disregard the particular shape and destiny of each red life, and call them all Rose. To a more brutal, more active eye, *all* flowers look alike, like Negroes and Chinamen. F. never shut up. His voice has got into my ear like a trapped fly, incessantly buzzing. His style is colonizing me. His will provides me with his room downtown, the factory he bought, his tree house, his soap collection, his papers. And I don't like the discharge from my pecker. Too much, F.! I've got to hold on to myself. Next thing you know my ears will be transparent. F., why do I suddenly miss you so intensely? There are certain restaurants I can never go to again. But do I have to be your monument? Were we friends, after all? I remember the day you finally bought the factory, eight hundred thousand dollars, and I walked with you on those uneven wood floors, floors which as a boy you had swept so often. I believe you were actually weeping. It was the middle of the night and half the lights were gone. We walked between the rows of sewing machines, cutting tables, defunct steam pressers. There is nothing more quiet than a still factory. Every now and then we kicked a tangle of wire hangers, or brushed a rack where they hung, thick as vines, and a curious tinkling resounded, like a hundred bored

men playing in their pockets, a curiously violent sound, as if
the men were waiting among the grotesque shadows cast by the
abandoned machines, men waiting for salaries, goons for the
word to smash F.'s shut-down. I was vaguely frightened. Fac-
tories, like parks, are public places, and it was an offense to the
democratic mind to see F. so deeply moved by his ownership.
F. picked up an old heavy steam iron which was connected to a
metal frame above by a thick spring. He swung it away from
the table, dropped it, laughed while it bounced up and down
like a dangerous yo-yo, shadows striping the dirty walls like a
wild chalk eraser on a blackboard. Suddenly F. threw a switch,
the lights flickered, and the central power belt which drove the
sewing machines began to roll. F. began to orate. He loved to
talk against mechanical noise.

—Larry! he cried, moving down the empty benches. Larry!
Ben! Dave! I know you can hear me! Ben! I haven't forgotten
your hunched back! Sol! I've done what I promised! Little
Margerie! You can eat your tattered slippers now! Jews, Jews,
Jews! Thanks!

—F., this is disgusting.

—Every generation must thank its Jews, F. said, leaping away
from me. And its Indians. The Indians must be thanked for
building our bridges and skyscrapers. The world is made of
races, you better learn that, my friend. People are different!
Roses are different from each other! Larry! It's me, F., boy goy,
whose blond hair you ofttimes ruffled. I've done what I promised you in the dark stock room so many afternoons ago. It's
mine! It's ours! I'm dancing on the scraps! I've turned it into
a playground! I'm here with a friend!

When he had calmed down F. took my hand and led me to
the stock room. Great empty spools and cardboard cylinders
threw their precise shadows in the half light, temple columns.
The respectable animal smell of wool still clung to the air. I

sensed a layer of oil forming on my nose. Back on the factory
floor the power belt still turned and a few spikeless machines
pumped. F. and I stood very close.

—So you think I am disgusting, F. said.

—I would never believe you capable of such cheap senti-
mentality. Talking to little Jewish ghosts!

—I was playing as once I promised I would.

—You were slobbering.

Isn't this a beautiful place? Isn't is peaceful? We're standing
in the future. Soon rich men will build places like this on their
estates and visit them by moonlight. History has shown us how
men love to muse and loaf and make love in places formerly
the scene of much violent activity.

—What are you going to do with it?

—Come in, now and then. Sweep a little. Screw on the shiny
tables. Play with the machines.

—You could have been a millionaire. The financial page
talked about the brilliance of your manipulations. I must confess that this coup of yours lends a lot of weight to all the shit
you've been spouting over the years.

—Vanity! cried F. I had to see if I could pull it off. I had to
see if there was any comfort in it. In spite of what I knew!
Larry didn't expect it of me, it wasn't binding. My boyhood
promise was an alibi! *Please don't let this evening influence
anything I've said to you.*

—Don't cry, F.

—Forgive me. I wanted to taste revenge. I wanted to be an
American. I wanted to tie my life up with a visit. That isn't
what Larry meant.

My arm struck a rack of hangers as I seized F.'s shoulders.
The jangling of coins was not so loud, what with the smaller
room and the noise of the machinery beyond, and the thugs
retreated as we stood in a forlorn embrace.

15

Catherine Tekakwitha in the shadows of the long house. Edith crouching in the stuffy room, covered with grease. F. pushing a broom through his new factory. Catherine Tekakwitha can't go outside at noon. When she did get out she was swaddled in a blanket, a hobbling mummy. So she passed her girlhood, far from the sun and the noise of hunting, a constant witness to the tired Indians eating and fucking one another, and a picture of pure Mistress Mary rattling in her head louder than all the dancer's instruments, shy as the deer she had heard about. What voices did she hear, louder than groans, sweeter than snoring? How well she must have learned the ground rules. She did not know how the hunter rode down his prey but she knew how he sprawled with a full belly, burping later at love. She saw all the preparations and all the conclusions, without the perspective set against a mountain. She saw the coupling but she didn't hear the songs hummed in the forest and the little gifts made of grass. Confronted with this assault of human machinery, she must have developed elaborate and bright notions of heaven—and a hatred for finite shit. Still, it is a mystery how one loses the world. Dumque crescebat aetate, crescebat et prudentia, says P. Cholenec in 1715. Is it pain? Why didn't her vision turn Rabelaisan? Tekakwitha was the name she was given, but the exact meaning of the word is not known. She who puts things in order, is the interpretation of l'abbé Marcoux, the old missionary at Caughnawaga. L'abbé Couq, the Sulpician Indianologist: Celle qui s'avance, qui meut quelquechose devant elle. Like someone who proceeds in shadows, her arms held before her, is the elaboration of P. Lecompte. Let us say that her name was some combination of these two notions: She who, advancing, arranges the shadows neatly.

Perhaps, Catherine Tekakwitha, I come to you in the same fashion. A kind uncle took the orphan in. After the plague the whole village moved a mile up the Mohawk River, close to where it is joined by the Auries River. It was called Gandaouagué, another name which we know in many forms. Gandawagué, a Huron word used by missionaries to designate falls or rapids. Gahnawagué in the Mohawk dialect, Kaknawaké which developed into the current Caughnawaga. I'm paying my dues. Here she lived with her uncle, his wife, his sisters, in the long house which he established, one of the principal structures of the village. Iroquois women worked hard. A hunter never lugged his kill. He made an incision in the animal's stomach, grabbed a handful of entrails, and, as he danced home, sprinkled the guts here and there, this dangled from a branch, that spiked on a bush. I've killed, he announced to his wife. She followed his slimy traces into the forest, and her prize for finding the slain beast was to get it back to her husband, who was sleeping beside the fire, his stomach rumbling. Women did most of the disagreeable things. War, hunting, and fishing were the only occupations a man's dignity allowed. The rest of the time he smoked, gossiped, played games, ate, and slept. Catherine Tekakwitha liked work. All the other girls rushed through it so they could get out there and dance, flirt, comb their hair, paint their faces, put on their earrings, and ornament themselves with colored porcelain. They wore rich pelts, embroidered leggings worked with beads and porcupine quills. Beautiful! Couldn't I love one of these? Can Catherine hear them dance? Oh, I'd like one of the dancers. I don't want to disturb Catherine, working in the long house, the muffled thud of leaping feet tracing perfect burning circles in her heart. The girls aren't spending too much time on tomorrow, but Catherine is gathering her days into a chain, linking the shadows. Her aunts insist. Here's a necklace, put it on dear, and why don't you paint your lousy complexion? She was very young, she allowed herself to be adorned, and never forgave herself. Twenty years later she wept over what she considered one of her gravest sins. What am I getting into? Is this my kind of woman? After a while her aunts took the pressure off and she got back to total work, grinding, hauling water, gathering fire- wood, preparing the pelts for trade—all done in a remarkable spirit of willingness. "Douce, patiente, chaste, et innocente," says P. Chauchetière. "Sage comme une fille française bien élevée," he continues. Like a well-raised French girl! O Sinister Church! F., is this what you want from me! Is this my punish- ment for not sliding with Edith? She was waiting for me all covered in red grease and I was thinking of my white shirt. I have since applied the tube to myself, out of curiosity, a single gleaming column, useless to me as F.'s akropolis that morning. Now I read that Catherine Tekakwitha had a great gift for em- broidery and handicraft, and that she made beautiful embroi- dered leggings, tobacco pouches, moccasins, and wampums. Hour after hour she worked on these, roots and eelskins, por- celain, quills. To be worn by anyone but her! Whom was her mind adorning? Her wampums were especially cherished. Was this the way she mocked money? Perhaps her contempt freed her to invent elaborate designs and color arrangements just as F.'s contempt for commerce enabled him to buy a factory. Or do I misread them both? I'm tired of facts, I'm tired of specu- lations, I want to be consumed by unreason. I want to be swept along. Right now I don't care what goes on under her blanket. I want to be covered with unspecific kisses. I want my pam- phlets praised. Why is my work so lonely? It is past midnight, the elevator is at rest. The linoleum is new, the faucets tight, thanks to F.'s bequest. I want all the comes I did not demand. I want a new career. What have I done to Edith, that I can't even get her ghost to stiffen me? I hate this apartment. Why

did I have it redecorated? I thought the table would look nice
yellow. O God, please terrify me. The two who loved me, why
are they so powerless tonight? The belly button useless. Even
F.'s final horror meaningless. I wonder if it's raining. I want
F.'s experiences, his emotional extravagance. I can't think of a
single thing F. said. I can only remember the way he used his
handkerchief, the meticulous folding to keep his nose away
from snot, his high-pitched sneezes and the pleasure they gave
him. High-pitched and metallic, positively instrumental, a sideways snap of the bony head, then the look of surprise, as if
he'd just received an unexpected gift, and the raised eyebrows
which said, Fancy that. People sneeze, F., that's all, don't make
such a damn miracle out of it, it only depresses me, it's a depressing habit you have of loving to sneeze and of eating apples
as if they were juicier for you and being the first one to ex-
claim how good the movie is. You depress people. We like
apples too. I hate to think of the things you told Edith, probably sounding as if hers were the first body you ever touched.
Was she delighted? Her new nipples. You're both dead. Never
stare too long at an empty glass of milk. I don't like what's
happening to Montréal architecture. What happened to the
tents? I would like to accuse the Church. I accuse the Roman
Catholic Church of Québec of ruining my sex life and of shov-
ing my member up a relic box meant for a finger, I accuse the
R.C.C. of Q. of making me commit queer horrible acts with
F., another victim of the system, I accuse the Church of killing
Indians, I accuse the Church of refusing to let Edith go down
on me properly, I accuse the Church of covering Edith with
red grease and of depriving Catherine Tekakwitha of red grease,
I accuse the Church of haunting automobiles and of causing
pimples, I accuse the Church of building green masturbation
toilets, I accuse the Church of squashing Mohawk dances and
of not collecting folk songs, I accuse the Church of stealing my

sun tan and of promoting dandruff, I accuse the Church of
sending people with dirty toenails into streetcars where they
work against Science, I accuse the Church of female circumcision in French Canada.

· · ·

19

Now it is time for Edith to run, run between the old Canadian trees. But where are the doves today? Where is the smiling
luminous fish? Why are the hiding places hiding? Where is
Grace today? Why isn't candy being fed to History? Where is
the Latin music?
—Help!
Edith ran through the woods, thirteen years old, the men
after her. She was wearing a dress made from flour sacks. A
certain Flour Company packed their product in sacks printed
with flowers. There is a thirteen-year-old girl running through
needle pine. Have you ever seen such a thing? Follow her
young bum, Eternal Cock of the Brain. Edith told me this
story, or part of it, years later, and I've been pursuing her little
body through the forest ever since, I confess. Here I am an old
scholar, wild with unspecific grief, compulsive detective of
gonad shadows. Edith, forgive me, it was the thirteen-year-old
victim I always fucked. Forgive yourself, F. said. Thirteen-year-
old skin is very beautiful. What other food besides brandy is
good after thirteen years in the world? The Chinese eat old
eggs but that is no comfort. O Catherine Tekakwitha, send me
thirteen-year-olds today! I am not cured. I will never be cured.
I do not want to write this History. I do not want to mate with
Thee. I do not want to be as facile as F. I do not want to be
the leading Canadian authority on the A——s. I do not want a

new yellow table. I do not want astral knowledge. I do not want to do the Telephone Dance. I do not want to conquer the Plague. I want thirteen-year-olds in my life. Bible King David had one to warm his dying bed. Why shouldn't we associate with beautiful people? Tight, tight, tight, oh, I want to be trapped in a thirteen-year-old life. I know, I know about war and business. I am aware of shit. Thirteen-year-old electricity is very sweet to suck, and I am (or let me be) tender as a hummingbird. Don't I have some hummingbird in my soul? Isn't there something timeless and unutterably light in my lust hovering over a young wet crack in a blur of blond air? Oh come, hardy darlings, there is nothing of King Midas in my touch, I freeze nothing into money. I merely graze your hopeless nipples as they grow away from me into business problems. I change nothing as I float and sip under the first bra.

—Help!

Four men followed Edith, Damn every one of them. I can't blame them. The village was behind them, filled with families and business. These men had watched her for years. French Canadian schoolbooks do not encourage respect for the Indians. Some part of the Canadian Catholic mind is not certain of the Church's victory over the Medicine Man. No wonder the forests of Québec are mutilated and sold to America. Magic trees sawed with a crucifix. Murder the saplings. Bittersweet is the cut sap of a thirteen-year-old. O Tongue of the Nation! Why don't you speak for yourself? Can't you see what is behind all this teen-age advertising? Is it only money? What does "wooing the teen-age market" really mean? Eh? Look at all the thirteen-year-old legs on the floor spread in front of the tv screen. Is it only to sell them cereals and cosmetics? Madison Avenue is thronged with hummingbirds who want to drink from those little barely haired crevices. Woo them, woo them, suited writers of commercial poems. Dying America wants a thirteen-year-old Abishag to warm its bed. Men who shave want little girls to ravish but sell them high heels instead. The sexual Hit Parade is written by fathers who shave. O suffering child-lust offices of the business world, I feel your blue-balled pain everywhere! There is a thirteen-year-old blonde lying on the back seat of a parked car, one nyloned toe playing with the armrest ashtray, the other foot on the rich interior carpet, dimples on her cheeks and only a hint of innocent acne, and her garter belt is correctly uncomfortable: far away roam the moon and a few police flashlights: her Beethoven panties are damp from the Prom. She alone of all the world believes that fucking is holy, dirty, and beautiful. And who is this making his way through the bushes? It is her Chemistry Teacher, who smiled all night while she danced with the football star because it is the foam rubber of *his* car she lies dreaming upon. Charity begins alone, F. used to say. Many long nights have taught me that the Chemistry Teacher is not merely a sneak. He loves youth truly. Advertising courts lovely things. Nobody wants to make life hell. In the hardest hard sell exists a thirsty love-torn hummingbird. F. wouldn't want me to hate forever the men who pursued Edith.

—Sob. Sob. Whimper. Oh, oh!

They caught up with her in a stone quarry or an abandoned mine, someplace very mineral and hard, owned indirectly by U.S. interests. Edith was a beautiful thirteen-year-old Indian orphan living with foster Indian parents because her father and mother had been killed in an avalanche. She had been abused by schoolmates who didn't think she was Christian. Even at thirteen she had lovely freakishly long nipples, she told me. Perhaps this news had leaked out of the school shower room. Perhaps that was the underground rumor which had inflamed the root of the whole town. Perhaps the business and religion of the town kept operating as usual but every single person is secretly obsessed with this nipple information. The Mass is undermined with nipple dream. The picket line of strikers at the local asbestos factory is not wholly devoted to Labor. There is something absent in the blows and tear gas of the Provincial Police, for all minds are pursing for extraordinary nipple. Daily life cannot tolerate this fantastic intrusion. Edith's nipples are an absolute pearl irritating the workable monotonous proto-plasm of village existence. Who can trace the subtle mechanics of the Collective Will to which we all contribute? I believe that in some way the village delegated these four men to pur-sue Edith into the forest. Get Edith! commanded the Collec-tive Will. Get her magic nipples off Our Mind!

—Help me, Mother Mary!

They ran her to the ground. They ripped off the dress with the Company's raspberry pattern. It was a summer afternoon. Blackflies ate her. The men were drunk on beer. They laughed and called her *sauvagesse*, ha, ha! They pulled off her under-wear, rolling it down her long brown legs, and when they tossed it aside they did not notice that it looked like a big pink pretzel. They were surprised that her underwear was so clean: a heathen's underwear should be limp and smeared. They were not frightened by the police, somehow they knew the police wished them well, one of their brothers-in-law was a policeman, and he had balls like everyone. They dragged her into the shadows because each man wanted to be somewhat alone. They turned her over to see if the dragging had scraped her buttocks. Blackflies ate her buttocks, which were dazzlingly round. They twisted her over again and pulled her deeper into the shadows because now they were ready to remove her underwear top. The shadows were so thick and deep at the corner of the quarry that they could hardly see, and this is what they wanted. Edith peed in fear and they heard the noise of it louder than their laughter and hard breathing. It was a steady sound and it seemed to go on forever, steady and forceful, louder than their thoughts, louder than the crickets who were grinding out an elegy for the end of the afternoon. The fall of urine on last year's leaves and pine needles developed to a monolithic tumult in eight years. It was the pure sound of impregnable nature and it ate like acid at their plot. It was a sound so majestic and simple, a holy symbol of frailty which nothing could violate. They froze, each of them suddenly lonely, their erections collapsing like closed accordions as their blood poured upward like flowers out of a root. But the men refused to cooperate with the miracle (as F. called it). They could not bear to learn that Edith was no longer Other, that she was indeed, Sister. Natural Law they felt, but Collective Law they obeyed. They fell on the child with index fingers, pipe stems, ballpoint pens, and twigs. I would like to know what kind of miracle that is, F. The blood streamed down her legs. The men made coarse jests. Edith screamed.

—Help me, Saint Kateri!

F. urged me to make nothing of this connection. I can't go on with this. Everything has been taken from me. I just had a daydream: I saw the thirteen-year-old Edith suffering under the impotent attack of these four men. As the youngest kneeled down to examine better the progress of his sharp twig, Edith seized his head in her arms and drew him to her bosom, and there he lay weeping like that man on Old Orchard Beach. F., it's too late for the double feature. My stomach is jammed again. I want to begin my fast.

20

I see it so clearly now! The night of Edith's death, that long night of talk with F., he left a whole side of his chicken and barely touched the barbecue sauce. I see now that it was deliberate. I remember a saying of Kung's he was fond of: When eating beside a man of mourning the Master never ate his fill. Uncles! uncles! how dare any of us eat?

21

Among the curious items I inherited from F. is a box of fireworks packed by Rich Brothers Fireworks Co., Sioux Falls, South Dakota. It contains 64 sparklers, eight 12- and 8-ball roman candles, large pinwheels, red and green fire cones, vesuvius fountains, golden jewel, silver cascade, oriental and radiant fountains, 6 giant parade sparklers, silver wheels, skyrockets, comets, handle lawn fountains, snakes, torches, red white and blue cones. I wept as I unpacked the pieces, wept for the American boyhood I never had, for my invisible New England parents, for a long green lawn and an iron deer, for college romance with Zelda.

22

I am frightened and alone. I lit one of the snakes. From the little cone a writhing ribbon of gray ash bubbled in coils on a corner of the yellow table until all the cone was consumed in its own extension—a hideous little pile of skin, gray and black like a blob of birdshit squeezed like icing. Carcasses! Carcasses! I want to swallow dynamite.

23

Dear God, It Is Three In The Morning. Aimless Cloudy Semen Becomes Transparent. Is The Church Mad At Me? Please Let Me Work. I Lit Five Of The 8-Ball Roman Candles And Four Of Them Delivered Less Than 8 Balls. The Firecrackers Are Dying. The Newly Painted Ceiling Is Burned. Korean Starvation Hurts Me In The Heart. Is This A Sin To Say? Pain Is Stored In Animal Skins. I Solemnly Declare That I Renounce Interest In How Many Times Edith and F. Fucked In Happiness. Are You So Cruel As To Compel Me To Begin My Fast With A Stuffed Belly?

24

Burned my hand badly while holding a red and green fire cone. The smoldering hull of a skyrocket ignited a sheaf of Indian notes. The sharp fragrance of gunpowder has cleared my sinuses. Lucky there was butter in the icebox because I refuse to go into the bathroom. I never liked my hair but I am not fond of the blisters bestowed by the silver cascade. Cinders float and stick like blasted bats in whose torn wings I detect exact gray-blue replicas of candy-stripe and comet-tail designs. I've handled so much charred cardboard that I leave my fingerprints on everything. I look around at this mess of a kitchen and I know that my life is coming true. I care more about my red watery throbbing thumb than your whole foul universe of orphans. I salute my monsterhood. I urinate anywhere on the linoleum and I am pleased that nothing happens. Every creep for himself!

25

Pigskin crackling on my thumb, nummy, nummy, I hate pain. The way I hate pain is most monumentally extraordinary, much more significant than the way you hate pain, but my body is so much more central, I am the Moscow of pain, you are the mere provincial weather station. Gunpowder and semen is the only research I intend from now on, and look how harmless I be: no bullets after hearts, no sperms after destiny: nothing but the radiance of exhaustion: the gay little cylinders collapsing in ordinary fire after multiple belches of shooting stars, rainbows: the viscous blob of come in my palm thinning and clearing, like the end of Creation when all matter returns to water. Gunpowder, ballsweat, the yellow table starts to look like me, ugh, the kitchen looks like me, me has sneaked outside into furniture, inside smells are outside, bad to be so big, I have occupied the stove, isn't there somewhere fresh where I can tuck my eyes in a clean bed and dream new bodies, oh I've got to get to a movie and take my eyes out for a pee, a movie will put me back in my skin because I've leaked all over the kitchen from all my holes, movie will stuff pores with white splinters and stop my invasion of the world, missed movies will kill me tonight, I am scared of F.'s firecrackers, I hurt too much in my burns, what could you know about burns? All you've ever done is merely burn yourself. Steady, old scholar! I'll turn off the light and write in the dark a résumé of tomorrow's Indian chapter that I must get to work on. Discipline. Click! "Triompher du mal par le bien." St. Paul. That will begin the chapter. I feel better already. Foreign languages are a good corset. Get your hand off yourself. Edith Edith Edith long things forever Edith Edie cuntie Edith where your little Edith Edith Edith Edith Edith stretchy on E E E octopus complexion purse Edith lips lips area thy panties Edith Edith Edith Edith knew you your wet rivulets Eeeeddddiiiittthhhh yug yug sniffle truffle deep bulb bud button sweet soup pea spit rub hood rubber knob girl come head bup bup one bloom pug pig yum one tip tongue lug from end of bed of lips multiple lost sunk gone rise girl head small come knob splash sunk lost- lick search nose help wobble hard once more lurk up girl knob bob bubble sung in normal skin folds lab drowned lady labia up up appear pea bean brain jewel where where hurt hiding

bruised? come up hard as brass bubble from hair swamp little
leather love pimple form solid lump for tongue mess mess message oh unhood unhide unhair undrown or teeth hounds I warn
you tooth spade teeth dogs unleashed unloved lashed form
form you bead you small blunt boywise girlcock form command tiny periscope from foreign female lost sub no man can
fathom ever come up come up from women ocean period
mecca egg farm mystery beds come up come up from where I
don't even go from profound clam stretches from breathless
gill yards from gray broadloom oyster floors of girlsoul far far
amazon sex control rise rise here clity clity clity from amazing
forbidden protoplasmic amoeba fulfilled woman gla gla galaxy
please appear in small helmet of hope lap lap oh pearl pink
precious radio crystal marvelous fruit pit of whole bumcunt
harvest appear form develop unfold unshell unskin look into
cocklove lead dykeplug prickgirl nrrr grrr bridge entre men
woman so I can do you pleasure my lady deliver unto me thy
downtown brain unpuzzled from cunt labyrinth for I may never
join you in the seaweed nets in the sunk hotels in the spongey
jungles passive womb tubed mudlined herbal cast closet vast as
Mrs. God what? you no come up? splash splash hidden for a
newer tongue? for a nobler tongue? for dirtier tongue? for F.
tongue? for stranger? any stranger doing this to you would be
more honored any stranger how strange therefore therefore I
go down maybe where I meant to go like a snail this automatic
tongue slides down the aquarium moss shoot there is a ridge
tender and yielding as the casting join of a hollow chocolate
bunny I ride it down don't be ashamed all smells are al-
chemized tongue goes ring around a rosy lifesaver flavor mud
candy this is a better common button we both have we must
kiss assholes because we each poor one of us has one we cannot
kiss it is ringed with minnie hills they Bible dance it is ringed
with stunted petals tongue dives petals open shiver petals

tighten in a rubber knot I talk stiff now dig dig dig bump bump
bump thud on hills of petal knot get in there hands pull
cheeks apart pull apart cheeks of Edith's fabulous private hers
hers they give squeeze they yield like halves of ripe peach like
very cooked chicken perfectly lovely blood balloons this is
Edith its virgin pink brown hairy same as mine same same as
us all poor charmen who flood the world on our knees this is
solid prose this is mystery of everyday thus I insert cuneiform
face mouth to sphinx for my tongue was only a test game on
rosy sphinx hole I focus my mouth for pure talk gnawing suck
adoration shit danger love bravery open close open close goes
the surface petals closing to feel its own little cliffs of muscle
opening in terrible abandon red desperate as baby robin throat
oh Edith ass membrane gasping all my flock of mouth bathing
pruning fluttering in the sunny bird bath on a pillar of charity
bowel where am I now now don't go way here I am simply
with my face between her buttocks which hands have drawn
apart my chin does automatic good to cunt now I let cheeks go
they squeeze me in I squeeze me in I squash my nose sealing
juice infant shit games in my brain listen Edith listen to me
smother listen darling love it is thy hairy hole I suck are we
not joined Edith are we not proved Edith are we not breathing
Edith are we not awesome lovers Edith are we not filthy postcards are we not good meals Edith are we not conversing
miraculously darling pink evil fartrisk terror position darling I
swear I loved you Edith grab grab jumps the little crater kiss
kiss kiss kiss Edith Edith do the same to me do the same to
me pull my withered bum on your face I make it easy do the
same to me do the same to me do the same to me Edith lilacs
Edith Edith Edith Edith Edith Edith turning in our sleep
making spoons of ourselves Edith Edith Edith Edith please
appear as mushrooming dream from this poor Aladdin cock

Edith Edith Edith Edith in your sweet skin envelope Edith
Edith thy lonely husband Edith thy lonely husband thy lonely
husband thy apples thy run thy creases thy dark lonely husband

• • •

39

I remember one night with F. as he drove down the highway
to Ottawa where he was to make his Maiden Speech in Parliament the next day. There was no moon. The headlights flowed
over the white posts like a perfect liquid eraser, and behind us
we abandoned a blank blueprint of vanished roads and fields.
He had pushed it up to eighty. The St. Christopher's medal
pinned to the felt above the windshield was involved in a tiny
orbit lately initiated by a sharp curve.

—Take it easy, F.

—It's my night! My night!

—Yes it is, F. You finally made it: you're a Member of
Parliament.

—I'm in the world of men.

—F., put it back. Enough is enough.

—Never put it back when it gets like this.

—My God! I've never seen you so big! What's going on in
your mind? What are you thinking of? Please teach me how to
do it. Can I hold it?

—No! This is between me and God.

—Let's stop the car. F., I love you, I love your power. Teach
me everything.

—Shut up. There is a tube of sun cream in the glove compartment. Open the glove compartment by depressing the

button with your thumb. Dig into the tangle of maps and gloves and string and extract the tube. Screw off the cap and squeeze a couple of inches of cream into my palm.

—Like this, F.?

—Yeah.

—Don't shut your eyes, F. Do you want me to drive?

Oh, what a greasy tower he there massaged! I might as well have addressed myself to the missing landscape we flung in our wake, farm houses and oil signs bouncing like sparks off our fenders as we cut open the painted white line at ninety, fast as an acetylene saw. His right hand beneath the steering wheel, urging, urging, he seemed to be pulling himself into the far black harbor like a reflexive stevedore. What beautiful hair poked out of his underwear. His cufflink gleamed in the map-light, which I had switched on the better to witness the delicious operation. As his cupped hand bobbed faster the needle tickled ninety-eight. How I was torn between the fear for my safety and the hunger to jam my head between his knees and the dashboard! Whish! went an orchard. A Main Street flared up in our headlights—we left it in cinders. I longed for the little wrinkles of his tightening scrotum to trap the tatters of my lips. F.'s eyes closed suddenly as if they had been squirted with lemon. His fist closed hard around the pale slippery shaft and he commenced to throttle himself madly. I feared for the organ, feared and coveted it, so hard it gleamed, streamlined as a Brancusi, the swelled head red and hot as a radioactive fireman's helmet. I wanted an anteater's tongue to whip off the wet pearl which F. himself now noticed and with a happy violent motion incorporated into the general lubrication. I could bear my loneliness no longer. I ripped the buttons of my old-fashioned European trousers in my frenzy to touch myself as a lover. What a handful of blood I was. Zoom! A parking lot blazed and expired. The warmth spread through leather gloves which I had not time to remove. Kamikaze insects splashed against the glass. My life was in my hands, all the messages I longed to deliver to the Zodiac gathered to begin their journey and I moaned with the intolerable pressure of pleasure. F. was screaming gibberish, his spit flying in all directions.

—Face me, face me, face me, suck bright, suck bright, F. wailed (if I remember the sounds correctly).

Thus we existed in some eye for a second: two men in a hurtling steel shell aimed at Ottawa, blinded by a mechanical mounting ecstasy, the old Indian land sunk in soot behind us, two swelling pricks pointing at eternity, two naked capsules filled with lonely tear gas to stop the riot in our brains, two fierce cocks separate as the gargoyles on different corners of a tower, two sacrificial lollipops (orange in the map light) offered to the ruptured highway.

—Ay ay ay ay ay! cried F. from the very top of his ladder.

—Slof tlif, sounded the geysers of his semen as they hit the dashboard (surely the sound of upstream salmon smashing their skulls on underwater cliffs).

As for me, I knew that one more stroke would deliver me— I hovered on the edge of my orgasm like a parachutist in the whistling doorway—I was suddenly forlorn—I was suddenly without desire—I was suddenly more awake (for this fraction of a second) than ever before in my whole life—

—The wall!

The wall occupied the whole windshield, first as a blur, then focused precisely as if an expert had adjusted the microscope— every pimple of the concrete three-dimensional—bright! precise! —fast film of the moon's hide—then the windshield blurred again as the wall rushed into the glass of the headlights—I saw F.'s cufflink skimming the edge of the steering wheel like a surfboard—

—Darling! Ehhhffff. . . .

—Rrrrriiiiippppp, went the wall.

We passed through the wall because the wall was made of a scrim of painted silk. The car bumped over an empty field, the torn fabric clinging to the chrome Mercedes hood emblem. The undamaged headlights illumined a boarded-up hot-dog stand as F. applied the brake. On the wood counter I noticed an empty bottle with a perforated cap. I stared blankly at it.

—Did you come? asked F.

My prick hung out of my fly like a stray thread.

—Too bad, said F.

I started to shiver.

—You missed a great come.

I placed my clenched fists on the top of the dashboard and held my forehead on them, weeping in spasms.

—We went to a lot of trouble rigging the thing up, renting the parking lot and all.

I jerked my face toward him.

—We? What do you mean "we"?

—Edith and I.

—Edith was in on it?

—How about that second just before you were about to shoot? Did you sense the emptiness? Did you get the freedom?

—Edith knows about our filthy activities?

—You should have kept on with it, my friend. You weren't driving. There was nothing you could do. The wall was on top of you. You missed a great come.

—Edith knows we're fairies?

I threw my hands at his neck with a murderous intention. F. smiled. How thin and puny my wrists looked in the dim orange light. F. removed my fingers like a necklace.

—Easy. Easy. Dry your eyes.

—F., why do you torture me?

—O my friend, you are so lonely. Each day you get lonelier. What will happen when we are gone?

—None of your fucking business! How dare you presume to teach me anything? You're a fake. You're a menace! You're a disgrace to Canada! You've ruined my life!

—All these things may be true.

—You filthy bastard! How dare you admit they're true?

He leaned forward to switch on the ignition and looked at my lap.

—Button up. It's a long cold drive to Parliament.

40

I have been writing these true happenings for some time now. Am I any closer to Kateri Tekakwitha? The sky is very foreign. I do not think I will ever tarry with the stars. I do not think I will ever have a garland. I do not think ghosts will whisper erotic messages in my warm hair. I will never find a graceful way to carry a brown lunch bag on a bus ride. I'll go to funerals and they won't remind me of anything. It was years and years ago that F. said: Each day you get lonelier. That was years and years ago. What did F. mean by advising me to go down on a saint? What is a saint? A saint is someone who has achieved a remote human possibility. It is impossible to say what that possibility is. I think it has something to do with the energy of love. Contact with this energy results in the exercise of a kind of balance in the chaos of existence. A saint does not dissolve the chaos, if he did the world would have changed long ago. I do not think that a saint dissolves the chaos even for himself, for there is something arrogant and warlike in the notion of a man setting the universe in order. It is a kind of balance that is his glory. He rides the drifts like an escaped ski. His course is a caress of the hill. His track is a drawing of

the snow in a moment of its particular arrangement with wind
and rock. Something in him so loves the world that he gives
himself to the laws of gravity and chance. Far from flying with
the angels, he traces with the fidelity of a seismograph needle
the state of the solid bloody landscape. His house is dangerous
and finite, but he is at home in the world. He can love the
shapes of human beings, the fine and twisted shapes of the
heart. It is good to have among us such men, such balancing
monsters of love. It makes me think that the numbers in the
bag actually correspond to the numbers on the raffles we have
bought so dearly, and so the prize is not an illusion. But why
fuck one? I remember once slobbering over Edith's thigh. I
sucked, I kissed the long brown thing, and it was Thigh,
Thigh, Thigh—Thigh softening and spreading as it flowed in a
perfume of bacon to the mound of Cunt—Thigh sharpening
and hardening as I followed the direction of its tiny hairs and
bounced into Kneecap. I don't know what Edith did (maybe
one of her magnificent lubrication squirts) or what I did (maybe
one of my mysterious sprays of salivation) but all at once my
face was wet and my mouth slid on skin; it wasn't Thigh or
Cunt or any chalk schoolboy slogan (nor was I Fucking): it
was just a shape of Edith: then it was just a humanoid shape:
then it was just a shape—and for a blessed second truly I was
not alone, I was part of a family. That was the first time we
made love. It never happened again. Is that what you will
cause me to feel, Catherine Tekakwitha? But aren't you dead?
How do I get close to a dead saint? The pursuit seems like
such nonsense. I'm not happy here in F.'s old treehouse. It's
long past the end of summer. My brain is ruined. My career is
in tatters. O F., is this the training you planned for me?

7 ❧ *James Baldwin*

James Baldwin, essayist, playwright, and novelist, was born in New York City in 1924. He has written four novels, Go Tell It on the Mountain (1953), Giovanni's Room (1956), Another Country (1962), and Tell Me How Long the Train's Been Gone (1968) and a collection of short fiction, Going To Meet The Man (1965). Of Baldwin's writing, Norman Podhoretz has said: "I believe that Another Country will come to be seen as the book in which for the first time the superb intelligence of Baldwin the essayist became fully available to Baldwin the novelist, in which for the first time he attempted to speak his mind with complete candor and with a minimum of polite rhetorical elegance, and in which for the first time he dared to reveal himself as someone to be feared for how deeply he sees, how much he demands of the world and how powerfully he can hate."

SONNY'S BLUES

I read about it in the paper, in the subway, on my way to work. I read it, and I couldn't believe it, and I read it again. Then perhaps I just stared at it, at the newsprint spelling out his name, spelling out the story. I stared at it in the swinging lights of the subway car, and in the faces and bodies of the people, and in my own face, trapped in the darkness which roared outside.

It was not to be believed and I kept telling myself that, as I walked from the subway station to the high school. And at the same time I couldn't doubt it. I was scared, scared for Sonny.

He became real to me again. A great block of ice settled in my belly and kept melting there slowly all day long, while I taught my classes algebra. It was a special kind of ice. It kept melting, sending trickles of ice water all up and down my veins, but it never got less. Sometimes it hardened and seemed to expand until I felt my guts were going to come spilling out or that I was going to choke or scream. This would always be at a moment when I was remembering some specific thing Sonny had once said or done.

When he was about as old as the boys in my classes his face had been bright and open, there was a lot of copper in it; and he'd had wonderfully direct brown eyes, and great gentleness and privacy. I wondered what he looked like now. He had been picked up, the evening before, in a raid on an apartment downtown, for peddling and using heroin.

I couldn't believe it: but what I mean by that is that I couldn't find any room for it anywhere inside me. I had kept it outside me for a long time. I hadn't wanted to know. I had had suspicions, but I didn't name them, I kept putting them away. I told myself that Sonny was wild, but he wasn't crazy. And he's always been a good boy, he hadn't ever turned hard or evil or disrespectful, the way kids can, so quick, so quick, especially in Harlem. I didn't want to believe that I'd ever see my brother going down, coming to nothing, all that light in his face gone out, in the condition I'd already seen so many others. Yet it had happened and here I was, talking about algebra to a lot of boys who might, every one of them for all I knew, be popping off needles every time they went to the head. Maybe it did more for them than algebra could.

I was sure that the first time Sonny had ever had horse, he couldn't have been much older than these boys were now. These boys, now, were living as we'd been living then, they were growing up with a rush and their heads bumped abruptly

against the low ceiling of their actual possibilities. They were
filled with rage. All they really knew were two darknesses, the
darkness of their lives, which was now closing in on them, and
the darkness of the movies, which had blinded them to that
other darkness, and in which they now, vindictively, dreamed,
at once more together than they were at any other time, and
more alone.

When the last bell rang, the last class ended, I let out my
breath. It seemed I'd been holding it for all that time. My
clothes were wet—I may have looked as though I'd been sitting
in a steam bath, all dressed up, all afternoon. I sat alone in the
classroom a long time. I listened to the boys outside, downstairs, shouting and cursing and laughing. Their laughter struck
me for perhaps the first time. It was not the joyous laughter
which—God knows why—one associates with children. It was
mocking and insular, its intent to denigrate. It was disen-
chanted, and in this, also, lay the authority of their curses.
Perhaps I was listening to them because I was thinking about
my brother and in them I heard my brother. And myself.

One boy was whistling a tune, at once very complicated and
very simple, it seemed to be pouring out of him as though he
were a bird, and it sounded very cool and moving through
all that harsh, bright air, only just holding its own through all
those other sounds.

I stood up and walked over to the window and looked down
into the courtyard. It was the beginning of the spring and the
sap was rising in the boys. A teacher passed through them every
now and again, quickly, as though he or she couldn't wait to
get out of that courtyard, to get those boys out of their sight
and off their minds. I started collecting my stuff. I thought I'd
better get home and talk to Isabel.

The courtyard was almost deserted by the time I got downstairs. I saw this boy standing in the shadow of a doorway,

looking just like Sonny. I almost called his name. Then I saw that it wasn't Sonny, but somebody we used to know, a boy from around our block. He'd been Sonny's friend. He'd never been mine, having been too young for me, and, anyway, I'd never liked him. And now, even though he was a grown-up man, he still hung around that block, still spent hours on the street corners, was always high and raggy. I used to run into him from time to time and he'd often work around to asking me for a quarter or fifty cents. He always had some real good excuse, too, and I always gave it to him, I don't know why.

But now, abruptly, I hated him. I couldn't stand the way he looked at me, partly like a dog, partly like a cunning child. I wanted to ask him what the hell he was doing in the school courtyard.

He sort of shuffled over to me, and he said, "I see you got the papers. So you already know about it."

"You mean about Sonny? Yes, I already know about it. How come they didn't get you?"

He grinned. It made him repulsive and it also brought to mind what he'd looked like as a kid. "I wasn't there. I stay away from them people."

"Good for you." I offered him a cigarette and I watched him through the smoke. "You come all the way down here just to tell me about Sonny?"

"That's right." He was sort of shaking his head and his eyes looked strange, as though they were about to cross. The bright sun deadened his damp dark brown skin and it made his eyes look yellow and showed up the dirt in his kinked hair. He smelled funky. I moved a little away from him and I said, "Well, thanks. But I already know about it and I got to get home."

"I'll walk you a little ways," he said. We started walking. There were a couple of kids still loitering in the courtyard and one of them said goodnight to me and looked strangely at the boy beside me.

"What're you going to do?" he asked me. "I mean, about Sonny?"

"Look. I haven't seen Sonny for over a year, I'm not sure I'm going to do anything. Anyway, what the hell can I do?"

"That's right," he said quickly, "ain't nothing you can do. Can't much help old Sonny no more I guess."

It was what I was thinking and so it seemed to me he had no right to say it.

"I'm surprised at Sonny, though," he went on—he had a funny way of talking, he looked straight ahead as though he were talking to himself—"I thought Sonny was a smart boy, I thought he was too smart to get hung."

"I guess he thought so too," I said sharply, "and that's how he got hung. And how about you? You're pretty goddamn smart, I bet."

Then he looked directly at me, just for a minute. "I ain't smart," he said. "If I was smart, I'd have reached for a pistol a long time ago."

"Look. Don't tell me your sad story, if it was up to me, I'd give you one." Then I felt guilty—guilty, probably, for never having supposed that the poor bastard *had* a story of his own, much less a sad one, and I asked, quickly, "What's going to happen to him now?"

He didn't answer this. He was off by himself some place. "Funny thing," he said, and from his tone we might have been discussing the quickest way to get to Brooklyn, "when I saw the papers this morning, the first thing I asked myself was if I had anything to do with it. I felt sort of responsible."

I began to listen more carefully. The subway station was on the corner just before us, and I stopped. He stopped, too. We were in front of a bar and he ducked slightly, peering in, but

whoever he was looking for didn't seem to be there. The juke
box was blasting away with something black and bouncy and I
half watched the barmaid as she danced her way from the juke
box to her place behind the bar. And I watched her face as she
laughingly responded to something someone said to her, still
keeping time to the music. When she smiled one saw the little
girl, one sensed the doomed, still-struggling woman beneath
the battered face of the semi-whore.

"I never give Sonny nothing," the boy said finally, "but a
long time ago I come to school high and Sonny asked me how
it felt." He paused, I couldn't bear to watch him, I watched
the barmaid, and I listened to the music which seemed to be
causing the pavement to shake. "I told him it felt great." The
music stopped, the barmaid paused and watched the juke box
until the music began again. "It did."

All this was carrying me some place I didn't want to go. I
certainly didn't want to know how it felt. It filled everything,
the people, the houses, the music, the dark, quicksilver barmaid, with menace; and this menace was their reality.

"What's going to happen to him now?" I asked again.

"They'll send him away some place and they'll try to cure
him." He shook his head. "Maybe he'll even think he's kicked
the habit. Then they'll let him loose"—he gestured, throwing
his cigarette into the gutter. "That's all."

"What do you mean, that's *all?*"

But I knew what he meant.

"I *mean*, that's *all*." He turned his head and looked at me,
pulling down the corners of his mouth. "Don't you know what
I mean?" he asked, softly.

"How the hell *would* I know what you mean?" I almost
whispered it, I don't know why.

"That's right," he said to the air, "how would *he* know what
I mean?" He turned toward me again, patient and calm, and

yet I somehow felt him shaking, shaking as though he were going to fall apart. I fet that ice in my guts again, the dread I'd felt all afternoon; and again I watched the barmaid, moving about the bar, washing glasses, and singing. "Listen. They'll let him out and then it'll just start all over again. That's what I mean."

"You mean—they'll let him out. And then he'll just start working his way back in again. You mean he'll never kick the habit. Is that what you mean?"

"That's right," he said, cheerfully. "You see what I mean."

"Tell me," I said at last, "why does he want to die? He must want to die, he's killing himself, why does he want to die?"

He looked at me in surprise. He licked his lips. "He don't want to die. He wants to live. Don't nobody want to die, ever."

Then I wanted to ask him—too many things. He could not have answered, or if he had, I could not have borne the answers. I started walking. "Well, I guess it's none of my business."

"It's going to be rough on old Sonny," he said. We reached the subway station. "This is your station?" he asked. I nodded. I took one step down. "Damn!" he said, suddenly. I looked up at him. He grinned again. "Damn it if I didn't leave all my money home. You ain't got a dollar on you, have you? Just for a couple of days, is all."

All at once something inside gave and threatened to come pouring out of me. I didn't hate him any more. I felt that in another moment I'd start crying like a child.

"Sure," I said. "Don't sweat." I looked in my wallet and didn't have a dollar, I only had a five. "Here," I said. "That hold you?"

He didn't look at it—he didn't want to look at it. A terrible closed look came over his face, as though he were keeping the number on the bill a secret from him and me. "Thanks," he said, and now he was dying to see me go. "Don't worry about Sonny. Maybe I'll write him or something."

"Sure," I said. "You do that. So long."

"Be seeing you," he said. I went on down the steps.

And I didn't write Sonny or send him anything for a long time. When I finally did, it was just after my little girl died, he wrote me back a letter which made me feel like a bastard.

Here's what he said:

Dear brother,

You don't know how much I needed to hear from you. I wanted to write you many a time but I dug how much I must have hurt you and so I didn't write. But now I feel like a man who's been trying to climb up out of some deep, real deep and funky hole and just saw the sun up there, outside. I got to get outside.

I can't tell you much about how I got here. I mean I don't know how to tell you. I guess I was afraid and you know I have never been very strong in the head (smile). I'm glad Mama and Daddy are dead and can't see what's happened to their son and I swear if I'd known what I was doing I would never have hurt you so, you and a lot of other fine people who were nice to me and who believed in me.

I don't want you to think it had anything to do with me being a musician. It's more than that. Or maybe less than that. I can't get anything straight in my head down here and I try not to think about what's going to happen to me when I get outside again. Sometime I think I'm going to flip and never get outside and sometime I think I'll come straight back. I tell you one thing, though, I'd rather blow my brains out than go through this again. But that's what they all say, so they tell me. If I tell you when I'm coming to New York and if you could meet me, I sure would appreciate it. Give my love to Isabel and the kids and I was sure sorry to hear about little Gracie. I wish I could be like Mama and say the Lord's will be done, but I don't know it seems to me that trouble is the one thing that never does get stopped and I don't know what good it does to blame it on the Lord. But maybe it does some good if you believe it.

Your brother,
Sonny

Then I kept in constant touch with him and I sent him whatever I could and I went to meet him when he came back to New York. When I saw him many things I thought I had forgotten came flooding back to me. This was because I had begun, finally, to wonder about Sonny, about the life that Sonny lived inside. This life, whatever it was, had made him older and thinner and it had deepened the distant stillness in which he had always moved. He looked very unlike my baby brother. Yet, when he smiled, when we shook hands, the baby brother I'd never known looked out from the depths of his private life, like an animal waiting to be coaxed into the light.

"How you been keeping?" he asked me.

"All right. And you?"

"Just fine." He was smiling all over his face. "It's good to see you again."

The seven years' difference in our ages lay between us like a chasm: I wondered if these years would ever operate between us as a bridge. I was remembering, and it made it hard to catch my breath, that I had been there when he was born; and I had heard the first words he had ever spoken. When he started to walk, he walked from our mother straight to me. I caught him just before he fell when he took the first steps he ever took in this world.

"How's Isabel?"

"Just fine. She's dying to see you."

"And the boys?"

"They're fine, too. They're anxious to see their uncle."

"Oh, come on. You know they don't remember me."

"Are you kidding? Of course they remember you."

He grinned again. We got into a taxi. We had a lot to say to each other, far too much to know how to begin.

As the taxi began to move, I asked, "You still want to go to India?"

He laughed. "You still remember that. Hell, no. This place is Indian enough for me."

"It used to belong to them," I said.

And he laughed again. "They damn sure knew what they were doing when they got rid of it."

Years ago, when he was around fourteen, he'd been all hipped on the idea of going to India. He read books about people sitting on rocks, naked, in all kinds of weather, but mostly bad, naturally, and walking barefoot through hot coals and arriving at wisdom. I used to say that it sounded to me as though they were getting away from wisdom as fast as they could. I think he sort of looked down on me for that.

"Do you mind," he asked, "if we have the driver drive alongside the park? On the west side—I haven't seen the city in so long."

"Of course not," I said. I was afraid that I might sound as though I were humoring him, but I hoped he wouldn't take it that way.

So we drove along, between the green of the park and the stony, lifeless elegance of hotels and apartment buildings, toward the vivid, killing streets of our childhood. These streets hadn't changed, though housing projects jutted up out of them now like rocks in the middle of a boiling sea. Most of the houses in which we had grown up had vanished, as had the stores from which we had stolen, the basements in which we had first tried sex, the rooftops from which we had hurled tin cans and bricks. But houses exactly like the houses of our past yet dominated the landscape, boys exactly like the boys we once had been found themselves smothering in these houses, came down into the streets for light and air and found themselves encircled by disaster. Some escaped the trap, most didn't. Those who got out always left something of themselves behind, as some animals amputate a leg and leave it in the trap. It might be said, perhaps, that I had escaped, after all, I was a school teacher; or that Sonny had, he hadn't lived in Harlem for years. Yet, as the cab moved uptown through the streets which seemed, with a rush, to darken people, and as I covertly studied Sonny's face, it came to me that what we both were seeking through our separate cab windows was that part of ourselves which had been left behind. It's always at the hour of trouble and confrontation that the missing member aches.

We hit 110th Street and started rolling up Lenox Avenue. And I'd known this avenue all my life, but it seemed to me again, as it had seemed on the day I'd first heard about Sonny's trouble, filled with a hidden menace which was its very breath of life.

"We almost there," said Sonny.

"Almost." We were both too nervous to say anything more.

We live in a housing project. It hasn't been up long. A few days after it was up it seemed uninhabitably new, now, of course, it's already rundown. It looks like a parody of the good, clean, faceless life—God knows the people who live in it do their best to make it a parody. The beat-looking grass lying around isn't enough to make their lives green, the hedges will never hold out the streets, and they know it. The big windows fool no one, they aren't big enough to make space out of no

space. They don't bother with the windows, they watch the
TV screen instead. The playground is most popular with the
children who don't play at jacks, or skip rope, or roller skate, or
swing, and they can be found in it after dark. We moved in
partly because it's not too far from where I teach, and partly
for the kids; but it's really just like the houses in which Sonny
and I grew up. The same things happen, they'll have the same
things to remember. The moment Sonny and I started into the
house I had the feeling that I was simply bringing him back
into the danger he had almost died trying to escape.

Sonny has never been talkative. So I don't know why I was
sure he'd be dying to talk to me when supper was over the
first night. Everything went fine, the oldest boy remembered
him, and the youngest boy liked him, and Sonny had remembered to bring something for each of them; and Isabel,
who is really much nicer than I am, more open and giving,
had gone to a lot of trouble about dinner and was genuinely
glad to see him. And she's always been able to tease Sonny in a
way that I haven't. It was nice to see her face so vivid again
and to hear her laugh and watch her make Sonny laugh. She
wasn't, or, anyway, she didn't seem to be, at all uneasy or
embarrassed. She chatted as though there were no subject
which had to be avoided and she got Sonny past his first, faint
stiffness. And thank God she was there, for I was filled with
that icy dread again. Everything I did seemed awkward to me,
and everything I said sounded freighted with hidden meaning.
I was trying to remember everything I'd heard about dope
addiction and I couldn't help watching Sonny for signs. I
wasn't doing it out of malice. I was trying to find out something about my brother. I was dying to hear him tell me he
was safe.

"Safe!" my father grunted, whenever Mama suggested trying
to move to a neighborhood which might be safer for children.
"Safe, hell! Ain't no place safe for kids, nor nobody."

He always went on like this, but he wasn't, ever, really as bad as he sounded, not even on weekends, when he got drunk. As a matter of fact, he was always on the lookout for "something a little better," but he died before he found it. He died suddenly, during a drunken weekend in the middle of the war, when Sonny was fifteen. He and Sonny hadn't ever got on too well. And this was partly because Sonny was the apple of his father's eye. It was because he loved Sonny so much and was frightened for him, that he was always fighting with him. It doesn't do any good to fight with Sonny. Sonny just moves back, inside himself, where he can't be reached. But the principal reason that they never hit it off is that they were so much alike. Daddy was big and rough and loud-talking, just the opposite of Sonny, but they both had—that same privacy.

Mama tried to tell me something about this, just after Daddy died. I was home on leave from the army.

This was the last time I ever saw my mother alive. Just the same, this picture gets all mixed up in my mind with pictures I had of her when she was younger. The way I always see her is the way she used to be on a Sunday afternoon, say, when the old folks were talking after the big Sunday dinner. I always see her wearing pale blue. She'd be sitting on the sofa. And my father would be sitting in the easy chair, not far from her. And the living room would be full of church folks and relatives. There they sit, in chairs all around the living room, and the night is creeping up outside, but nobody knows it yet. You can see the darkness growing against the windowpanes and you hear the street noises every now and again, or maybe the jangling beat of a tambourine from one of the churches close by, but it's real quiet in the room. For a moment nobody's talking, but every face looks darkening, like the sky outside. And my mother rocks a little from the waist, and my father's eyes are closed. Everyone is looking at something a child can't see. For a minute they've forgotten the children. Maybe a kid is lying

on the rug, half asleep. Maybe somebody's got a kid in his lap
and is absent-mindedly stroking the kid's head. Maybe there's
a kid, quiet and big-eyed, curled up in a big chair in the
corner. The silence, the darkness coming, and the darkness in
the faces frightens the child obscurely. He hopes that the hand
which strokes his forehead will never stop—will never die. He
hopes that there will never come a time when the old folks
won't be sitting around the living room, talking about where
they've come from, and what they've seen, and what's happened to them and their kinfolk.

But something deep and watchful in the child knows that
this is bound to end, is already ending. In a moment someone
will get up and turn on the light. Then the old folks will remember the children and they won't talk any more that day.
And when light fills the room, the child is filled with darkness.
He knows that everytime this happens he's moved just a little
closer to that darkness outside. The darkness outside is what
the old folks have been talking about. It's what they've come
from. It's what they endure. The child knows that they won't
talk any more because if he knows too much about what's
happened to them, he'll know too much too soon, about what's
going to happen to him.

The last time I talked to my mother, I remember I was restless. I wanted to get out and see Isabel. We weren't married
then and we had a lot to straighten out between us.

There Mama sat, in black, by the window. She was humming
an old church song, Lord, you brought me from a long ways
off. Sonny was out somewhere. Mama kept watching the
streets.

"I don't know," she said, "if I'll ever see you again, after you
go off from here. But I hope you'll remember the things I
tried to teach you."

"Don't talk like that," I said, and smiled. "You'll be here a
long time yet."

She smiled, too, but she said nothing. She was quiet for a long time. And I said, "Mama, don't you worry about nothing. I'll be writing all the time, and you be getting the checks. . . ."

"I want to talk to you about your brother," she said, suddenly. "If anything happens to me he ain't going to have nobody to look out for him."

"Mama," I said, "ain't nothing going to happen to you or Sonny. Sonny's all right. He's a good boy and he's got good sense."

"It ain't a question of his being a good boy," Mama said, "nor of his having good sense. It ain't only the bad ones, nor yet the dumb ones that gets sucked under." She stopped, looking at me. "Your Daddy once had a brother," she said, and she smiled in a way that made me feel she was in pain. "You didn't never know that, did you?"

"No," I said, "I never knew that," and I watched her face.

"Oh, yes," she said, "your Daddy had a brother." She looked out of the window again. "I know you never saw your Daddy cry. But I did—many a time, through all these years."

I asked her, "What happened to his brother? How come nobody's ever talked about him?"

This was the first time I ever saw my mother look old.

"His brother got killed," she said, "when he was just a little younger than you are now. I knew him. He was a fine boy. He was maybe a little full of the devil, but he didn't mean nobody no harm."

Then she stopped and the room was silent, exactly as it had sometimes been on those Sunday afternoons. Mama kept looking out into the streets.

"He used to have a job in the mill," she said, "and, like all young folks, he just liked to perform on Saturday nights. Saturday nights, him and your father would drift around to different places, go to dances and things like that, or just sit around with people they knew, and your father's brother would sing, he had a fine voice, and play along with himself on his guitar. Well, this particular Saturday night, him and your father was coming home from some place, and they were both a little drunk and there was a moon that night, it was bright like day. Your father's brother was feeling kind of good, and he was whistling to himself, and he had his guitar slung over his shoulder. They was coming down a hill and beneath them was a road that turned off from the highway. Well, your father's brother, being always kind of frisky, decided to run down this hill, and he did, with that guitar banging and clanging behind him, and he ran across the road, and he was making water behind a tree. And your father was sort of amused at him and he was still coming down the hill, kind of slow. Then he heard a car motor and that same minute his brother stepped from behind the tree, into the road, in the moonlight. And he started to cross the road. And your father started to run down the hill, he says he don't know why. This car was full of white men. They was all drunk, and when they seen your father's brother they let out a great whoop and holler and they aimed the car straight at him. They was having fun, they just wanted to scare him, the way they do sometimes, you know. But they was drunk. And I guess the boy, being drunk, too, and scared, kind of lost his head. By the time he jumped it was too late. Your father says he heard his brother scream when the car rolled over him, and he heard the wood of that guitar when it gave, and he heard them strings go flying, and he heard them white men shouting, and the car kept on a-going and it ain't stopped till this day. And, time your father got down the hill, his brother weren't nothing but blood and pulp."

Tears were gleaming on my mother's face. There wasn't anything I could say.

"He never mentioned it," she said, "because I never let him mention it before you children. Your Daddy was like a crazy man that night and for many a night thereafter. He says he never in his life seen anything as dark as that road after the lights of that car had gone away. Weren't nothing, weren't nobody on the road, just your Daddy and his brother and that busted guitar. Oh, yes. Your Daddy never did really get right again. Till the day he died he weren't sure but that every white man he saw was the man that killed his brother."

She stopped and took out her handkerchief and dried her eyes and looked at me.

"I ain't telling you all this," she said, "to make you scared or bitter or to make you hate nobody. I'm telling you this because you got a brother. And the world ain't changed."

I guess I didn't want to believe this. I guess she saw this in my face. She turned away from me, toward the window again, searching those streets.

"But I praise my Redeemer," she said at last, "that He called your Daddy home before me. I ain't saying it to throw no flowers at myself, but, I declare, it keeps me from feeling too cast down to know I helped your father get safely through this world. Your father always acted like he was the roughest, strongest man on earth. And everybody took him to be like that. But if he hadn't had me there—to see his tears!"

She was crying again. Still, I couldn't move. I said, "Lord, Lord, Mama, I didn't know it was like that."

"Oh, honey," she said, "there's a lot that you don't know. But you are going to find it out." She stood up from the window and came over to me, "You got to hold on to your brother," she said, "and don't let him fall, no matter what it looks like is happening to him and no matter how evil you gets with him. You going to be evil with him many a time. But don't you forget what I told you, you hear?"

"I won't forget," I said. "Don't you worry, I won't forget. I won't let nothing happen to Sonny."

My mother smiled as though she were amused at something she saw in my face. Then, "You may not be able to stop nothing from happening. But you got to let him know you's *there*."

Two days later I was married, and then I was gone. And I had a lot of things on my mind and I pretty well forgot my promise to Mama until I got shipped home on a special furlough for her funeral.

And, after the funeral, with just Sonny and me alone in the empty kitchen, I tried to find out something about him.

"What do you want to do?" I asked him.

"I'm going to be a musician," he said.

For he had graduated, in the time I had been away, from dancing to the juke box to finding out who was playing what, and what they were doing with it, and he had bought himself a set of drums.

"You mean, you want to be a drummer?" I somehow had the feeling that being a drummer might be all right for other people but not for my brother Sonny.

"I don't think," he said, looking at me very gravely, "that I'll ever be a good drummer. But I think I can play a piano."

I frowned. I'd never played the role of the older brother quite so seriously before, had scarcely ever, in fact, asked Sonny a damn thing. I sensed myself in the presence of something I didn't really know how to handle, didn't understand. So I made my frown a little deeper as I asked: "What kind of musician do you want to be?"

He grinned. "How many kinds do you think there are?"

"Be *serious*," I said.

He laughed, throwing his head back, and then looked at me. "I *am* serious."

"Well, then, for Christ's sake, stop kidding around and

answer a serious question. I mean, do you want to be a concert pianist, you want to play classical music and all that, or—or what?" Long before I finished he was laughing again. "For Christ's *sake*, Sonny!"

He sobered, but with difficulty. "I'm sorry. But you sound so—*scared!*" and he was off again.

"Well, you may think it's funny now, baby, but it's not going to be so funny when you have to make your living at it, let me tell you *that*." I was furious because I knew he was laughing at me and I didn't know why.

"No," he said, very sober now, and afraid, perhaps, that he'd hurt me, "I don't want to be a classical pianist. That isn't what interests me. I mean"—he paused, looking hard at me, as though his eyes would help me to understand, and then gestured helplessly, as though perhaps his hand would help—"I mean, I'll have a lot of studying to do, and I'll have to study *everything*, but, I mean, I want to play *with*—jazz musicians." He stopped. "I want to play jazz," he said.

Well, the word had never before sounded as heavy, as real, as it sounded that afternoon in Sonny's mouth. I just looked at him and I was probably frowning a real frown by this time. I simply couldn't see why on earth he'd want to spend his time hanging around nightclubs, clowning around on bandstands, while people pushed each other around a dance floor. It seemed —beneath him, somehow. I had never thought about it before, had never been forced to, but I suppose I had always put jazz musicians in a class with what Daddy called "good-time people."

"Are you *serious?*"

"Hell, yes, I'm serious."

He looked more helpless than ever, and annoyed, and deeply hurt.

I suggested, helpfully: "You mean—like Louis Armstrong?"

His face closed as though I'd struck him. "No. I'm not talk-ing about none of that old-time, down home crap."

"Well, look, Sonny, I'm sorry, don't get mad. I just don't altogether get it, that's all. Name somebody—you know, a jazz musician you admire."

"Bird."

"Who?"

"Bird! Charlie Parker! Don't they teach you nothing in the goddamn army?"

I lit a cigarette. I was surprised and then a little amused to discover that I was trembling. "I've been out of touch," I said. "You'll have to be patient with me. Now. Who's this Parker character?"

"He's just one of the greatest jazz musicians alive," said Sonny, sullenly, his hands in his pockets, his back to me. "Maybe *the* greatest," he added, bitterly, "that's probably why you never heard of him

"All right," I said, "I'm ignorant. I'm sorry. I'll go out and buy me all the cat's records right away, all right?"

"It don't," said Sonny, with dignity, "make any difference to me. I don't care what you listen to. Don't do me no favors."

I was beginning to realize that I'd never seen him so upset before. With another part of my mind I was thinking that this would probably turn out to be one of those things kids go through and that I shouldn't make it seem important by pushing it too hard. Still, I didn't think it would do any harm to ask: "Doesn't all this take a lot of time? Can you make a living at it?"

He turned back to me and half leaned, half sat, on the kitchen table. "Everything takes time," he said, "and—well, yes, sure, I can make a living at it. But what I don't seem to be able to make you understand is that it's the only thing I want to do."

"Well, Sonny," I said, gently, "you know people can't always do exactly what they want to do—"

"No, I don't know that," said Sonny, surprising me. "I think people ought to do what they want to do, what else are they alive for?"

"You getting to be a big boy," I said desperately, "it's time you started thinking about your future."

"I'm thinking about my future," said Sonny, grimly. "I think about it all the time."

I gave up. I decided, if he didn't change his mind, that we could always talk about it later. "In the meantime," I said, "you got to finish school." We had already decided that he'd have to move in with Isabel and her folks. I knew this wasn't the ideal arrangement because Isabel's folks are inclined to be dicty and they hadn't especially wanted Isabel to marry me. But I didn't know what else to do. "And we have to get you fixed up at Isabel's."

There was a long silence. He moved from the kitchen table to the window. "That's a terrible idea. You know it yourself."

"Do you have a better idea?"

He just walked up and down the kitchen for a minute. He was as tall as I was. He had started to shave. I suddenly had the feeling that I didn't know him at all.

He stopped at the kitchen table and picked up my cigarettes. Looking at me with a kind of mocking, amused defiance, he put one between his lips. "You mind?"

"You smoking already?"

He lit the cigarette and nodded, watching me through the smoke. "I just wanted to see if I'd have the courage to smoke in front of you." He grinned and blew a great cloud of smoke to the ceiling. "It was easy." He looked at my face." Come on, now. I bet you was smoking at my age, tell the truth."

I didn't say anything but the truth was on my face, and he

laughed. But now there was something very strained in his laugh. "Sure. And I bet that ain't all you was doing."

He was frightening me a little. "Cut the crap," I said. "We already decided that you was going to go and live at Isabel's. Now what's got into you all of a sudden?"

"You decided it," he pointed out. "I didn't decide nothing." He stopped in front of me, leaning against the stove, arms loosely folded. "Look, brother. I don't want to stay in Harlem no more, I really don't." He was very earnest. He looked at me, then over toward the kitchen window. There was something in his eyes I'd never seen before, some thoughtfulness, some worry all his own. He rubbed the muscle of one arm. "It's time I was getting out of here."

"Where do you want to go, Sonny?"

"I want to join the army. Or the navy, I don't care. If I say I'm old enough, they'll believe me."

Then I got mad. It was because I was so scared. "You must be crazy. You goddamn fool, what the hell do you want to go and join the army for?"

"I just told you. To get out of Harlem."

"Sonny, you haven't even finished *school*. And if you really want to be a musician, how do you expect to study if you're in the army?"

He looked at me, trapped, and in anguish. "There's ways. I might be able to work out some kind of deal. Anyway, I'll have the G.I. Bill when I come out."

"*If* you come out." We stared at each other. "Sonny, please. Be reasonable. I know the setup is far from perfect. But we got to do the best we can."

"I ain't learning nothing in school," he said. "Even when I go." He turned away from me and opened the window and threw his cigarette out into the narrow alley. I watched his back. "At least, I ain't learning nothing you'd want me to learn." He slammed the window so hard I thought the glass would fly out, and turned back to me. "And I'm sick of the stink of these garbage cans!"

"Sonny," I said, "I know how you feel. But if you don't finish school now, you're going to be sorry later that you didn't." I grabbed him by the shoulders. "And you only got another year. It ain't so bad. And I'll come back and I swear I'll help you do whatever you want to do. Just try to put up with it till I come back. Will you please do that? For me?"

He didn't answer and he wouldn't look at me.

"Sonny. You hear me?"

He pulled away. "I hear you. But you never hear anything I say."

I didn't know what to say to that. He looked out of the window and then back at me. "OK," he said, and sighed. "I'll try."

Then I said, trying to cheer him up a little, "They got a piano at Isabel's. You can practice on it."

And as a matter of fact, it did cheer him up for a minute. "That's right," he said to himself. "I forgot that." His face relaxed a little. But the worry, the thoughtfulness, played on it still, the way shadows play on a face which is staring into the fire.

But I thought I'd never hear the end of that piano. At first, Isabel would write me, saying how nice it was that Sonny was so serious about his music and how, as soon as he came in from school, or wherever he had been when he was supposed to be at school, he went straight to that piano and stayed there until suppertime. And, after supper, he went back to that piano and stayed there until everybody went to bed. He was at the piano all day Saturday and all day Sunday. Then he bought a record player and started playing records.

He'd play one record over and over again, all day long sometimes, and he'd improvise along with it on the piano. Or he'd
play one section of the record, one chord, one change, one
progression, then he'd do it on the piano. Then back to the
record. Then back to the piano.

Well, I really don't know how they stood it. Isabel finally
confessed that it wasn't like living with a person at all, it was
like living with sound. And the sound didn't make any sense
to her, didn't make any sense to any of them—naturally.
They began, in a way, to be afflicted by this presence that
was living in their home. It was as though Sonny were some
sort of god, or monster. He moved in an atmosphere which
wasn't like theirs at all. They fed him and he ate, he washed
himself, he walked in and out of their door; he certainly
wasn't nasty or unpleasant or rude, Sonny isn't any of those
things; but it was as though he were all wrapped up in some
cloud, some fire, some vision all his own; and there wasn't
any way to reach him.

At the same time, he wasn't really a man yet, he was still
a child, and they had to watch out for him in all kinds of
ways. They certainly couldn't throw him out. Neither did
they dare to make a great scene about that piano because
even they dimly sensed, as I sensed, from so many thousands
of miles away, that Sonny was at that piano playing for his
life.

But he hadn't been going to school. One day a letter came
from the school board and Isabel's mother got it—there had,
apparently, been other letters but Sonny had torn them up.
This day, when Sonny came in, Isabel's mother showed him
the letter and asked where he'd been spending his time. And
she finally got it out of him that he'd been down in Green-
wich Village, with musicians and other characters, in a white
girl's apartment. And this scared her and she started to scream

at him and what came up, once she began—though she denies it to this day—was what sacrifices they were making to give Sonny a decent home and how little he appreciated it.

Sonny didn't play the piano that day. By evening, Isabel's mother had calmed down but then there was the old man to deal with, and Isabel herself. Isabel says she did her best to be calm but she broke down and started crying. She says she just watched Sonny's face. She could tell, by watching him, what was happening with him. And what was happening was that they penetrated his cloud, they had reached him. Even if their fingers had been a thousand times more gentle than human fingers ever are, he could hardly help feeling that they had stripped him naked and were spitting on that nakedness. For he also had to see that his presence, that music, which was life or death to him, had been torture for them and that they had endured it, not at all for his sake, but only for mine. And Sonny couldn't take that. He can take it a little better today than he could then but he's still not very good at it and, frankly, I don't know anybody who is.

The silence of the next few days must have been louder than the sound of all the music ever played since time began. One morning, before she went to work, Isabel was in his room for something and she suddenly realized that all of his records were gone. And she knew for certain that he was gone. And he was. He went as far as the navy would carry him. He finally sent me a postcard from some place in Greece and that was the first I knew that Sonny was still alive. I didn't see him any more until we were both back in New York and the war had long been over.

He was a man by then, of course, but I wasn't willing to see it. He came by the house from time to time, but we fought almost every time we met. I didn't like the way he carried himself, loose and dreamlike all the time, and I didn't

like his friends, and his music seemed to be merely an excuse
for the life he led. It sounded just that weird and disordered.

Then we had a fight, a pretty awful fight, and I didn't see
him for months. By and by I looked him up, where he was
living, in a furnished room in the Village, and I tried to make
it up. But there were lots of people in the room and Sonny
just lay on his bed, and he wouldn't come downstairs with
me, and he treated these other people as though they were
his family and I weren't. So I got mad and then he got mad,
and then I told him that he might just as well be dead as
live the way he was living. Then he stood up and he told me
not to worry about him any more in life, that he was dead as
far as I was concerned. Then he pushed me to the door and
the other people looked on as though nothing were happening, and he slammed the door behind me. I stood in the
hallway, staring at the door. I heard somebody laugh in the
room and then the tears came to my eyes. I started down the
steps, whistling to keep from crying, I kept whistling to
myself, *You going to need me, baby, one of these cold, rainy
days.*

I read about Sonny's trouble in the spring. Little Grace
died in the fall. She was a beautiful little girl. But she only
lived a little over two years. She died of polio and she suffered.
She had a slight fever for a couple of days, but it didn't seem
like anything and we just kept her in bed. And we would certainly have called the doctor, but the fever dropped, she
seemed to be all right. So we thought it had just been a cold.
Then, one day, she was up, playing, Isabel was in the kitchen
fixing lunch for the two boys when they'd come in from
school, and she heard Grace fall down in the living room.
When you have a lot of children you don't always start running when one of them falls, unless they start screaming or

something. And, this time, Grace was quiet. Yet, Isabel says that when she heard that *thump* and then that silence, something happened in her to make her afraid. And she ran to the living room and there was little Grace on the floor, all twisted up, and the reason she hadn't screamed was that she couldn't get her breath. And when she did scream, it was the worst sound, Isabel says, that she's ever heard in all her life, and she still hears it sometimes in her dreams. Isabel will sometimes wake me up with a low, moaning, strangled sound and I have to be quick to awaken her and hold her to me and where Isabel is weeping against me seems a mortal wound.

I think I may have written Sonny the very day that little Grace was buried. I was sitting in the living room in the dark, by myself, and I suddenly thought of Sonny. My trouble made his real.

One Saturday afternoon, when Sonny had been living with us, or, anyway, been in our house, for nearly two weeks, I found myself wandering aimlessly about the living room, drinking from a can of beer, and trying to work up the courage to search Sonny's room. He was out, he was usually out whenever I was home, and Isabel had taken the children to see their grandparents. Suddenly I was standing still in front of the living room window, watching Seventh Avenue. The idea of searching Sonny's room made me still. I scarcely dared to admit to myself what I'd be searching for. I didn't know what I'd do if I found it. Or if I didn't.

On the sidewalk across from me, near the entrance to a barbecue joint, some people were holding an old-fashioned revival meeting. The barbecue cook, wearing a dirty white apron, his conked hair reddish and metallic in the pale sun, and a cigarette between his lips, stood in the doorway, watching them. Kids and older people paused in their errands and stood there, along with some older men and a couple of very

tough-looking women who watched everything that happened
on the avenue, as though they owned it, or were maybe owned
by it. Well, they were watching this, too. The revival was
being carried on by three sisters in black, and a brother. All
they had were their voices and their Bibles and a tambourine.
The brother was testifying and while he testified two of the
sisters stood together, seeming to say, amen, and the third
sister walked around with the tambourine outstretched and a
couple of people dropped coins into it. Then the brother's
testimony ended and the sister who had been taking up the
collection dumped the coins into her palm and transferred
them to the pocket of her long black robe. Then she raised
both hands, striking the tambourine against the air, and then
against one hand, and she started to sing. And the two other
sisters and the brother joined in.

It was strange, suddenly, to watch, though I had been seeing
these street meetings all my life. So, of course, had everybody
else down there. Yet, they paused and watched and listened
and I stood still at the window. *"Tis the old ship of Zion,"*
they sang, and the sister with the tambourine kept a steady,
jangling beat, *"it has rescued many a thousand!"* Not a soul
under the sound of their voices was hearing this song for the
first time, not one of them had been rescued. Nor had they
seen much in the way of rescue work being done around them.
Neither did they especially believe in the holiness of the three
sisters and the brother, they knew too much about them, knew
where they lived, and how. The woman with the tambourine,
whose voice dominated the air, whose face was bright with
joy, was divided by very little from the woman who stood
watching her, a cigarette between her heavy, chapped lips, her
hair a cuckoo's nest, her face scarred and swollen from many
beatings, and her black eyes glittering like coal. Perhaps they
both knew this, which was why, when, as rarely, they addressed

each other, they addressed each other as Sister. As the singing filled the air the watching, listening faces underwent a change, the eyes focusing on something within; the music seemed to soothe a poison out of them; and time seemed, nearly, to fall away from the sullen, belligerent, battered faces, as though they were fleeing back to their first condition, while dreaming of their last. The barbecue cook half shook his head and smiled, and dropped his cigarette and disappeared into his joint. A man fumbled in his pockets for change and stood holding it in his hand impatiently, as though he had just remembered a pressing appointment further up the avenue. He looked furious. Then I saw Sonny, standing on the edge of the crowd. He was carrying a wide, flat notebook with a green cover, and it made him look, from where I was standing, almost like a schoolboy. The coppery sun brought out the copper in his skin, he was very faintly smiling, standing very still. Then the singing stopped, the tambourine turned into a collection plate again. The furious man dropped in his coins and vanished, so did a couple of the women, and Sonny dropped some change in the plate, looking directly at the woman with a little smile. He started across the avenue, toward the house. He has a slow, loping walk, something like the way Harlem hipsters walk, only he's imposed on this his own half-beat. I had never really noticed it before.

I stayed at the window, both relieved and apprehensive. As Sonny disappeared from my sight, they began singing again. And they were still singing when his key turned in the lock.

"Hey," he said.

"Hey, yourself. You want some beer?"

"No. Well, maybe." But he came up to the window and stood beside me, looking out. "What a warm voice," he said.

They were singing *If I could only hear my mother pray again!*

"Yes," I said, "and she can sure beat the tambourine."

"But what a terrible song," he said, and laughed. He dropped his notebook on the sofa and disappeared into the kitchen. "Where's Isabel and the kids?"

"I think they went to see their grandparents. You hungry?"

"No." He came back into the living room with his can of beer. "You want to come some place with me tonight?"

I sensed, I don't know how, that I couldn't possibly say no. "Sure. Where?"

He sat down on the sofa and picked up his notebook and started leafing through it. "I'm going to sit in with some fellows in a joint in the Village."

"You mean, you're going to play, tonight?"

"That's right." He took a swallow of his beer and moved back to the window. He gave me a sidelong look. "If you can stand it."

"I'll try," I said.

He smiled to himself and we both watched as the meeting across the way broke up. The three sisters and the brother, heads bowed, were singing *God be with you till we meet again.* The faces around them were very quiet. Then the song ended. The small crowd dispersed. We watched the three women and the lone man walk slowly up the avenue.

"When she was singing before," said Sonny, abruptly, "her voice reminded me for a minute of what heroin feels like sometimes—when it's in your veins. It makes you feel sort of warm and cool at the same time. And distant. And—and sure." He sipped his beer, very deliberately not looking at me. I watched his face. "It makes you feel—in control. Sometimes you've got to have that feeling."

"Do you?" I sat down slowly in the easy chair.

"Sometimes." He went to the sofa and picked up his notebook again. "Some people do."

"In order," I asked, "to play?" And my voice was very ugly, full of contempt and anger.

"Well"—he looked at me with great, troubled eyes, as though, in fact, he hoped his eyes would tell me things he could never otherwise say—they *think* so. And *if* they think so—!"

"And what do *you* think?" I asked.

He sat on the sofa and put his can of beer on the floor. "I don't know," he said, and I couldn't be sure if he were answering my question or pursuing his thoughts. His face didn't tell me. "It's not so much to *play*. It's to *stand* it, to be able to make it at all. On any level." He frowned and smiled: "In order to keep from shaking to pieces."

"But these friends of yours," I said, "they seem to shake themselves to pieces pretty goddamn fast."

"Maybe." He played with the notebook. And something told me that I should curb my tongue, that Sonny was doing his best to talk, that I should listen. "But of course you only know the ones that've gone to pieces. Some don't—or at least they haven't yet and that's just about all any of us can say." He paused. "And then there are some who just live, really, in hell, and they know it and they see what's happening and they go right on. I don't know." He sighed, dropped the notebook, folded his arms. "Some guys, you can tell from the way they play, they on something all the time. And you can see that, well, it makes something real for them. But of course," he picked up his beer from the floor and sipped it and put the can down again, "they *want* to, too, you've got to see that. Even some of them that say they don't—*some*, not all."

"And what about you?" I asked—I couldn't help it. "What about you? Do *you* want to?"

He stood up and walked to the window and remained silent for a long time. Then he sighed. "Me," he said. Then: "While

I was downstairs before, on my way here, listening to that woman sing, it struck me all of a sudden how much suffering she must have had to go through—to sing like that. It's re-pulsive to think you have to suffer that much."

I said: "But there's no way not to suffer—is there, Sonny?"

"I believe not," he said and smiled, "but that's never stopped anyone from trying." He looked at me. "Has it?" I realized, with his mocking look, that there stood between us, forever, beyond the power of time or forgiveness, the fact that I had held silence—so long!—when he had needed human speech to help him. He turned back to the window. "No, there's no way not to suffer. But you try all kinds of ways to keep from drowning in it, to keep on top of it, and to make it seem—well, like you. Like you did something, all right, and now you're suffering for it. You know?" I said nothing. "Well you know," he said, impatiently, "why do people suffer? Maybe it's better to do something to give it a reason, any reason."

"But we just agreed," I said, "that there's no way not to suffer. Isn't it better, then, just to—take it?"

"But nobody just takes it," Sonny cried, "that's what I'm telling you! Everybody tries not to. You're just hung up on the way some people try—it's not your way!"

The hair on my face began to itch, my face felt wet. "That's not true," I said, "that's not true. I don't give a damn what other people do, I don't even care how they suffer. I just care how you suffer." And he looked at me. "Please believe me," I said, "I don't want to see you—die—trying not to suffer."

"I won't," he said, flatly, "die trying not to suffer. At least, not any faster than anybody else."

"But there's no need," I said, trying to laugh, "is there? in killing yourself."

I wanted to say more, but I couldn't. I wanted to talk about will power and how life could be—well, beautiful. I wanted to say that it was all within; but was it? or, rather, wasn't that exactly the trouble? And I wanted to promise that I would never fail him again. But it would all have sounded—empty words and lies.

So I made the promise to myself and prayed that I would keep it.

"It's terrible sometimes, inside," he said, "that's what's the trouble. You walk these streets, black and funky and cold, and there's not really a living ass to talk to, and there's nothing shaking, and there's no way of getting it out—that storm inside. You can't talk it and you can't make love with it, and when you finally try to get with it and play it, you realize *nobody's* listening. So you've got to listen. You got to find a way to listen."

And then he walked away from the window and sat on the sofa again, as though all the wind had suddenly been knocked out of him. "Sometimes you'll do *anything* to play, even cut your mother's throat." He laughed and looked at me. "Or your brother's." Then he sobered. "Or your own." Then: "Don't worry. I'm all right now and I think I'll be all right. But I can't forget—where I've been. I don't mean just the physical place I've been, I mean where I've *been*. And *what* I've been."

"What have you been, Sonny?" I asked.

He smiled—but sat sideways on the sofa, his elbow resting on the back, his fingers playing with his mouth and chin, not looking at me. "I've been something I didn't recognize, didn't know I could be. Didn't know anybody could be." He stopped, looking inward, looking helplessly young, looking old. "I'm not talking about it now because I feel *guilty* or anything like that —maybe it would be better if I did, I don't know. Anyway, I can't really talk about it. Not to you, not to anybody," and now he turned and faced me. "Sometimes, you know, and it was actually when I was most out of the world, I felt that I was in it, that I was with it, really, and I could play or I didn't really have to play, it just came out of me, it was there. And I don't know how I played, thinking about it now, but I know I did awful things, those times, sometimes, to people. Or it wasn't that I did anything to them—it was that they weren't real." He picked up the beer can; it was empty; he rolled it between his palms: "And other times—well, I needed a fix, I needed to find a place to lean, I needed to clear a space to listen—and I couldn't find it, and I—went crazy." He began pressing the beer can between his hands, I watched the metal begin to give. It glittered, as he played with it, like a knife, and I was afraid he would cut himself, but I said nothing. "Oh well. I can never tell you. I was all by myself at the bottom of something, stinking and sweating and crying and shaking, and I smelled it, you know? my stink, and I thought I'd die if I couldn't get away from it and yet, all the same, I knew that everything I was doing was just locking me in with it. And I didn't know," he paused, still flattening the beer can, "I didn't know, I still don't know, something kept telling me that maybe it was good to smell your own stink, but I didn't think that that was what I'd been trying to do—and—who can stand it?" and he abruptly dropped the ruined beer can, looking at me with a small, still smile, and then rose walking to the window as though it were the lodestone rock. I watched his face, he watched the avenue. "I couldn't tell you when Mama died— but the reason I wanted to leave Harlem so bad was to get away from drugs. And then, when I ran away, that's what I was running from—really. When I came back, nothing had changed, I hadn't changed, I was just—older." And he stopped, drumming with his fingers on the windowpane. The sun had vanished, soon darkness would fall. I watched his face. "It can come again," he said, almost as though speaking to himself.

Then he turned to me. "It can come again," he repeated. "I just want you to know that."

"All right," I said, at last. "So it can come again, All right."

He smiled, but the smile was sorrowful. "I had to try to tell you," he said.

"Yes," I said. "I understand that."

"You're my brother," he said, looking straight at me, and not smiling at all.

"Yes," I repeated, "yes. I understand that."

He turned back to the window, looking out. "All that hatred down there," he said, "all that hatred and misery and love. It's a wonder it doesn't blow the avenue apart."

We went to the only nightclub on a short, dark street, downtown. We squeezed through the narrow, chattering, jampacked bar to the entrance of the big room, where the bandstand was. And we stood there for a moment, for the lights were very dim in this room and we couldn't see. Then, "Hello, boy," said a voice and an enormous black man, much older than Sonny or myself, erupted out of all that atmospheric lighting and put an arm around Sonny's shoulder. "I been sitting right here," he said, "waiting for you."

He had a big voice, too, and heads in the darkness turned toward us.

Sonny grinned and pulled a little away, and said, "Creole, this is my brother. I told you about him."

Creole shook my hand. "I'm glad to meet you, son," he said, and it was clear that he was glad to meet me *there*, for Sonny's sake. And he smiled, "You got a real musician in your family," and he took his arm from Sonny's shoulder and slapped him, lightly, affectionately, with the back of his hand.

"Well. Now I've heard it all," said a voice behind us. This was another musician, and a friend of Sonny's, a coal-black,

cheerful-looking man, built close to the ground. He immediately began confiding to me, at the top of his lungs, the most
terrible things about Sonny, his teeth gleaming like a light
house and his laugh coming up out of him like the beginning
of an earthquake. And it turned out that everyone at the
bar knew Sonny, or almost everyone; some were musicians,
working there, or nearby, or not working, some were simply
hangers-on, and some were there to hear Sonny play. I was
introduced to all of them and they were all very polite to me.
Yet, it was clear that, for them, I was only Sonny's brother.
Here, I was in Sonny's world. Or, rather: his kingdom. Here,
it was not even a question that his veins bore royal blood.

They were going to play soon and Creole installed me, by
myself, at a table in a dark corner. Then I watched them,
Creole, and the little black man, and Sonny, and the others,
while they horsed around, standing just below the bandstand.
The light from the bandstand spilled just a little short of them
and, watching them laughing and gesturing and moving about,
I had the feeling that they, nevertheless, were being most
careful not to step into that circle of light too suddenly: that if
they moved into the light too suddenly, without thinking, they
would perish in flame. Then, while I watched, one of them,
the small, black man, moved into the light and crossed the
bandstand and started fooling around with his drums. Then—
being funny and being, also, extremely ceremonious—Creole
took Sonny by the arm and led him to the piano. A woman's
voice called Sonny's name and a few hands started clapping.
And Sonny, also being funny and being ceremonious, and so
touched, I think, that he could have cried, but neither hiding
it nor showing it, riding it like a man, grinned, and put both
hands to his heart and bowed from the waist.

Creole then went to the bass fiddle and a lean, very bright-
skinned brown man jumped up on the bandstand and picked

up his horn. So there they were, and the atmosphere on the bandstand and in the room began to change and tighten. Someone stepped up to the microphone and announced them. Then there were all kinds of murmurs. Some people at the bar shushed others. The waitress ran around, frantically getting in the last orders, guys and chicks got closer to each other, and the lights on the bandstand, on the quartet, turned to a kind of indigo. Then they all looked different there. Creole looked about him for the last time, as though he were making certain that all his chickens were in the coop, and then he—jumped and struck the fiddle. And there they were.

All I know about music is that not many people ever really hear it. And even then, on the rare occasions when something opens within, and the music enters, what we mainly hear, or hear corroborated, are personal, private, vanishing evocations. But the man who creates the music is hearing something else, is dealing with the roar rising from the void and imposing order on it as it hits the air. What it evoked in him, then, is of another order, more terrible because it has no words, and triumphant, too, for that same reason. And his triumph, when he triumphs, is ours. I just watched Sonny's face. His face was troubled, he was working hard, but he wasn't with it. And I had the feeling that, in a way, everyone on the bandstand was waiting for him, both waiting for him and pushing him along. But as I began to watch Creole, I realized that it was Creole who held them all back. He had them on a short rein. Up there, keeping the beat with his whole body, wailing on the fiddle, with his eyes half closed, he was listening to everything, but he was listening to Sonny. He was having a dialogue with Sonny. He wanted Sonny to leave the shoreline and strike out for the deep water. He was Sonny's witness that deep water and drowning were not the same thing—he had been there, and he knew. And he wanted Sonny to know. He was waiting for Sonny to do the things on the keys which would let Creole know that Sonny was in the water.

And, while Creole listened, Sonny moved, deep within, exactly like someone in torment. I had never before thought of how awful the relationship must be between the musician and his instrument. He has to fill it, this instrument, with the breath of life, his own. He has to make it do what he wants it to do. And a piano is just a piano. It's made out of so much wood and wires and little hammers and big ones, and ivory. While there's only so much you can do with it, the only way to find this out is to try; to try and make it do everything.

And Sonny hadn't been near a piano for over a year. And he wasn't on much better terms with his life, not the life that stretched before him now. He and the piano stammered, started one way, got scared, stopped; started another way, panicked, marked time, started again; then seemed to have found a direction, panicked again, got stuck. And the face I saw on Sonny I'd never seen before. Everything had been burned out of it, and, at the same time, things usually hidden were being burned in, by the fire and fury of the battle which was occurring in him up there.

Yet, watching Creole's face as they neared the end of the first set, I had the feeling that something had happened, something I hadn't heard. Then they finished, there was scattered applause, and then, without an instant's warning, Creole started into something else, it was almost sardonic, it was Am I Blue. Something began to happen. And Creole let out the reins. The dry, low, black man said something awful on the drums, Creole answered, and the drums talked back. Then the horn insisted, sweet and high, slightly detached perhaps, and Creole listened, commenting now and then, dry, and driving, beautiful and calm and old. Then they all came together again, and Sonny was part of the family again. I could tell this

from his face. He seemed to have found, right there beneath
his fingers, a damn brand-new piano. It seemed that he
couldn't get over it. Then, for awhile, just being happy with
Sonny, they seemed to be agreeing with him that brand-new
pianos certainly were a gas.

Then Creole stepped forward to remind them that what
they were playing was the blues. He hit something in all of
them, he hit something in me, myself, and the music tightened
and deepened, apprehension began to beat the air. Creole
began to tell us what the blues were all about. They were not
about anything very new. He and his boys up there were keeping it new, at the risk of ruin, destruction, madness, and death,
in order to find new ways to make us listen. For, while the
tale of how we suffer, and how we are delighted, and how we
may triumph is never new, it always must be heard. There
isn't any other tale to tell, it's the only light we've got in all
this darkness.

And this tale, according to that face, that body, those strong
hands on those strings, has another aspect in every country,
and a new depth in every generation. Listen, Creole seemed
to be saying, listen. Now these are Sonny's blues. He made
the little black man on the drums know it, and the bright,
brown man on the horn. Creole wasn't trying any longer to
get Sonny in the water. He was wishing him Godspeed. Then
he stepped back, very slowly, filling the air with the immense
suggestion that Sonny speak for himself.

Then they all gathered around Sonny and Sonny played.
Every now and again one of them seemed to say amen.
Sonny's fingers filled the air with life, his life. But that life
contained so many others. And Sonny went all the way back,
he really began with the spare, flat statement of the opening
phrase of the song. Then he began to make it his. It was very
beautiful because it wasn't hurried and it was no longer a

lament. I seemed to hear with what burning he had made it his, with what burning we had yet to make it ours, how we could cease lamenting. Freedom lurked around us and I understood, at last, that he could help us to be free if we would listen, that he would never be free until we did. Yet, there was no battle in his face now. I heard what he had gone through, and would continue to go through until he came to rest in earth. He had made it his: that long line, of which we knew only Mama and Daddy. And he was giving it back, as everything must be given back, so that, passing through death, it can live forever. I saw my mother's face again, and felt, for the first time, how the stones of the road she had walked on must have bruised her feet. I saw the moonlit road where my father's brother died. And it brought something else back to me, and carried me past it. I saw my little girl again and felt Isabel's tears again, and I felt my own tears begin to rise. And I was yet aware that this was only a moment, that the world waited outside, as hungry as a tiger, and that trouble stretched above us, longer than the sky.

Then it was over. Creole and Sonny let out their breath, both soaking wet, and grinning. There was a lot of applause and some of it was real. In the dark, the girl came by and I asked her to take drinks to the bandstand. There was a long pause, while they talked up there in the indigo light and after awhile I saw the girl put a Scotch and milk on top of the piano for Sonny. He didn't seem to notice it, but just before they started playing again, he sipped from it and looked toward me, and nodded. Then he put it back on top of the piano. For me, then, as they began to play again, it glowed and shook above my brother's head like the very cup of trembling.

8 ❧ *Flann O'Brien*

Born in Ireland shortly before the First World War, Flann O'Brien
wrote two extravagant comic novels, At Swim-Two-Birds and The Third
Policeman. Graham Greene has called At Swim-Two-Birds "a book in a
thousand . . . in the line of Tristram Shandy and Ulysses."

"THE LITTLE CHEST"
(FROM *THE THIRD POLICEMAN*)

I

Not everybody knows how I killed old Phillip Mathers, smashing his jaw in with my spade; but first it is better to speak of my friendship with John Divney because it was he who first knocked old Mathers down by giving him a great blow in the neck with a special bicycle-pump which he manufactured himself out of a hollow iron bar. Divney was a strong civil man but he was lazy and idle-minded. He was personally responsible for the whole idea in the first place. It was he who told me to bring my spade. He was the one who gave the orders on the occasion and also the explanations when they were called for.

I was born a long time ago. My father was a strong farmer

and my mother owned a public house. We all lived in the
public house but it was not a strong house at all and was
closed most of the day because my father was out at work on
the farm and my mother was always in the kitchen and for
some reason the customers never came until it was nearly bedtime; and well after it at Christmas-time and on other unusual
days like that. I never saw my mother outside the kitchen in
my life and never saw a customer during the day and even at
night I never saw more than two or three together. But then
I was in bed part of the time and it is possible that things
happened differently with my mother and with the customers
late at night. My father I do not remember well but he was
a strong man and did not talk much except on Saturdays when
he would mention Parnell with the customers and say that
Ireland was a queer country. My mother I can recall perfectly.
Her face was always red and sore-looking from bending at the
fire; she spent her life making tea to pass the time and singing
snatches of old songs to pass the meantime. I knew her well
but my father and I were strangers and did not converse much;
often indeed when I would be studying in the kitchen at night
I could hear him through the thin door to the shop talking
there from his seat under the oil-lamp for hours on end to
Mick the sheepdog. Always it was only the drone of his voice
I heard, never the separate bits of words. He was a man who
understood all dogs thoroughly and treated them like human
beings. My mother owned a cat but it was a foreign outdoor
animal and was rarely seen and my mother never took any
notice of it. We were all happy enough in a queer separate
way.

Then a certain year came about the Christmas-time and
when the year was gone my father and mother were gone also.
Mick the sheepdog was very tired and sad after my father went
and would not do his work with the sheep at all; he too went

the next year. I was young and foolish at the time and did not know properly why these people had all left me, where they had gone and why they did not give explanations beforehand. My mother was the first to go and I can remember a fat man with a red face and a black suit telling my father that there was no doubt where she was, that he could be as sure of that as he could of anything else in this vale of tears. But he did not mention where and as I thought the whole thing was very private and that she might be back on Wednesday, I did not ask him where. Later, when my father went, I thought he had gone to fetch her with an outside car but when neither of them came back on the next Wednesday, I felt sorry and disappointed. The man in the black suit was back again. He stayed in the house for two nights and was continually washing his hands in the bedroom and reading books. There were two other men, one a small pale man and one a tall black man in leggings. They had pockets full of pennies and they gave me one every time I asked them questions. I can remember the tall man in the leggings saying to the other man:

"The poor misfortunate little bastard."

I did not understand this at the time and thought that they were talking about the other man in the black clothes who was always working at the wash-stand in the bedroom. But I understood it all clearly afterwards.

After a few days I was brought away myself on an outside car and sent to a strange school. It was a boarding school filled with people I did not know, some young and some older. I soon got to know that it was a good school and a very expensive one but I did not pay over any money to the people who were in charge of it because I had not any. All this and a lot more I understood clearly later.

My life at this school does not matter except for one thing. It was there that I first came to know something of de Selby.

One day I picked up idly an old tattered book in the science master's study and put it in my pocket to read in bed the next morning as I had just earned the privilege of lying late. I was about sixteen then and the date was the seventh of March. I still think that day is the most important in my life and can remember it more readily than I do my birthday. The book was a first edition of *Golden Hours* with the two last pages missing. By the time I was nineteen and had reached the end of my education I knew that the book was valuable and that in keeping it I was stealing it. Nevertheless I packed it in my bag without a qualm and would probably do the same if I had my time again. Perhaps it is important in the story I am going to tell to remember that it was for de Selby I committed my first serious sin. It was for him that I committed my greatest sin.

I had long-since got to know how I was situated in the world. All my people were dead and there was a man called Divney working the farm and living on it until I should return. He did not own any of it and was given weekly cheques of pay by an office full of solicitors in a town far away. I had met these solicitors and never met Divney but they were really all working for me and my father had paid in cash for these arrangements before he died. When I was younger I thought he was a generous man to do that for a boy he did not know well.

I did not go home direct from school. I spent some months in other places broadening my mind and finding out what a complete edition of de Selby's works would cost me and whether some of the less important of his commentators' books could be got on loan. In one of the places where I was broadening my mind I met one night with a bad accident. I broke my left leg (or, if you like, it was broken for me) in six places and when I was well enough again to go my way I had one leg made of wood, the left one. I knew that I had only a little money, that I was going home to a rocky farm and that my life would not be easy. But I was certain by this time that farming, even if I had to do it, would not be my life work. I knew that if my name was to be remembered, it would be remembered with de Selby's.

I can recall in every detail the evening I walked back into my own house with a travelling-bag in each hand. I was twenty years of age; it was an evening in a happy yellow summer and the door of the public house was open. Behind the counter was John Divney, leaning forward on the low-down porter dash-board with his fork, his arms neatly folded and his face looking down on a newspaper which was spread upon the counter. He had brown hair and was made handsomely enough in a small butty way; his shoulders were broadened out with work and his arms were thick like little tree-trunks. He had a quiet civil face with eyes like cow's eyes, brooding, brown, and patient. When he knew that somebody had come in he did not stop his reading but his left hand strayed out and found a rag and began to give the counter slow damp swipes. Then, still reading, he moved his hands one above the other as if he was drawing out a concertina to full length and said:

"A schooner?"

A schooner was what the customers called a pint of Coleraine blackjack. It was the cheapest porter in the world. I said that I wanted my dinner and mentioned my name and station. Then we closed the shop and went into the kitchen and we were there nearly all night, eating and talking and drinking whiskey.

The next day was Thursday. John Divney said that his work was now done and that he would be ready to go home to where his people were on Saturday. It was not true to say that his work was done because the farm was in a poor way and most of the year's work had not even been started. But on

Saturday he said there were a few things to finish and that he
could not work on Sunday but that he would be in a position
to hand over the place in perfect order on Tuesday evening.
On Monday he had a sick pig to mind and that delayed him.
At the end of the week he was busier than ever and the
passing of another two months did not seem to lighten or
reduce his urgent tasks. I did not mind much because if he
was idle-minded and a sparing worker, he was satisfactory so
far as company was concerned and he never asked for pay. I
did little work about the place myself, spending all my time
arranging my papers and re-reading still more closely the pages
of de Selby.

A full year had not passed when I noticed that Divney was
using the word "we" in his conversation and worse than that,
the word "our." He said that the place was not everything that
it might be and talked of getting a hired man. I did not agree
with this and told him so, saying that there was no necessity
for more than two men on a small farm and adding, most unhappily for myself, that we were poor. After that it was useless
trying to tell him that it was I who owned everything. I began
to tell myself that even if I did own everything, he owned me.

Four years passed away happily enough for each of us. We
had a good house and plenty of good country food but little
money. Nearly all my own time was spent in study. Out of my
savings I had now bought the complete works of the two
principal commentators, Hatchjaw and Bassett, and a photostat
of the de Selby Codex. I had also embarked upon the task of
learning French and German thoroughly in order to read the
works of other commentators in those languages. Divney had
been working after a fashion on the farm by day and talking
loudly in the public house by night and serving drinks there.
Once I asked him what about the public house and he said he

was losing money on it every day. I did not understand this because the customers, judging by their voices through the thin door, were plentiful enough and Divney was continually buying himself suits of clothes and fancy tiepins. But I did not say much. I was satisfied to be left in peace because I knew that my own work was more important than myself.

One day in early winter Divney said to me:

"I cannot lose very much more of my own money on that bar. The customers are complaining about the porter. It is very bad porter because I have to drink a little now and again myself to keep them company and I do not feel well in my health over the head of it. I will have to go away for two days and do some travelling and see if there is better brand of porter to be had."

He disappeared the next morning on his bicycle and when he came back very dusty and travel-worn at the end of three days, he told me that everything was all right and that four barrels of better porter could be expected on Friday. It came punctually on that day and was well bought by the customers in the public house that night. It was manufactured in some town in the south and was known as "The Wrastler." If you drank three or four pints of it, it was nearly bound to win. The customers praised it highly and when they had it inside them they sang and shouted and sometimes lay down on the floor or on the roadway outside in a great stupor. Some of them complained afterwards that they had been robbed while in this state and talked angrily in the shop the next night about stolen money and gold watches which had disappeared off their strong chains. John Divney did not say much on this subject to them and did not mention it to me at all. He printed the words—BEWARE OF PICKPOCKETS—in large letters on a card and hung it on the back of shelves beside another notice that dealt with cheques. Nevertheless a week rarely passed without some customer complaining after an evening with "The Wrastler." It was not a satisfactory thing.

As time went on Divney became more and more despondent about what he called "the bar." He said that he would be satisfied if it paid its way but he doubted seriously if it ever would. The Government were partly responsible for the situation owing to the high taxes. He did not think that he could continue to bear the burden of the loss without some assistance. I said my father had some old-fashioned way of management which made possible a profit but that the shop should be closed if now continuing to lose money. Divney only said that it was a very serious thing to surrender a licence.

It was about this time, when I was nearing thirty, that Divney and I began to get the name of being great friends. For years before that I had rarely gone out at all. This was because I was so busy with my work that I hardly ever had the time; also my wooden leg was not very good for walking with. Then something very unusual happened to change all this and after it had happened, Divney and I never parted company for more than one minute either night or day. All day I was out with him on the farm and at night I sat on my father's old seat under the lamp in a corner of the public house doing what work I could with my papers in the middle of the blare and the crush and the hot noises which went always with "The Wrastler." If Divney went for a walk on Sunday to a neighbour's house I went with him and came home with him again, never before or after him. If he went away to a town on his bicycle to order porter or seed potatoes or even 'to see a certain party," I went on my own bicycle beside him. I brought my bed into his room and took the trouble to sleep only after he was sleeping and to be wide-awake a good hour before he stirred. Once I nearly failed in my watchfulness. I remember waking up with a start in the small hours of a black night and finding him quietly dressing himself in the dark. I asked him where he was going and he said he could not sleep and that he thought a walk would do him good. I said I was in the same condition myself and the two of us went for a walk together into the coldest and wettest night I ever experienced. When we returned drenched I said it was foolish for us to sleep in different beds in such bitter weather and got into his bed beside him. He did not say much, then or at any other time. I slept with him always after that. We were friendly and smiled at each other but the situation was a queer one and neither of us liked it. The neighbours were not long noticing how inseparable we were. We had been in that condition of being always together for nearly three years and they said that we were the best two Christians in all Ireland. They said that human friendship was a beautiful thing and that Divney and I were the noblest example of it in the history of the world. If other people fell out or fought or disagreed, they were asked why they could not be like me and Divney. It would have been a great shock for everybody if Divney had appeared in any place at any time without myself beside him. And it is not strange that two people never came to dislike each other as bitterly as did I and Divney. And two people were never so polite to each other, so friendly in the face.

I must go back several years to explain what happened to bring about this peculiar situation. The "certain party" whom Divney went to visit once a month was a girl called Pegeen Meers. For my part I had completed my definitive "De Selby Index" wherein the views of all known commentators on every aspect of the savant and his work had been collated. Each of us therefore had a large thing on the mind. One day Divney said to me:

"That is a powerful book you have written I don't doubt."

"It is useful," I admitted, "and badly wanted." In fact it contained much that was entirely new and proof that many opinions widely held about de Selby and his theories were misconceptions based on misreadings of his work.

"It might make your name in the world and your golden fortune in copyrights?"

"It might."

"Then why do you not put it out?"

I explained that money is required to "put out" a book of this kind unless the writer already has a reputation. He gave me a look of sympathy that was not usual with him and sighed.

"Money is hard to come by these days," he said, "with the drink trade on its last legs and the land starved away to nothing for the want of artificial manures that can't be got for love or money owing to the trickery of the Jewmen and the Freemasons."

I knew that it was not true about the manures. He had already pretended to me that they could not be got because he did not want the trouble of them. After a pause he said:

"We will have to see what we can do about getting money for your book and indeed I am in need of some myself because you can't expect a girl to wait until she is too old to wait any longer."

I did not know whether he meant to bring a wife, if he got one, into the house. If he did and I could not stop him, then I would have to leave. On the other hand if marriage meant that he himself would leave I think I would be very glad of it.

It was some days before he talked on this subject of money again. Then he said:

"What about old Mathers?"

"What about him?"

I had never seen the old man but knew all about him. He had spent a long life of fifty years in the cattle trade and now lived in retirement in a big house three miles away. He still did large business through agents and the people said that he carried no less than three thousand pounds with him every time he hobbled to the village to lodge his money. Little as I knew of social proprieties at the time, I would not dream of asking him for assistance.

"He is worth a packet of potato-meal," Divney said.

"I do not think we should look for charity," I answered.

"I do not think so either," he said. He was a proud man in his own way, I thought, and no more was said just then. But after that he took to the habit of putting occasionally into conversations on other subjects some irrelevant remark about our need for money and the amount of it which Mathers carried in his black cash-box; sometimes he would revile the old man, accusing him of being in "the artificial manure ring" or of being dishonest in his business dealings. Once he said something about "social justice" but it was plain to me that he did not properly understand the term.

I do not know exactly how or when it became clear to me that Divney, far from seeking charity, intended to rob Mathers; and I cannot recollect how long it took me to realise that he meant to kill him as well in order to avoid the possibility of being identified as the robber afterwards. I only know that within six months I had come to accept this grim plan as a commonplace of our conversation. Three further months passed before I could bring myself to agree to the proposal and three months more before I openly admitted to Divney that my misgivings were at an end. I cannot recount the tricks and wiles he used to win me to his side. It is sufficient to say that he read portions of my "De Selby Index" (or pretended to) and discussed with me afterwards the serious responsibility of any person who declined by mere reason of personal whim to give the "Index" to the world.

Old Mathers lived alone. Divney knew on what evening and at what deserted stretch of road near his house we would meet

him with his box of money. The evening when it came was in
the depth of winter; the light was already waning as we sat
at our dinner discussing the business we had in hand. Divney
said that we should bring our spades tied on the crossbars of
our bicycles because this would make us look like men out
after rabbits; he would bring his own iron pump in case we
should get a slow puncture.

There is little to tell about the murder. The lowering skies
seemed to conspire with us, coming down in a shroud of
dreary mist to within a few yards of the wet road where we
were waiting. Everything was very still with no sound in our
ears except the dripping of the trees. Our bicycles were hidden.
I was leaning miserably on my spade and Divney, his iron
pump under his arm, was smoking his pipe contentedly. The
old man was upon us almost before we realised there was anybody near. I could not see him well in the dim light but I
could glimpse a spent bloodless face peering from the top of
the great black coat which covered him from ear to ankle.
Divney went forward at once and pointing back along the road
said:

"Would that be your parcel on the road?"

The old man turned his head to look and received a blow
in the back of the neck from Divney's pump which knocked
him clean off his feet and probably smashed his neck-bone. As
he collapsed full-length in the mud he did not cry out. Instead
I heard him say something softly in a conversational tone—
something like "I do not care for celery" or "I left my glasses
in the scullery." Then he lay very still. I had been watching
the scene rather stupidly, still leaning on my spade. Divney
was rummaging savagely at the fallen figure and then stood up.
He had a black cash-box in his hand. He waved it in the air
and roared at me:

"Here, wake up! Finish him with the spade!"

I went forward mechanically, swung the spade over my shoulder and smashed the blade of it with all my strength against the protruding chin. I felt and almost heard the fabric of his skull crumple up crisply like an empty eggshell. I do not know how often I struck him after that but I did not stop until I was tired.

I threw the spade down and looked around for Divney. He was nowhere to be seen. I called his name softly but he did not answer. I walked a little bit up the road and called again. I jumped on the rising of a ditch and peered around into the gathering dusk. I called his name once more as loudly as I dared but there was no answer in the stillness. He was gone. He had made off with the box of money, leaving me alone with the dead man and with a spade which was now probably tinging the watery mud around it with a weak pink stain.

My heart stumbled painfully in its beating. A chill of fright ran right through me. If anybody should come, nothing in the world would save me from the gallows. If Divney was with me still to share my guilt, even that would not protect me. Numb with fear I stood for a long time looking at the crumpled heap in the black coat.

Before the old man had come Divney and I had dug a deep hole in the field beside the road, taking care to preserve the sods of grass. Now in a panic I dragged the heavy sodden figure from where it lay and got it with a tremendous effort across the ditch into the field and slumped it down into the hole. Then I rushed back for my spade and started to throw and push the earth back into the hole in a mad blind fury.

The hole was nearly full when I heard steps. Looking round in great dismay I saw the unmistakable shape of Divney making his way carefully across the ditch into the field. When he came up I pointed dumbly to the hole with my spade. Without a word he went to where our bicycles were, came

back with his own spade and worked steadily with me until
the task was finished. We did everything possible to hide any
trace of what had happened. Then we cleaned our boots with
grass, tied the spades and walked home. A few people who
came against us on the road bade us good evening in the dark.
I am sure they took us for two tired labourers making for home
after a hard day's work. They were not far wrong.

On our way I said to Divney:

"Where were you that time?"

"Attending to important business," he answered. I thought
he was referring to a certain thing and said:

"Surely you could have kept it till after."

"It is not what you are thinking of," he answered.

"Have you got the box?"

He turned his face to me this time, screwed it up and put a
finger on his lip.

"Not so loud," he whispered. "It is in a safe place."

"But where?"

The only reply he gave me was to put the finger on his lip
more firmly and make a long hissing noise. He gave me to
understand that mentioning the box, even in a whisper, was
the most foolish and reckless thing it was possible for me to do.

When we reached home he went away and washed himself
and put on one of the several blue Sunday suits he had. When
he came back to where I was sitting, a miserable figure at the
kitchen fire, he came across to me with a very serious face,
pointed to the window and cried:

"Would that be your parcel on the road?"

Then he let out a bellow of laughter which seemed to loosen
up his whole body, turn his eyes to water in his head and
shake the whole house. When he had finished he wiped the
tears from his face, walked into the shop and made a noise
which can only be made by taking the cork quickly out of a
whiskey bottle.

In the weeks which followed I asked him where the box was a hundred times in a thousand different ways. He never answered in the same way but the answer was always the same. It was in a very safe place. The least said about it the better until things quietened down. Mum was the word. It would be found all in good time. For the purpose of safekeeping the place it was in was superior to the Bank of England. There was a good time coming. It would be a pity to spoil everything by hastiness or impatience.

And that is why John Divney and I became inseparable friends and why I never allowed him to leave my sight for three years. Having robbed me in my own public house (having even robbed my customers) and having ruined my farm, I knew that he was sufficiently dishonest to steal my share of Mathers' money and make off with the box if given the opportunity. I knew that there was no possible necessity for waiting until "things quietened down" because very little notice was taken of the old man's disappearance. People said he was a queer mean man and that going away without telling anybody or leaving his address was the sort of thing he would do.

I think I have said before that the peculiar terms of physical intimacy upon which myself and Divney found ourselves had become more and more intolerable. In latter months I had hoped to force him to capitulate by making my company unbearably close and unrelenting but at the same time I took to carrying a small pistol in case of accidents. One Sunday night when both of us were sitting in the kitchen—both, incidentally, on the same side of the fire—he took his pipe from his mouth and turned to me:

"Do you know," he said, "I think things have quietened down."

I only gave a grunt.

"Do you get my meaning?" he asked.

"Things were never any other way," I answered shortly.

He looked at me in a superior way.

"I know a lot about these things," he said, "and you would be surprised at the pitfalls a man will make if he is in too big a hurry. You cannot be too careful but all the same I think things have quietened down enough to make it safe."

"I am glad you think so."

"There are good times coming. I will get the box tomorrow and then we will divide the money, right here on this table."

"We will get the box," I answered, saying the first word with great care. He gave me a long hurt look and asked me sadly did I not trust him. I replied that both of us should finish what both had started.

"All right," he said in a very vexed way. "I am sorry you don't trust me after all the work I have done to try to put this place right but to show you the sort I am I will let you get the box yourself, I will tell you where it is tomorrow."

I took care to sleep with him as usual that night. The next morning he was in a better temper and told me with great simplicity that the box was hidden in Mathers' own empty house, under the floorboards of the first room on the right from the hall.

"Are you sure?" I asked.

"I swear it," he said solemnly, raising his hand to heaven.

I thought the position over for a moment, examining the possibility that it was a ruse to part company with me at last and then make off himself to the real hiding-place. But his face for the first time seemed to wear a look of honesty.

"I am sorry if I injured your feelings last night," I said, "but to show that there is no ill-feeling I would be glad if you would come with me at least part of the way. I honestly think that both of us should finish what the two of us started."

"All right," he said. "It is all the same but I would like you to get the box with your own hands because it is only simple justice after not telling you where it was."

As my own bicycle was punctured we walked the distance. When we were about a hundred yards from Mathers' house, Divney stopped by a low wall and said that he was going to sit on it and smoke his pipe and wait for me.

"Let you go alone and get the box and bring it back here. There are good times coming and we will be rich men tonight. It is sitting under a loose board in the floor of the first room on the right, in the corner forenenst the door."

Perched as he was on the wall I knew that he need never leave my sight. In the brief time I would be away I could see him any time I turned my head.

"I will be back in ten minutes," I said.

"Good man," he answered. "But remember this. If you meet anybody, you don't know what you're looking for, you don't know in whose house you are, you don't know anything."

"I don't even know my own name," I answered.

This was a very remarkable thing for me to say because the next time I was asked my name I could not answer. I did not know.

II

De Selby has some interesting things to say on the subject of houses.[1] A row of houses he regards as a row of necessary evils. The softening and degeneration of the human race he attributes to its progressive predilection for interiors and waning interest in the art of going out and staying there. This in turn he sees as the result of the rise of such pursuits as reading, chess-playing, drinking, marriage and the like, few of which

[1] *Golden Hours*, ii, 261.

can be satisfactorily conducted in the open. Elsewhere[2] he defines a house as "a large coffin," "a warren," and "a box." Evidently his main objection was to the confinement of a roof and four walls. He ascribed somewhat far-fetched therapeutic values—chiefly pulmonary—to certain structures of his own design which he called "habitats," crude drawings of which may still be seen in the pages of the *Country Album*. These structures were of two kinds, roofless "houses" and "houses" without walls. The former had wide open doors and windows with an extremely ungainly superstructure of tarpaulins loosely rolled on spars against bad weather—the whole looking like a foundered sailing-ship erected on a platform of masonry and the last place where one would think of keeping even cattle. The other type of "habitat" had the conventional slated roof but no walls save one, which was to be erected in the quarter of the prevailing wind; around the other sides were the inevitable tarpaulins loosely wound on rollers suspended from the gutters of the roof, the whole structure being surrounded by a diminutive moat or pit bearing some resemblance to military latrines. In the light of present-day theories of housing and hygiene, there can be no doubt that de Selby was much mistaken in these ideas but in his own remote day more than one sick person lost his life in an ill-advised quest for health in these fantastic dwellings.[3]

[2] *Country Album*, p. 1,034.

[3] Le Fournier, the reliable French commentator (in *De Selby—l'Énigme de l'Occident*) has put forward a curious theory regarding these "habitats." He suggests that de Selby, when writing the *Album*, paused to consider some point of difficulty and in the meantime engaged in the absent-minded practice known generally as "doodling," then putting his manuscript away. The next time he took it up he was confronted with a mass of diagrams and drawings which he took to be the plans of a type of dwelling he always had in mind and immediately wrote many pages explaining the sketches. "In no other way," adds the severe Le Fournier, "can one explain so regrettable a lapse."

My recollections of de Selby were prompted by my visit to the home of old Mr. Mathers. As I approached it along the road the house appeared to be a fine roomy brick building of uncertain age, two storeys high with a plain porch and eight or nine windows to the front of each floor.

I opened the iron gate and walked as softly as I could up the weed-tufted gravel drive. My mind was strangely empty. I did not feel that I was about to end successfully a plan I had worked unrelentingly at night and day for three years. I felt no glow of pleasure and was unexcited at the prospect of becoming rich. I was occupied only with the mechanical task of finding a black box.

The hall-door was closed and although it was set far back in a very deep porch the wind and rain had whipped a coating of gritty dust against the panels and deep into the crack where the door opened, showing that it had been shut for years. Standing on a derelict flower-bed, I tried to push up the sash of the first window on the left. It yielded to my strength, raspingly and stubbornly. I clambered through the opening and found myself, not at once in a room, but crawling along the deepest window-ledge I have ever seen. When I reached the floor and jumped noisily down upon it, the open window seemed very far away and much too small to have admitted me.

The room where I found myself was thick with dust, musty and deserted of all furniture. Spiders had erected great stretchings of their web about the fireplace. I made my way quickly to the hall, threw open the door of the room where the box was and paused on the threshold. It was a dark morning and the weather had stained the windows with blears of grey wash which kept the brightest part of the weak light from coming in. The far corner of the room was a blur of shadow. I had a sudden urge to have done with my task and be out of this

house forever. I walked across the bare boards, knelt down in
the corner and passed my hands about the floor in search of
the loose board. To my surprise I found it easily. It was about
two feet in length and rocked hollowly under my hand. I lifted
it up, laid it aside and struck a match. I saw a black metal
cash-box nestling dimly in the hole. I put my hand down and
crooked a finger into the loose reclining handle but the match
suddenly flickered and went out and the handle of the box,
which I had lifted up about an inch slid heavily off my finger.
Without stopping to light another match I thrust my hand
bodily into the opening and just when it should be closing
about the box, something happened.

I cannot hope to describe what it was but it had frightened
me very much long before I had understood it even slightly.
It was some change which came upon me or upon the room,
indescribably subtle, yet momentous, ineffable. It was as if
the daylight had changed with unnatural suddenness, as if the
temperature of the evening had altered greatly in an instant
or as if the air had become twice as rare or twice as dense as
it had been in the winking of an eye; perhaps all of these and
other things happened together for all my senses were bewildered all at once and could give me no explanation. The
fingers of my right hand, thrust into the opening in the floor,
had closed mechanically, found nothing at all and came up
again empty. The box was gone!

I heard a cough behind me, soft and natural yet more dis-
turbing than any sound that could ever come upon the human
ear. That I did not die of fright was due, I think, to two
things, the fact that my senses were already disarranged and
able to interpret to me only gradually what they had perceived
and also the fact that the utterance of the cough seemed to
bring with it some more awful alteration in everything, just
as if it had held the universe standstill for an instant, suspend-

ing the planets in their courses, halting the sun and holding
in mid-air any falling thing the earth was pulling towards it.
I collapsed weakly from my kneeling backwards into a limp
sitting-down upon the floor. Sweat broke upon my brow and
my eyes remained open for a long time without a wink, glazed
and almost sightless.

In the darkest corner of the room near the window a man
was sitting in a chair, eyeing me with a mild but unwavering
interest. His hand had crept out across the small table by his
side to turn up very slowly an oil-lamp which was standing
on it. The oil-lamp had a glass bowl with the wick dimly visible
inside it, curling in convolutions like an intestine. There were
tea things on the table. The man was old Mathers. He was
watching me in silence. He did not move or speak and might
have been still dead save for the slight movement of his hand
at the lamp, the very gentle screwing of his thumb and forefinger against the wick-wheel. The hand was yellow, the
wrinkled skin draped loosely upon the bones. Over the knuckle
of his forefinger I could clearly see the loop of a skinny vein.

It is hard to write of such a scene or to convey with known
words the feelings which came knocking at my numbed mind.
How long we sat there, for instance, looking at one another
I do not know. Years or minutes could be swallowed up with
equal ease in that indescribable and unaccountable interval.
The light of morning vanished from my sight, the dusty floor
was like nothingness beneath me and my whole body dissolved
away, leaving me existing only in the stupid spellbound gaze
that went steadily from where I was to the other corner.

I remember that I noticed several things in a cold mechanical way as if I was sitting there with no worry save to note
everything I saw. His face was terrifying but his eyes in the
middle of it had a quality of chill and horror which made his
other features look to me almost friendly. The skin was like

faded parchment with an arrangement of puckers and wrinkles which created between them an expression of fathomless inscrutability. But the eyes were horrible. Looking at them I got the feeling that they were not genuine eyes at all but mechanical dummies animated by electricity or the like, with a tiny pinhole in the centre of the "pupil" through which the real eye gazed out secretively and with great coldness. Such a conception, possibly with no foundation at all in fact, disturbed me agonisingly and gave rise in my mind to interminable speculations as to the colour and quality of the real eye and as to whether, indeed, it was real at all or merely another dummy with its pinhole on the same plane as the first one so that the real eye, possibly behind thousands of these absurd disguises, gazed out through a barrel of serried peep-holes. Occasionally the heavy cheese-like lids would drop down slowly with great languor and then rise again. Wrapped loosely around the body was an old wine-coloured dressing-gown.

In my distress I thought to myself that perhaps it was his twin brother but at once I heard someone say:

Scarcely. If you look carefully at the left-hand side of his neck you will notice that there is sticking-plaster or a bandage there. His throat and chin are also bandaged.

Forlornly, I looked and saw that this was true. He was the man I had murdered beyond all question. He was sitting on a chair four yards away watching me. He sat stiffly without a move as if afraid to hurt the gaping wounds which covered his body. Across my own shoulders a stiffness had spread from my exertions with the spade.

But who had uttered these words? They had not frightened me. They were clearly audible to me yet I knew they did not ring out across the air like the chilling cough of the old man in the chair. They came from deep inside me, from my soul. Never before had I believed or suspected that I had a soul but just then I knew I had. I knew also that my soul was friendly, was my senior in years and was solely concerned for my own welfare. For convenience I called him Joe. I felt a little reassured to know that I was not altogether alone. Joe was helping me.

I will not try to tell of the space of time which followed. In the terrible situation I found myself, my reason could give me no assistance. I knew that old Mathers had been felled by an iron bicycle-pump, hacked to death with a heavy spade and then securely buried in a field. I knew also that the same man was now sitting in the same room with me, watching me in silence. His body was bandaged but his eyes were alive and so was his right hand and so was all of him. Perhaps the murder by the roadside was a bad dream.

There is nothing dreamy about your stiff shoulders. No, I replied, but a nightmare can be as strenuous physically as the real thing.

I decided in some crooked way that the best thing to do was to believe what my eyes were looking at rather than to place my trust in a memory. I decided to show unconcern, to talk to the old man and to test his own reality by asking about the black box which was responsible, if anything could be, for each of us being the way we were. I made up my mind to be bold because I knew that I was in great danger. I knew that I would go mad unless I got up from the floor and moved and talked and behaved in as ordinary a way as possible. I looked away from old Mathers, got carefully to my feet and sat down on a chair that was not far away from him. Then I looked back at him, my heart pausing for a time and working on again with slow heavy hammer-blows which seemed to make my whole frame shudder. He had remained perfectly still but the live right hand had gripped the pot of tea, raised it very awkwardly and slapped a filling into the empty cup.

His eyes had followed me to my new position and were now regarding me again with the same unwavering languorous interest.

Suddenly I began to talk. Words spilled out of me as if they were produced by machinery. My voice, tremulous at first, grew hard and loud and filled the whole room. I do not remember what I said at the beginning. I am sure that most of it was meaningless but I was too pleased and reassured at the natural healthy noise of my tongue to be concerned about the words.

Old Mathers did not move or say anything at first but I was certain that he was listening to me. After a while he began to shake his head and then I was sure I had heard him say No. I became excited at his responses and began to speak carefully. He negatived my inquiry about his health, refused to say where the black box had gone and even denied that it was a dark morning. His voice had a peculiar jarring weight like the hoarse toll of an ancient rusty bell in an ivy-smothered tower. He had said nothing beyond the one word No. His lips hardly moved; I felt sure he had no teeth behind them.

"Are you dead at present?" I asked.

"I am not."

"Do you know where the box is?"

"No."

He made another violent movement with his right arm, slapping hot water into his teapot and pouring forth a little more of the feeble brew into his cup. He then relapsed into his attitude of motionless watching. I pondered for a time.

"Do you like weak tea?" I asked.

"I do not," he said.

"Do you like tea at all?" I asked, "strong or weak or half-way tea?"

"No," he said.

"Then why do you drink it?"

He shook his yellow face from side to side sadly and did not say anything. When he stopped shaking he opened up his mouth and poured the cupful of tea in as one would pour a bucket of milk into a churn at churning-time.

Do you notice anything?

No, I replied, nothing beyond the eeriness of this house and the man who owns it. He is by no means the best conversationalist I have met.

I found I spoke lightly enough. While speaking inwardly or outwardly or thinking of what to say I felt brave and normal enough. But every time a silence came the horror of my situation descended upon me like a heavy blanket flung upon my head, enveloping and smothering me and making me afraid of death.

But do you notice nothing about the way he answers your questions?

No.

Do you not see that every reply is in the negative? No matter what you ask him he says No.

That is true enough, I said, but I do not see where that leads me.

Use your imagination.

When I brought my whole attention back to old Mathers I thought he was asleep. He sat over his teacup in a more stooped attitude as if he were a rock or part of the wooden chair he sat on, a man completely dead and turned to stone. Over his eyes the limp lids had drooped down, almost closing them. His right hand resting on the table lay lifeless and abandoned. I composed my thoughts and addressed to him a sharp noisy interrogation.

"Will you answer a straight question?" I asked. He stirred somewhat, his lids opening slightly.

"I will not," he replied.

I saw that this answer was in keeping with Joe's shrewd suggestion. I sat thinking for a moment until I had thought the same thought inside out.

"Will you refuse to answer a straight question?" I asked.

"I will not," he replied.

This answer pleased me. It meant that my mind had got to grips with his, that I was now almost arguing with him and that we were behaving like two ordinary human beings. I did not understand all the terrible things which had happened to me but I now began to think that I must be mistaken about them.

"Very well," I said quietly. "Why do you always answer No?"

He stirred perceptibly in his chair and filled the teacup up again before he spoke. He seemed to have some difficulty in finding words.

"No" is, generally speaking, a better answer than "Yes," he said at last. He seemed to speak eagerly, his words coming out as if they had been imprisoned in his mouth for a thousand years. He seemed relieved that I had found a way to make him speak. I thought he even smiled slightly at me but this was doubtless the trickery of the bad morning light or a mischief worked by the shadows of the lamp. He swallowed a long draught of tea and sat waiting, looking at me with his queer eyes. They were now bright and active and moved about restlessly in their yellow wrinkled sockets.

"Do you refuse to tell me why you say that?" I asked.

"No," he said. "When I was a young man I led an unsatisfactory life and devoted most of my time to excesses of one kind or another, my principal weakness being Number

One. I was also party to the formation of an artificial manure-ring."

My mind went back at once to John Divney, to the farm and the public house and on from that to the horrible afternoon we had spent on the wet lonely road. As if to interrupt my unhappy thoughts I heard Joe's voice again, this time severe:

No need to ask him what Number One is, we do not want lurid descriptions of vice or anything at all in that line. Use your imagination. Ask him what all this has to do with Yes and No?"

"What has that got to do with Yes and No?"

"After a time," said old Mathers disregarding me, "I mercifully perceived the error of my ways and the unhappy destination I would reach unless I mended them. I retired from the world in order to try to comprehend it and to find out why it becomes more unsavoury as the years accumulate on a man's body. What do you think I discovered at the end of my meditations?"

I felt pleased again. He was now questioning me.

"What?"

"That No is a better word than Yes," he replied.

This seemed to leave us where we were, I thought.

On the contrary, very far from it. I am beginning to agree with him. There is a lot to be said for No as a General Principle. Ask him what he means.

"What do you mean?" I inquired.

"When I was meditating," said old Mathers, "I took all my sins out and put them on the table, so to speak. I need not tell you it was a big table."

He seemed to give a very dry smile at his own joke. I chuckled to encourage him.

"I gave them all a strict examination, weighed them and

viewed them from all angles of the compass. I asked myself how I came to commit them, where I was and whom I was with when I came to do them."

This is very wholesome stuff, every word a sermon in itself. Listen very carefully. Ask him to continue.

"Continue," I said.

I confess I felt a click inside me very near my stomach as if Joe had put a finger to his lip and pricked up a pair of limp spaniel ears to make sure that no syllable of the wisdom escaped him. Old Mathers continued talking quietly.

"I discovered," he said, "that everything you do is in response to a request or a suggestion made to you by some other party either inside you or outside. Some of these suggestions are good and praiseworthy and some of them are undoubtedly delightful. But the majority of them are definitely bad and are pretty considerable sins as sins go. Do you understand me?"

"Perfectly."

"I would say that the bad ones outnumber the good ones by three to one."

Six to one if you ask me.

"I therefore decided to say No henceforth to every suggestion, request or inquiry whether inward or outward. It was the only simple formula which was sure and safe. It was difficult to practise at first and often called for heroism but I persevered and hardly ever broke down completely. It is now many years since I said Yes. I have refused more requests and negatived more statements than any man living or dead. I have rejected, reneged, disagreed, refused and denied to an extent that is unbelievable."

An excellent and original régime. This is all extremely interesting and salutary, every syllable a sermon in itself. Very very wholesome.

"Extremely interesting," I said to old Mathers.

"The system leads to peace and contentment," he said. "People do not trouble to ask you questions if they know the answer is a foregone conclusion. Thoughts which have no chance of succeeding do not take the trouble to come into your head at all."

"You must find it irksome in some ways," I suggested. "If, for instance, I were to offer you a glass of whiskey . . ."

"Such few friends as I have," he answered, "are usually good enough to arrange such invitations in a way that will enable me to adhere to my system and also accept the whiskey. More than once I have been asked whether I would refuse such things."

"And the answer is still NO?"

"Certainly."

Joe said nothing at this stage but I had the feeling that this confession was not to his liking; he seemed to be uneasy inside me. The old man seemed to get somewhat restive also. He bent over his teacup with abstraction as if he were engaged in accomplishing a sacrament. Then he drank with his hollow throat, making empty noises.

A saintly man.

I turned to him again, fearing that his fit of talkativeness had passed.

"Where is the black box which was under the floor a moment ago?" I asked. I pointed to the opening in the corner. He shook his head and did not say anything.

"Do you refuse to tell me?"

"No."

"Do you object to my taking it?"

"No."

"Then where is it?"

"What is your name?" he asked sharply.

I was surprised at this question. It had no bearing on my own conversation but I did not notice its irrelevance because I was shocked to realise that, simple as it was, I could not answer it. I did not know my name, did not remember who I was. I was not certain where I had come from or what my business was in that room. I found I was sure of nothing save my search for the black box. But I knew that the other man's name was Mathers and that he had been killed with a pump and a spade. I had no name.

"I have no name," I replied.

"Then how could I tell you where the box was if you could not sign a receipt? That would be most irregular. I might as well give it to the west wind or to the smoke from a pipe. How could you execute an important Bank document?"

"I can always get a name," I replied. "Doyle or Spaldman is a good name and so is O'Sweeny and Hardiman and O'Gara. I can take my choice. I am not tied down for life to one word like most people."

"I do not care much for Doyle," he said absently.

The name is Bari. Signor Bari, the eminent tenor. Five hundred thousand people crowded the great piazza when the great artist appeared on the balcony of St. Peter's Rome.

Fortunately these remarks were not audible in the ordinary sense of the word. Old Mathers was eyeing me.

"What is your colour?" he asked.

"My colour?"

"Surely you know you have a colour?"

"People often remark on my red face."

"I do not mean that at all."

Follow this closely, this is bound to be extremely interesting. Very edifying also.

I saw it was necessary to question old Mathers carefully.

"Do you refuse to explain this question about the colours?"

"No," he said. He slapped more tea in his cup.

"No doubt you are aware that the winds have colours," he said. I thought he settled himself more restfully in his chair and changed his face till it looked a little bit benign.

"I never noticed it."

"A record of this belief will be found in the literature of all ancient peoples.[4] There are four winds and eight sub-winds, each with its own colour. The wind from the east is a deep purple, from the south a fine shining silver. The north wind is a hard black and the west is amber. People in the old days had the power of perceiving these colours and could spend a day sitting quietly on a hillside watching the beauty of the winds, their fall and rise and changing hues, the magic of neighbouring winds when they are interweaved like ribbons at a wedding. It was a better occupation than gazing at newspapers. The sub-winds had colours of indescribable delicacy, a reddish-yellow half-way between silver and purple, a greyish-green which was related equally to black and brown. What could be more exquisite than a countryside swept lightly by cool rain reddened by the south-west breeze!"

"Can you see these colours?" I asked.

"No."

"You were asking me what my colour was. How do people get their colours?"

---

[4] It is not clear whether de Selby had heard of this but he suggests (*Garcia*, p. 12) that night, far from being caused by the commonly accepted theory of planetary movements, was due to accumulations of "black air" produced by certain volcanic activities of which he does not treat in detail. See also p. 79 and 945, *Country Album*. Le Fournier's comment (in *Homme ou Dieu*) is interesting. "On ne saura jamais jusqu'à quel point de Selby fut cause de la Grande Guerre, mais, sans aucun doute, ses théories excentriques—spécialement celle que nuit n'est pas un phénomène de nature, mais dans l'atmosphère un état malsain amené par un industrialisme cupide et sans pitié—auraient l'effect de produire un trouble profond dans les masses."

"A person's colour," he answered slowly, "is the colour of the wind prevailing at his birth."

"What is your own colour?"

"Light yellow."

"And what is the point of knowing your colour or having a colour at all?"

"For one thing you can tell the length of your life from it. Yellow means a long life and the lighter the better."

This is very edifying, every sentence a sermon in itself. Ask him to explain.

"Please explain."

"It is a question of making little gowns," he said informatively.

"Little gowns?"

"Yes. When I was born there was a certain policeman present who had the gift of wind-watching. The gift is getting very rare these days. Just after I was born he went outside and examined the colour of the wind that was blowing across the hill. He had a secret bag with him full of certain materials and bottles and he had tailor's instruments also. He was outside for about ten minutes. When he came in again he had a little gown in his hand and he made my mother put it on me."

"Where did he get this gown?" I asked in surprise.

"He made it himself secretly in the backyard, very likely in the cowhouse. It was very thin and slight like the very finest of spider's muslin. You would not see it at all if you held it against the sky but at certain angles of the light you might at times accidentally notice the edge of it. It was the purest and most perfect manifestation of the outside skin of light yellow. This yellow was the colour of my birth-wind."

"I see," I said.

A very beautiful conception.

"Every time my birthday came," old Mathers said, "I was presented with another little gown of the same identical quality except that it was put on over the other one and not in place of it. You may appreciate the extreme delicacy and fineness of the material when I tell you that even at five years old with five of these gowns together on me, I still appeared to be naked. It was, however, an unusual yellowish sort of nakedness. Of course there was no objection to wearing other clothes over the gown. I usually wore an overcoat. But every year I got a new gown."

"Where did you get them?" I asked.

"From the police. They were brought to my own home until I was big enough to call to the barracks for them."

"And how does all this enable you to predict your span of life?"

"I will tell you. No matter what your colour is, it will be represented faithfully in your birth-gown. With each year and each gown, the colour will get deeper and more pronounced. In my own case I had attained a bright full-blown yellow at fifteen although the color was so light at birth as to be imperceptible. I am now nearing seventy and the colour is a light brown. As my gowns come to me through the years ahead, the colour will deepen to dark brown, then a dull mahogany and from that ultimately to that very dark sort of brownness one associates usually with stout."

"Yes?"

"In a word the colour gradually deepens gown by gown and year by year until it appears to be black. Finally a day will come when the addition of one further gown will actually achieve real and full blackness. On that day I will die."

Joe and I were surprised at this. We pondered it in silence, Joe, I thought, seeking to reconcile what he had heard with certain principles he held respecting morality and religion.

"That means," I said at last, "that if you get a number of these gowns and put them all on together, reckoning each as a year of life, you can ascertain the year of your death?"

"Theoretically, yes," he replied, "but there are two difficulties. First of all the police refuse to let you have the gowns together on the ground that the general ascertainment of death-days would be contrary to the public interest. They talk of breaches of the peace and so forth. Secondly, there is a difficulty about stretching."

"Streching?"

"Yes. Since you will be wearing as a grown man the tiny gown that fitted you when you were born, it is clear that the gown has stretched until it is perhaps one hundred times as big as it was originally. Naturally this will affect the colour, making it many times rarer that it was. Similarly there will be a proportionate stretch and a corresponding diminution in colour in all the gowns up to manhood—perhaps twenty or so in all."

I wonder whether it can be taken that this accretion of gowns will have become opaque at the incidence of puberty.

I reminded him that there was always an overcoat.

"I take it, then," I said to old Mathers, "that when you say you can tell the length of life, so to speak, from the colour of your shirt, you mean that you can tell roughly whether you will be long-lived or short-lived?"

"Yes," he replied. "But if you use your intelligence you can make a very accurate forecast. Naturally some colours are better than others. Some of them, like purple or maroon, are very bad and always mean an early grave. Pink, however, is excellent, and there is a lot to be said for certain shades of green and blue. The prevalence of such colours at birth, however, usually connote a wind that brings bad weather—thunder and lightning, perhaps—and there might be difficulties such, for instance, as getting a woman to come in time. As you know, most good things in life are associated with certain disadvantages."

Really very beautiful, everything considered.

"Who are these policemen?" I asked.

"There is Sergeant Pluck and another man called Mac-Cruiskeen and there is a third man called Fox that disappeared twenty-five years ago and was never heard of after. The first two are down in the barracks and so far as I know they have been there for hundreds of years. They must be operating on a very rare colour, something that ordinary eyes could not see at all. There is no white wind that I know of. They all have the gift of seeing the winds.

A bright thought came to me when I heard of these policemen. If they knew so much they would have no difficulty in telling me where I would find the black box. I began to think I would never be happy until I had that box again in my grip. I looked at old Mathers. He had relapsed again to his former passivity. The light had faded from his eyes and the right hand resting on the table looked quite dead.

"Is the barracks far?" I asked loudly.

"No."

I made up my mind to go there with no delay. Then I noticed a very remarkable thing. The lamplight, which in the beginning had been shining forlornly in the old man's corner only, had now grown rich and yellow and flooded the entire room. The outside light of morning had faded away almost to nothingness. I glanced out of the window and gave a start. Coming into the room I had noticed that the window was to the east and that the sun was rising in that quarter and firing the heavy clouds with light. Now it was setting with last glimmers of feeble red in exactly the same place. It had risen a bit, stopped, and then gone back. Night had come. The

policemen would be in bed. I was sure I had fallen among
strange people. I made up my mind to go to the barracks the
first thing on the morrow. Then I turned again to old Mathers.

"Would you object," I said to him, "if I went upstairs and
occupied one of your beds for the night? It is too late to go
home and I think it is going to rain in any case."

"No," he said.

I left him bent at his teaset and went up the stairs. I had
got to like him and thought it was a pity he had been murdered. I felt relieved and simplified and certain that I would
soon have the black box. But I would not ask the policemen
openly about it at first. I would be crafty. In the morning I
would go to the barracks and report the theft of my American
gold watch. Perhaps it was this lie which was responsible for
the bad things that happened to me afterwards. I had no
American gold watch.

III

I crept out of old Mathers' house nine hours afterwards,
making my way on to the firm high-road under the first skies
of morning. The dawn was contagious, spreading rapidly about
the heavens. Birds were stirring and the great kingly trees
were being pleasingly interfered with by the first breezes. My
heart was happy and full of zest for high adventure. I did not
know my name or where I had come from but the black box
was practically in my grasp. The policemen would direct me
to where it was. Ten thousand pounds worth of negotiable
securities would be a conservative estimate of what was in it.
As I walked down the road I was pleased enough with everything.

The road was narrow, white, old, hard and scarred with
shadow. It ran away westwards in the mist of the early morn-

ing, running cunningly through the little hills and going to some trouble to visit tiny towns which were not, strictly speaking, on its way. It was possibly one of the oldest roads in the world. I found it hard to think of a time when there was no road there because the trees and the tall hills and the fine views of bogland had been arranged by wise hands for the pleasing picture they made when looked at from the road. Without a road to have them looked at from they would have a somewhat aimless if not a futile aspect.

De Selby has some interesting things to say on the subject of roads.[1] Roads he regards as the most ancient of human monuments, surpassing by many tens of centuries the oldest thing of stone that man has reared to mark his passing. The tread of time, he says, levelling all else, has beaten only to a more enduring hardness the pathways that have been made throughout the world. He mentions in passing a trick the Celts had in ancient times—that of "throwing a calculation" upon a road. In those days wise men could tell to a nicety the dimension of a host which had passed by in the night by looking at their tracks with a certain eye and judging them by their perfection and imperfection, the way each footfall was interfered with by each that came after. In this way they could tell the number of men who had passed, whether they were with horse or heavy with shields and iron weapons, and how many chariots; thus they could say the number of men who should be sent after them to kill them. Elsewhere[2] de Selby makes the point that a good road will have character and a certain air of destiny, an indefinable intimation that it is going somewhere, be it east or west, and not coming back from there. If you go with such a road, he thinks, it will give you pleasant travelling, fine sights at every corner and a gentle ease of

[1] *Golden Hours*, vi 156.
[2] A Memoir of Garcia, p. 27.

peregrination that will persuade you that you are walking forever on falling ground. But if you go east on a road that is on its way west, you will marvel at the unfailing bleakness of every prospect and the great number of sore-footed inclines that confront you to make you tired. If a friendly road should lead you into a complicated city with nets of crooked streets and five hundred other roads leaving it for unknown destinations, your own road will always be discernible for its own self and will lead you safely out of the tangled town.

I walked quietly for a good distance on this road, thinking my own thoughts with the front part of my brain and at the same time taking pleasure with the back part in the great and widespread finery of the morning. The air was keen, clear, abundant and intoxicating. Its powerful presence could be discerned everywhere, shaking up the green things jauntily, conferring greater dignity and definition on the stones and boulders, forever arranging and re-arranging the clouds and breathing life into the world. The sun had climbed steeply out of his hiding and was now standing benignly in the lower sky pouring down floods of enchanting light and preliminary tinglings of heat.

I came upon a stone stile beside a gate leading into a field and sat down to rest upon the top of it. I was not sitting there long until I became surprised; surprising ideas were coming into my head from nowhere. First of all I remembered who I was—not my name but where I had come from and who my friends were. I recalled John Divney, my life with him and how we came to wait under the dripping trees on the winter's evening. This led me to reflect in wonder that there was nothing wintry about the morning in which I was now sitting. Furthermore, there was nothing familiar about the good-looking countryside which stretched away from me at every view. I was now but two days from home—not more than three hours' walking—and yet I seemed to have reached regions which I had never seen before and of which I had never even heard. I could not understand this because although my life had been spent mostly among my books and papers, I had thought that there was no road in the district I had not travelled, no road whose destination was not well-known to me. There was another thing. My surroundings had a strangeness of a peculiar kind, entirely separate from the mere strangeness of a country where one has never been before. Everything seemed almost too pleasant, too perfect, too finely made. Each thing the eye could see was unmistakable and unambiguous, incapable of merging with any other thing or of being confused with it. The colour of the bogs was beautiful and the greenness of the green fields supernal. Trees were arranged here and there with far-from-usual consideration for the fastidious eye. The senses took keen pleasure from merely breathing the air and discharged their functions with delight. I was clearly in a strange country but all the doubts and perplexities which strewed my mind could not stop me from feeling happy and heart-light and full of an appetite for going about my business and finding the hiding-place of the black box. The valuable contents of it, I felt, would secure me for life in my own house and afterwards I could revisit this mysterious townland upon my bicycle and probe at my leisure the reasons for all its strangenesses. I got down from the stile and continued my walk along the road. It was pleasant easeful walking. I felt sure I was not going against the road. It was, so to speak, accompanying me.

Before going to sleep the previous night I had spent a long time in puzzled thought and also in carrying on inward conversations with my newly-found soul. Strangely enough, I was not thinking about the baffling fact that I was enjoying the hospitality of the man I had murdered (or whom I was sure

I had murdered) with my spade. I was reflecting about my name and how tantalising it was to have forgotten it. All people have names of one kind or another. Some are arbitrary labels related to the appearance of the person, some represent purely genealogical associations but most of them afford some clue as to the parents of the person named and confer a certain advantage in the execution of legal documents.[3] Even a dog has a name which dissociates him from other dogs and indeed my own soul, whom nobody has ever seen on the road or standing at the counter of a public house, had apparently no difficulty in assuming a name which distinguished him from other people's souls.

A thing not easy to account for is the unconcern with which I turned over my various perplexities in my mind. Blank anonymity coming suddenly in the middle of life should be at best alarming, a sharp symptom that the mind is in decay. But the unexplainable exhilaration which I drew from my surroundings seemed to invest this situation merely with the genial interest of a good joke. Even now as I walked along

[3] De Selby (Golden Hours, p. 93, et seq.) has put forward an interesting theory on names. Going back to primitive times, he regards the earliest names as crude onomatopaeic associations with the appearance of the person or object named—thus harsh or rough manifestations being represented by far from pleasant gutturalities and vice versa. This idea he pursued to rather fanciful lengths, drawing up elaborate paradigms of vowels and consonants purporting to correspond to certain indices of human race, colour and temperament and claiming ultimately to be in a position to state the physiological "group" of any person merely from a brief study of the letters of his name after the word had been "rationalised" to allow for variations of language. Certain "groups" he showed to be universally "repugnant" to other "groups." An unhappy commentary on the theory was furnished by the activities of his own nephew, whether through ignorance or contempt for the humanistic researches of his uncle. The nephew set about a Swedish servant, from whom he was completely excluded by the paradigms, in the pantry of a Portsmouth hotel to such purpose that de Selby had to open his purse to the tune of five or six hundred pounds to avert an unsavoury law case.

contentedly I sensed a solemn question on this subject from
within, one similar to many that had been asked the night
before. It was a mocking inquiry. I light-heartedly gave a list
of names which, for all I knew, I might hear:

Hugh Murray.

Constantin Petrie.

Peter Small.

Signor Beniamino Bari.

The Honourable Alex O'Brannigan, Bart.

Kurt Freund.

Mr. John P. de Salis, M.A.

Dr Solway Garr.

Bonaparte Gosworth.

Legs O'Hagan.

Signor Beniamino Bari, Joe said, the eminent tenor. Three
baton-charges outside La Scala at great tenor's première. Extraordinary scenes were witnessed outside La Scala Opera House
when a crowd of some ten thousand devotées, incensed by
the management's statement that no more standing-room was
available, attempted to rush the barriers. Thousands were injured, 79 fatally, in the wild mêlée. Constable Peter Coutts
sustained injuries to the groin from which he is unlikely to
recover. These scenes were comparable only to the delirium
of the fashionable audience inside after Signor Bari had concluded his recital. The great tenor was in admirable voice.
Starting with a phase in the lower register with a husky richness which seemed to suggest a cold, he delivered the immortal
strains of Che Gelida Manina, favourite aria of the beloved
Caruso. As he warmed to his God-like task, note after golden
note spilled forth to the remotest corner of the vast theatre,
thrilling all and sundry to the inner core. When he reached
the high C where heaven and earth seem married in one great

climax of exaltation, the audience arose in their seats and
cheered as one man, showering hats, programmes and choco-
late-boxes on the great artist.

Thank you very much, I murmured, smiling in wild amusement.

A bit overdone, perhaps, but it is only a hint of the pretensions and vanity that you inwardly permit yourself.

Indeed?

Or what about Dr Solway Garr? The duchess has fainted.
Is there a doctor in the audience? The spare figure, thin
nervous fingers and iron-grey hair, making its way quietly
through the pale excited onlookers. A few brief commands,
quietly spoken but imperious. Inside five minutes the situation
is well in hand. Wan but smiling, the duchess murmurs her
thanks. Expert diagnosis has averted still another tragedy. A
small denture has been extracted from the thorax. All hearts
go out to the quiet-spoken servant of humanity. His Grace,
summoned too late to see aught but the happy ending, is
opening his cheque-book and has already marked a thousand
guineas on the counterfoil as a small token of his esteem. His
cheque is taken but torn to atoms by the smiling medico. A
lady in blue at the back of the hall begins to sing O Peace Be
Thine and the anthem, growing in volume and sincerity, peals
out into the quiet night, leaving few eyes that are dry and
hearts that are not replete with yearning ere the last notes
fade. Dr. Garr only smiles, shaking his head in deprecation.

I think that is quite enough, I said.

I walked on unperturbed. The sun was maturing rapidly in
the east and a great heat had started to spread about the ground
like a magic influence, making everything, including my own
self, very beautiful and happy in a dreamy drowsy way. The
little beds of tender grass here and there by the roadside and
the dry sheltery ditches began to look seductive and inviting.

The road was being slowly baked to a greater hardness, making my walking more and more laborious. After not long I decided that I must now be near the police barracks and that another rest would fit me better for the task I had on hand. I stopped walking and spread my body out evenly in the shelter of the ditch. The day was brand new and the ditch was feathery. I lay back unstintingly, stunned with the sun. I felt a million little influences in my nostril, hay-smells, grass-smells, odours from distant flowers, the reassuring unmistakability of the abiding earth beneath my head. It was a new and a bright day, the day of the world. Birds piped without limitation and incomparable stripe-coloured bees passed above me on their missions and hardly ever came back the same way home. My eyes were shuttered and my head was buzzing with the spinning of the universe. I was not long lying there until my wits deserted me and I fell far into my sleep. I slept there for a long time, as motionless and as devoid of feeling as the shadow of myself which slept behind me.

When I awoke again it was later in the day and a small man was sitting beside me watching me. He was tricky and smoked a tricky pipe and his hand was quavery. His eyes were tricky also, probably from watching policemen. They were very unusual eyes. There was no palpable divergence in their alignment but they seemed to be incapable of giving a direct glance at anything that was straight, whether or not their curious incompatibility was suitable for looking at crooked things. I knew he was watching me only by the way his head was turned; I could not meet his eyes or challenge them. He was small and poorly dressed and on his head was a cloth cap of pale salmon colour. He kept his head in my direction without speaking and I found his presence disquieting. I wondered how long he had been watching me before I awoke.

Watch your step here. A very slippery-looking customer.

I put my hand into my pocket to see if my wallet was there. It was, smooth and warm like the hand of a good friend. When found that I had not been robbed, I decided to talk to him genially and civilly, see who he was and ask him to direct me to the barracks. I made up my mind not to despise the assistance of anybody who could help me, in however small a way, to find the black box. I gave him the time of day and, so far as I could, a look as intricate as any he could give himself.

"More luck to you," I said.

"More power to yourself," he answered dourly.

Ask him his name and occupation and inquire what is his destination.

"I do not desire to be inquisitive, sir," I said, "but would it be true to mention that you are a bird-catcher?"

"Not a bird-catcher," he answered.

"A tinker?"

"Not that."

"A man on a journey?"

"No, not that."

"A fiddler?"

"Not that one."

I smiled at him in good-humoured perplexity and said:

"Tricky-looking man, you are hard to place and it is not easy to guess your station. You seem very contented in one way but then again you do not seem to be satisfied. What is your objection to life?"

He blew little bags of smoke at me and looked at me closely from behind the bushes of hair which were growing about his eyes.

"Is it life?" he answered. "I would rather be without it," he said, "for there is a queer small utility in it. You cannot eat it or drink it or smoke it in your pipe, it does not keep the rain out and it is a poor armful in the dark if you strip it and take it to bed with you after a night of porter when you are shivering with the red passion. It is a great mistake and a thing better done without, like bed-jars and foreign bacon."

"That is a nice way to be talking on this grand lively day," I chided, "when the sun is roaring in the sky and sending great tidings into our weary bones."

"Or like feather-beds," he continued, "or bread manufactured with powerful steam machinery. Is it life you say? Life?"

Explain the difficulty of life yet stressing its essential sweetness and desirability.

What sweetness?

Flowers in the spring, the glory and fulfilment of human life, bird-song at evening—you know very well what I mean. I am not so sure about the sweetness all the same.

"It is hard to get the right shape of it," I said to the tricky man, "or to define life at all but if you identify life with enjoyment I am told that there is a better brand of it in the cities than in the country parts and there is said to be a very superior brand of it to be had in certain parts of France. Did you ever notice that cats have a lot of it in them when they are quite juveniles?"

He was looking in my direction crossly.

"Is it life? Many a man has spent a hundred years trying to get the dimensions of it and when he understands it at last and entertains the certain pattern of it in his head, by the hokey he takes to his bed and dies! He dies like a poisoned sheepdog. There is nothing so dangerous, you can't smoke it, nobody will give you tuppence-halfpenny for the half of it and it kills you in the wind-up. It is a queer contraption, very dangerous, a certain death-trap. Life?"

He sat there looking very vexed with himself and stayed for a while without talking behind a little grey wall he had built for himself by means of his pipe. After an interval I made another attempt to find out what his business was.

"Or a man out after rabbits?" I asked.

"Not that. Not that."

"A travelling man with a job of journey-work?"

"No."

"Driving a steam thrashing-mill?"

"Not for certain."

"Tin-plates?"

"No."

"A town clerk?"

"No."

"A water-works inspector?"

"No."

"With pills for sick horses?"

"Not with pills."

"Then by Dad," I remarked perplexedly, "your calling is very unusual and I cannot think of what it is at all, unless you are a farmer like myself, or a publican's assistant or possibly something in the drapery line. Are you an actor or a mummer?"

"Not them either."

He sat up suddenly and looked at me in a manner that was almost direct, his pipe sticking out aggressively from his tight jaws. He had the world full of smoke. I was uneasy but not altogether afraid of him. If I had my spade with me I knew I would soon make short work of him. I thought the wisest thing to do was to humour him and to agree with everything he said.

"I am a robber," he said in a dark voice, "a robber with a knife and an arm that's as strong as an article of powerful steam machinery."

"A robber?" I exclaimed. My forebodings had been borne out.

Steady here. Take no chances.

"As strong as the bright moving instruments in a laundry. A black murderer also. Every time I rob a man I knock him dead because I have no respect for life, not a little. If I kill enough men there will be more life to go round and maybe then I will be able to live till I am a thousand and not have the old rattle in my neck when I am quite seventy. Have you a money-bag with you?"

Plead poverty and destitution. Ask for the loan of money.

That will not be difficult, I answered.

"I have no money at all, or coins or sovereigns or bankers' drafts," I replied, "no pawn-masters' tickets, nothing that is negotiable or of any value. I am as poor a man as yourself and I was thinking of asking you for two shillings to help me on my way."

I was now more nervous than I was before as I sat looking at him. He had put his pipe away and had produced a long farmer's knife. He was looking at the blade of it and flashing lights with it.

"Even if you have no money," he cackled, "I will take your little life."

"Now look here till I tell you," I rejoined in a stern voice, "robbery and murder are against the law and furthermore my life would add little to your own because I have a disorder in my chest and I am sure to be dead in six months. As well as that, there was a question of a dark funeral in my teacup on Tuesday. Wait till you hear a cough."

I forced out a great hacking cough. It travelled like a breeze across the grass near at hand. I was now thinking that it might be wise to jump up quickly and run away. It would at least be a simple remedy.

"There is another thing about me," I added, "part of me is made of wood and has no life in it at all."

The tricky man gave out sharp cries of surprise, jumped up

and gave me looks that were too tricky for description. I smiled
at him and pulled up my left trouser-leg to show him my
timber shin. He examined it closely and ran his hard finger
along the edge of it. Then he sat down very quickly, put his
knife away and took out his pipe again. It had been burning
away all the time in his pocket because he started to smoke
it without any delay and after a minute he had so much blue
smoke made, and grey smoke, that I thought his clothes had
gone on fire. Between the smoke I could see that he was giving friendly looks in my direction. After a few moments he
spoke cordially and softly to me.

"I would not hurt you, little man," he said.

"I think I got the disorder in Mullingar," I explained. I
knew that I had gained his confidence and that the danger
of violence was now passed. He then did something which
took me by surprise. He pulled up his own ragged trouser and
showed me his own left leg. It was smooth, shapely and fairly
fat but it was made of wood also.

"That is a funny coincidence," I said. I now perceived the
reason for his sudden change of attitude.

"You are a sweet man," he responded, "and I would not
lay a finger on your personality. I am the captain of all the
one-leggèd men in the country. I knew them all up to now
except one—your own self—and that one is now also my friend
into the same bargain. If any man looks at you sideways, I
will rip his belly."

"That is very friendly talk," I said.

"Wide open," he said, making a wide movement with his
hands. "If you are ever troubled, send for me and I will save
you from the woman."

"Women I have no interest in at all," I said smiling.

"A fiddle is a better thing for diversion."

"It does not matter. If your perplexity is an army or a dog,

I will come with all the one-leggèd men and rip the bellies. My real name is Martin Finnucane."

"It is a reasonable name," I assented.

"Martin Finnucane," he repeated, listening to his own voice as if he were listening to the sweetest music in the world. He lay back and filled himself up to the ears with dark smoke and when he was nearly bursting he let it out again and hid himself in it.

"Tell me this," he said at last. "Have you a desideratum?"

This queer question was unexpected but I answered it quickly enough. I said I had.

"What desideratum?"

"To find what I am looking for."

"That is a handsome desideratum," said Martin Finnucane. "What way will you bring it about or mature its mutandum and bring it ultimately to passable factivity?"

"By visiting the police barracks," I said, "and asking the policemen to direct me to where it is. Maybe you might instruct me on how to get to the barrack from where we are now?"

"Maybe indeed," said Mr. Finnucane. "Have you an ultimatum?"

"I have a secret ultimatum," I replied.

"I am sure it is a fine ultimatum," he said, "but I will not ask you to recite it for me if you think it is a secret one."

He had smoked away all his tobacco and was now smoking the pipe itself, judging by the surly smell of it. He put his hand into a pocket at his crotch and took out a round thing.

"Here is a sovereign for your good luck" he said, "the golden token of your golden destiny."

I gave him, so to speak, my golden thank-you but I noticed that the coin he gave me was a bright penny. I put it carefully into my pocket as if it were highly prized and very valuable.

I was pleased at the way I had handled this eccentric queerly-spoken brother of the wooden leg. Near the far side of the road was a small river. I stood up and looked at it and watched the white water. It tumbled in the stony bedstead and jumped in the air and hurried excitedly round a corner.

"The barracks are on this same road," said Martin Finnu-cane, "and I left it behind me a mile away this today morning. You will discover it at the place where the river runs away from the road. If you look now you will see the fat trout in their brown coats coming back from the barracks at this hour because they go there every morning for the fine breakfast that is to be had from the slops and the throwings of the two policemen. But they have their dinners down the other way where a man called MacFeeterson has a bakery shop in a village of houses with their rears to the water. Three bread vans he has and a light dog-cart for the high mountain and he attends at Kilkishkeam on Mondays and Wednesdays."

"Martin Finnucane," I said, "a hundred and two difficult thoughts I have to think between this and my destination and the sooner the better."

He sent me up friendly glances from the smokey ditch.

"Good-looking man," he said, "good luck to your luck and do not entertain danger without sending me cognisance."

I said "Good-bye, Good-bye" and left him after a hand-shake. I looked back from down the road and saw nothing but the lip of the ditch with smoke coming from it as if tinkers were in the bottom of it cooking their what-they-had. Before I was gone I looked back again and saw the shape of his old head regarding me and closely studying my disappear-ance. He was amusing and interesting and had helped me by directing me to the barracks and telling me how far it was. And as I went upon my way I was slightly glad that I had met him.

A droll customer.

I V

Of all the many striking statements made by de Selby, I
do not think that any of them can rival his assertion that "a
journey is an hallucination." The phrase may be found in the
Country Album[1] cheek by jowl with the well-known treatise
on "tent-suits," those egregious canvas garments which he designed as a substitute alike for the hated houses and ordinary
clothing. His theory, insofar as I can understand it, seems to
discount the testimony of human experience and is at variance
with everything I have learnt myself on many a country walk.
Human existence de Selby has defined as "a succession of
static experiences each infinitely brief," a conception which
he is thought to have arrived at from examining some old
cinematograph films which belonged probably to his nephew.[2]
From this premise he discounts the reality or truth of any
progression or serialism in life, denies that time can pass as
such in the accepted sense and attributes to hallucinations the
commonly experienced sensation of progression as, for instance, in journeying from one place to another or even "living." If one is resting at A, he explains, and desires to rest in
a distant place B, one can only do so by resting for infinitely
brief intervals in innumerable intermediate places. Thus there
is no difference essentially between what happens when one
is resting at A before the start of the "journey" and what happens when one is "en route," i.e., resting in one or other of
the intermediate places. He treats of these "intermediate
places" in a lengthy footnote. They are not, he warns us, to

1 Page 822.
2 These are evidently the same films which he mentions in *Golden
Hours* (p. 155) as having "a strong repetitive element" and as being
"tedious." Apparently he had examined them patiently picture by picture and imagined that they would be screened in the same way, failing
at that time to grasp the principle of the cinematograph.

be taken as arbitrarily-determined points on the A-B axis so
many inches or feet apart. They are rather to be regarded as
points infinitely near each other yet sufficiently far apart to
admit of the insertion between them of a series of other "in-
terintermediate" places, between each of which must be imagined a chain of other resting-places—not, of course, strictly
adjacent but arranged so as to admit of the application of this
principle indefinitely. The illusion of progression he attributes
to the inability of the human brain—"as at present developed"
—to appreciate the reality of these separate "rests," preferring
to group many millions of them together and calling the result motion, an entirely indefensible and impossible procedure
since even two separate positions cannot obtain simultaneously
of the same body. Thus motion is also an illusion. He mentions that almost any photograph is conclusive proof of his
teachings.

Whatever about the soundness of de Selby's theories, there
is ample evidence that they were honestly held and that several attempts were made to put them into practice. During
his stay in England, he happened at one time to be living in
Bath and found it necessary to go from there to Folkestone
on pressing business.[3] His method of doing so was far from
conventional. Instead of going to the railway station and in-
quiring about trains, he shut himself up in a room in his lodg-
ings with a supply of picture postcards of the areas which
would be traversed on such a journey, together with an elaborate arrangement of clocks and barometric instruments and
a device for regulating the gaslight in conformity with the
changing light of the outside day. What happened in the room
or how precisely the clocks and other machines were manip-
ulated will never be known. It seems that he emerged after

[3] See Hatchjaw's De Selby's Life and Times.

a lapse of seven hours convinced that he was in Folkestone and possibly that he had evolved a formula for travellers which would be extremely distasteful to railway and shipping companies. There is no record of the extent of his disillusionment when he found himself still in the familiar surroundings of Bath but one authority[4] relates that he claimed without turning a hair to have been to Folkestone and back again. Reference is made to a man (unnamed) declaring to have actually seen the savant coming out of a Folkestone bank on the material date.

Like most of de Selby's theories, the ultimate outcome is inconclusive. It is a curious enigma that so great a mind would question the most obvious realities and object even to things scientifically demonstrated (such as the sequence of day and night) while believing absolutely in his own fantastic explanations of the same phenomena.

Of my own journey to the police-barracks I need only say that it was no hallucination. The heat of the sun played incontrovertibly on every inch of me, the hardness of the road was uncompromising and the country changed slowly but surely as I made my way through it. To the left was brown bogland scarred with dark cuttings and strewn with rugged clumps of bushes, white streaks of boulder and here and there a distant house half-hiding in an assembly of little trees. Far beyond was another region sheltering in the haze, purple and mysterious. The right-hand side was a greener country with the small turbulent river accompanying the road at a respectful distance and on the other side of it hills of rocky pasture stretching away into the distance up and down. Tiny sheep could be discerned near the sky far away and crooked lanes ran hither and thither. There was no sign whatever of human

4 Bassett: *Lux Mundi: A Memoir of de Selby.*

life. It was still early morning, perhaps. If I had not lost my American gold watch it would be possible for me to tell the time.

You have no American gold watch.

Something strange then happened to me suddenly. The road before me was turning gently to the left and as I approached the bend my heart began to behave irregularly and an unaccountable excitement took complete possession of me. There was nothing to see and no change of any kind had come upon the scene to explain what was taking place within me. I continued walking with wild eyes.

As I came round the bend of the road an extraordinary spectacle was presented to me. About a hundred yards away on the left-hand side was a house which astonished me. It looked as if it were painted like an advertisement on a board on the roadside and indeed very poorly painted. It looked completely false and unconvincing. It did not seem to have any depth or breadth and looked as if it would not deceive a child. That was not in itself sufficient to surprise me because I had seen pictures and notices by the roadside before. What bewildered me was the sure knowledge deeply-rooted in my mind, that this was the house I was searching for and that there were people inside it. I had no doubt at all that it was the barracks of the policemen. I had never seen with my eyes ever in my life before anything so unnatural and appalling and my gaze faltered about the thing uncomprehendingly as if at least one of the customary dimensions was missing, leaving no meaning in the remainder. The appearance of the house was the greatest surprise I had encountered since I had seen the old man in the chair and I felt afraid of it.

I kept on walking, but walked more slowly. As I approached, the house seemed to change its appearance. At first, it did nothing to reconcile itself with the shape of an ordinary house but it became uncertain in outline like a thing glimpsed under ruffled water. Then it became clear again and I saw that it began to have some back to it, some small space for rooms behind the frontage. I gathered this from the fact that I seemed to see the front and the back of the "building" simultaneously from my position approaching what should have been the side. As there was no side that I could see I thought the house must be triangular with its apex pointing towards me but when I was only fifteen yards away I saw a small window apparently facing me and I knew from that that there must be some side to it. Then I found myself almost in the shadow of the structure, dry-throated and timorous from wonder and anxiety. It seemed ordinary enough at close quarters except that it was very white and still. It was momentous and frightening; the whole morning and the whole world seemed to have no purpose at all save to frame it and give it some magnitude and position so that I could find it with my simple senses and pretend to myself that I understood it. A constabulary crest above the door told me that it was a police station. I had never seen a police station like it.

I cannot say why I did not stop to think or why my nervousness did not make me halt and sit down weakly by the roadside. Instead I walked straight up to the door and looked in. I saw, standing with his back to me, an enormous policeman. His back appearance was unusual. He was standing behind a little counter in a neat whitewashed day-room; his mouth was open and he was looking into a mirror which hung upon the wall. Again, I find it difficult to convey the precise reason why my eyes found his shape unprecedented and unfamiliar. He was very big and fat and the hair which strayed abundantly about the back of his bulging neck was a pale straw-colour; all that was striking but not unheard of. My glance ran over his great back, the thick arms and legs en-

cased in the rough blue uniform. Ordinary enough as each
part of him looked by itself, they all seemed to create together, by some undetectable discrepancy in association or
proportion, a very disquieting impression of unnaturalness,
amounting almost to what was horrible and monstrous. His
hands were red, swollen and enormous and he appeared to
have one of them half-way into his mouth as he gazed into
the mirror.

"It's my teeth," I heard him say, abstractedly and half-aloud.
His voice was heavy and slightly muffled, reminding me of a
thick winter quilt. I must have made some sound at the door
or possibly he had seen my reflection in the glass for he turned
slowly round, shifting his stance with leisurely and heavy
majesty, his fingers still working at his teeth; and as he turned
I heard him murmuring to himself:

"Nearly every sickness is from the teeth."

His face gave me one more surprise. It was enormously fat,
red and widespread, sitting squarely on the neck of his tunic
with a clumsy weightiness that reminded me of a sack of flour.
The lower half of it was hidden by a violent red moustache
which shot out from his skin far into the air like the antennae
of some unusual animal. His cheeks were red and chubby and
his eyes were nearly invisible, hidden from above by the ob-
struction of his tufted brows and from below by the fat fold-
ings of his skin. He came over ponderously to the inside of
the counter and I advanced meekly from the door until we
were face to face.

"Is it about a bicycle?" he asked.

His expression when I encountered it was unexpectedly reassuring. His face was gross and far from beautiful but he had
modified and assembled his various unpleasant features in some
skillful way so that they expressed to me good nature, polite-
ness and infinite patience. In the front of his peaked official

cap was an important-looking badge and over it in golden letters was the word Sergeant. It was Sergeant Pluck himself.

"No," I answered, stretching forth my hand to lean with
it against the counter. The Sergeant looked at me incredulously.

"Are you sure?" he asked.

"Certain."

"Not about a motor-cycle?"

"No."

"One with overhead valves and a dynamo for light? Or with
racing handle-bars?"

"No."

"In that circumstantial eventuality there can be no question
of a motor-bicycle," he said. He looked surprised and puzzled
and leaned sideways on the counter on the prop of his left
elbow, putting the knuckles of his right hand between his
yellow teeth and raising three enormous wrinkles of perplexity
on his forehead. I decided now that he was a simple man and
that I would have no difficulty in dealing with him exactly as
I desired and finding out from him what had happened to
the black box. I did not understand clearly the reason for his
questions about bicycles but I made up my mind to answer
everything carefully, to bide my time and to be cunning in all
my dealings with him. He moved away abstractedly, came back
and handed me a bundle of differently-coloured papers which
looked like application forms for bull-licences and dog-licences
and the like.

"It would be no harm if you filled up these forms," he said.
"Tell me," he continued, "would it be true that you are an
itinerant dentist and that you came on a tricycle?"

"It would not," I replied.

"On a patent tandem?"

"No."

"Dentists are an unpredictable coterie of people," he said. "Do you tell me it was a velocipede or a penny-farthing?"

"I do not," I said evenly. He gave me a long searching look as if to see whether I was serious in what I was saying, again wrinkling up his brow.

"Then maybe you are no dentist at all," he said, "but only a man after a dog licence or papers for a bull?"

"I did not say I was a dentist," I said sharply, "and I did not say anything about a bull."

The Sergeant looked at me incredulously.

"That is a great curiosity," he said, "a very difficult piece of puzzledom, a snorter."

He sat down by the turf fire and began jawing his knuckles and giving me sharp glances from under his bushy brows. If I had horns upon my head or a tail behind me he could not have looked at me with more interest. I was unwilling to give any lead to the direction of the talk and there was complete silence for five minutes. Then his expression eased a bit and he spoke to me again.

"What is your pronoun?" he inquired.

"I have no pronoun," I answered, hoping I knew his meaning.

"What is your cog?"

"My cog?"

"Your surnoun?"

"I have not got that either."

My reply again surprised him and also seemed to please him. He raised his thick eyebrows and changed his face into what could be described as a smile. He came back to the counter, put out his enormous hand, took mine in it and shook it warmly.

"No name or no idea of your originality at all?"

"None."

"Well, by the holy Hokey!"

Signor Bari, the eminent one-leggèd tenor!

"By the holy Irish-American Powers," he said again, "by the Dad! Well carry me back to old Kentucky!"

He then retreated from the counter to his chair by the fire and sat silently bent in thought as if examining one by one the by-gone years stored up in his memory.

"I was once acquainted with a tall man," he said to me at last, "that had no name either and you are certain to be his son and the heir to his nullity and all his nothings. What way is your pop today and where is he?"

It was not, I thought, entirely unreasonable that the son of a man who had no name should have no name also but it was clear that the Sergeant was confusing me with somebody else. This was no harm and I decided to encourage him. I considered it desirable that he should know nothing about me but it was even better if he knew several things which were quite wrong. It would help me in using him for my own purposes and ultimately in finding the black box.

"He is gone to America," I replied.

"Is that where," said the sergeant. "Do you tell me that? He was a true family husband. The last time I interviewed him it was about a missing pump and he had a wife and ten sonnies and at that time he had the wife again in a very advanced state of sexuality."

"That was me," I said, smiling.

"That was you," he agreed. "What way are the ten strong sons?"

"All gone to America."

"That is a great conundrum of a country," said the Sergeant, "a very wide territory, a place occupied by black men and strangers. I am told they are very fond of shooting-matches in that quarter."

"It is a queer land," I said.

At this stage there were footsteps at the door and in marched a heavy policeman carrying a small constabulary lamp. He had a dark Jewish face and hooky nose and masses of black curly hair. He was blue-jowled and black-jowled and looked as if he shaved twice a day. He had white enamelled teeth which came, I had no doubt, from Manchester, two rows of them arranged in the interior of his mouth and when he smiled it was a fine sight to see, like delph on a neat country dresser. He was heavy-fleshed and gross in body like the Sergeant but his face looked far more intelligent. It was unexpectedly lean and the eyes in it were penetrating and observant. If his face alone were in question he would look more like a poet than a policeman but the rest of his body looked anything but poetical.

"Policeman MacCruiskeen," said Sergeant Pluck.

Policeman MacCruiskeen put the lamp on the table, shook hands with me and gave me the time of day with great gravity. His voice was high, almost feminine, and he spoke with a delicate careful intonation. Then he put the little lamp on the counter and surveyed the two of us.

"Is it about a bicycle?" he asked.

"Not that," said the Sergeant. "This is a private visitor who says he did not arrive in the townland upon a bicycle. He has no personal name at all. His dadda is in far Amurikey."

"Which of the two Amurikeys?" asked MacCruiskeen.

"The Unified Stations," said the Sergeant.

"Likely he is rich by now if he is in that quarter," said Mac-Cruiskeen, "because there's dollars there, dollars and bucks and nuggets in the ground and any amount of rackets and golf games and musical instruments. It is a free country too by all accounts."

"Free for all," said the Sergeant. "Tell me this," he said to the policeman, "Did you take any readings today?"

"I did," said MacCruiskeen.

"Take out your black book and tell me what it was, like a good man," said the Sergeant. "Give me the gist of it till I see what I see," he added.

MacCruiskeen fished a small black notebook from his breast pocket.

"Ten point six," he said.

"Ten point six," said the Sergeant. "And what reading did you notice on the beam?"

"Seven point four."

"How much on the lever?"

"One point five."

There was a pause here. The Sergeant put on an expression of great intricacy as if he were doing far-from-simple sums and calculations in his head. After a time his face cleared and he spoke again to his companion.

"Was there a fall?"

"A heavy fall at half-past three."

"Very understandable and commendably satisfactory," said the Sergeant. "Your 'supper is on the hob inside and be sure to stir the milk before you take any of it, the way the rest of us after you will have our share of the fats of it, the health and the heart of it."

Policeman MacCruiskeen smiled at the mention of food and went into the back room loosening his belt as he went; after a moment we heard the sounds of coarse slobbering as if he was eating porridge without the assistance of spoon or hand. The Sergeant invited me to sit at the fire in his company and gave me a wrinkled cigarette from his pocket.

"It is lucky for your pop that he is situated in Amurikey,"

he remarked, "if it is a thing that he is having trouble with the old teeth. It is very few sicknesses that are not from the teeth."

"Yes," I said. I was determined to say as little as possible and let these unusual policemen first show their hand. Then I would know how to deal with them.

"Because a man can have more disease and germination in his gob than you'll find in a rat's coat and Amurikey is a country where the population do have grand teeth like shaving-lather or like bits of delph when you break a plate."

"Quite true," I said.

"Or like eggs under a black crow."

"Like eggs," I said.

"Did you ever happen to visit the cinematograph in your travels?"

"Never," I answered humbly, "but I believe it is a dark quarter and little can be seen at all except the photographs on the wall."

"Well it is there you see the fine teeth they do have in Amurikey," said the Sergeant.

He gave the fire a hard look and took to handling absently his yellow stumps of teeth. I had been wondering about his mysterious conversation with MacCruiskeen.

"Tell me this much," I ventured. "What sort of readings were those in the policeman's black book?"

The Sergeant gave me a keen look which felt almost hot from being on the fire previously.

"The first beginnings of wisdom," he said, "is to ask questions but never to answer any. You get wisdom from asking and I from not answering. Would you believe that there is a great increase in crime in this locality? Last year we had sixty-nine cases of no lights and four stolen. This year we have eighty-two cases of no lights, thirteen cases of riding on the

footpath and four stolen. There was one case of wanton damage to a three-speed gear, there is sure to be a claim at the next
Court and the area of charge will be the parish. Before the
year is out there is certain to be a pump stolen, a very depraved
and despicable manifestation of criminality and a blot on the
county."

"Indeed," I said.

"Five years ago we had a case of loose handlebars. Now
there is a rarity for you. It took the three of us a week to
frame the charge."

"Loose handlebars," I muttered. I could not clearly see the
reason for such talk about bicycles.

"And then there is the question of bad brakes. The country
is honeycombed with bad brakes, half of the accidents are due
to it, it runs in families."

I thought it would be better to try to change the conversation from bicycles.

"You told me what the first rule of wisdom is," I said.
"What's is the second rule?"

"That can be answered," he said. "There are five in all. Always ask any questions that are to be asked and never answer
any. Turn everything you hear to your own advantage. Always
carry a repair outfit. Take left turns as much as possible. Never
apply your front brake first."

"These are interesting rules," I said dryly.

"If you follow them," said the Sergeant, "you will save your
soul and you will never get a fall on a slippy road."

"I would be obliged to you," I said, "if you would explain
to me which of these rules covers the difficulty I have come
here today to put before you."

"This is not today, this is yesterday," he said, "but which
of the difficulties is it? What is the crux rei?"

Yesterday? I decided without any hesitation that it was a

waste of time trying to understand the half of what he said.
I persevered with my inquiry.

"I came here to inform you officially about the theft of my
American gold watch."

He looked at me through an atmosphere of great surprise
and incredulity and raised his eyebrows almost to his hair.

"That is an astonishing statement," he said at last.
Why?"

"Why should anybody steal a watch when they can steal a
bicycle?"

Hark to his cold inexorable logic.

"Search me," I said.

"Who ever heard of a man riding a watch down the road
or bringing a sack of turf up to his house on the crossbar of a
watch?"

"I did not say the thief wanted my watch to ride it," I ex-
postulated. "Very likely he had a bicycle of his own and that
is how he got away quietly in the middle of the night."

"Never in my puff did I hear of any man stealing anything
but a bicycle when he was in his sane senses," said the Sergeant,"—except pumps and clips and lamps and the like of
that. Surely you are not going to tell me at my time of life
that the world is changing?"

"I am only saying that my watch was stolen," I said crossly.

"Very well," the Sergeant said with finality, "we will have to
institute a search."

He smiled brightly at me. It was quite clear that he did not
believe any part of my story, and that he thought I was in
delicate mental health. He was humouring me as if I were a
child.

"Thank you," I muttered.

"But the trouble will only be beginning when we find it," he
said severely.

"How is that?"

"When we find it we will have to start searching for the owner."

"But I am the owner."

Here the Sergeant laughed indulgently and shook his head.

"I know what you mean," he said. "But the law is an extremely intricate phenomenon. If you have no name you cannot own a watch and the watch that has been stolen does not exist and when it is found it will have to be restored to its rightful owner. If you have no name you possess nothing and you do not exist and even your trousers are not on you although they look as if they were from where I am sitting. On the other separate hand you can do what you like and the law cannot touch you."

"It had fifteen jewels," I said despairingly.

"And on the first hand again you might be charged with theft or common larceny if you were mistaken for somebody else when wearing the watch."

"I feel extremely puzzled," I said, speaking nothing less than the truth. The Sergeant gave his laugh of good humour.

"If we ever find the watch," he smiled, "I have a feeling that there will be a bell and a pump on it."

I considered my position with some misgiving. It seemed to be impossible to make the Sergeant take cognisance of anything in the world except bicycles. I thought I would make a last effort.

"You appear to be under the impression," I said coldly and courteously, "that I have lost a golden bicycle of American manufacture with fifteen jewels. I have lost a watch and there is no bell on it. Bells are only on alarm clocks and I have never in my life seen a watch with a pump attached to it."

The Sergeant smiled at me again.

"There was a man in this room a fortnight ago," he said,

"telling me that he was at the loss of his mother, a lady of eighty-two. When I asked him for a description—just to fill up the blanks in the official form we get for half-nothing from the Stationery Office—he said she had rust on her rims and that her back brakes were subject to the jerks."

This speech made my position quite clear to me. When I was about to say something else, a man put his face in and looked at us and then came in completely and shut the door carefully and came over to the counter. He was a bluff red man in a burly coat with twine binding his trousers at the knees. I discovered afterwards that his name was Michael Gilhaney. Instead of standing at the counter as he would in a public house, he went to the wall, put his arms akimbo and leaned against it, balancing his weight on the point of one elbow.

"Well, Michael," said the Sergeant pleasantly.

"That is a cold one," said Mr Gilhaney.

Sounds of shouting came to the three of us from the inner room where Policemen MacCruiskeen was engaged in the task of his early dinner.

"Hand me in a fag," he called.

The Sergeant gave me another wrinkled cigarette from his pocket and jerked his thumb in the direction of the back room. As I went in with the cigarette I heard the Sergeant opening an enormous ledger and putting questions to the red-faced visitor.

"What was the make," he was saying, "and the number of the frame and was there a lamp and a pump on it into the same bargain?"

IV

The long and unprecedented conversation I had with Policeman MacCruiskeen after I went in to him on my mission with the cigarette brought to my mind afterwards several of the more delicate speculations of de Selby, notably his investigation of the nature of time and eternity by a system of mirrors.[1] His theory as I understand it is as follows:

If a man stands before a mirror and sees in it his reflection, what he sees is not a true reproduction of himself but a picture of himself when he was a younger man. De Selby's explanation of this phenomenon is quite simple. Light, as he points out truly enough, has an ascertained and finite rate of travel. Hence before the reflection of any object in a mirror can be said to be accomplished, it is necessary that rays of light should first strike the object and subsequently impinge on the glass, to be thrown back to the object—to the eyes of a man, for instance. There is therefore an appreciable and calculable interval of time between the throwing by a man of a glance at his own face in a mirror and the registration of the reflected image in his eye.

So far, one may say, so good. Whether this idea is right or wrong, the amount of time involved is so negligible that few reasonable people would argue the point. But de Selby ever loath to leave well enough alone, insists on reflecting the first

---

[1] Hatchjaw remarks (unconfirmed, however, by Bassett) that throughout the whole ten years that went to the writing of *The Country Album* de Selby was obsessed with mirrors and had recourse to them so frequently that he claimed to have two left hands and to be living in a world arbitrarily bounded by a wooden frame. As time went on he refused to countenance a direct view of anything and had a small mirror permanently suspended at a certain angle in front of his eyes by a wired mechanism of his own manufacture. After he had resorted to this fantastic arrangement, he interviewed visitors with his back to them and with his head inclined towards the ceiling; he was even credited with long walks backwards in crowded thoroughfares. Hatchjaw claims that his statement is supported by the MS. of some three hundred pages of the *Album*, written backwards, "a circumstance that made necessary the extension of the mirror principle to the bench of the wretched printer." (*De Selby's Life and Times*, p. 221.) This manuscript cannot now be found.

reflection in a further mirror and professing to detect minute changes in this second image. Ultimately he constructed the familiar arrangement of parallel mirrors, each reflecting diminishing images of an interposed object indefinitely. The interposed object in this case was de Selby's own face and this he claims to have studied backwards through an infinity of reflections by means of "a powerful glass." What he states to have seen through his glass is astonishing. He claims to have noticed a growing youthfulness in the reflections of his face according as they receded, the most distant of them—too tiny to be visible to the naked eye—being the face of a beardless boy of twelve, and, to use his own words, "a countenance of singular beauty and nobility." He did not succeed in pursuing the matter back to the cradle "owing to the curvature of the earth and the limitations of the telescope."

So much for de Selby. I found MacCruiskeen with a red face at the kitchen table panting quietly from all the food he had hidden in his belly. In exchange for the cigarette he gave me searching looks. "Well, now," he said.

He lit the cigarette and sucked at it and smiled covertly at me.

"Well, now," he said again. He had his little lamp beside him on the table and he played his fingers on it.

"That is a fine day," I said. "What are you doing with a lamp in the white morning?"

"I can give you a question as good as that," he responded. "Can you notify me of the meaning of a bulbul?"

"A bulbul?"

"What would you say a bulbul is?"

This conundrum did not interest me but I pretended to rack my brains and screwed my face in perplexity until I felt it half the size it should be.

"Not one of those ladies who take money?" I said.

"No."

"Not the brass knobs on a German steam organ?"

"Not the knobs."

"Nothing to do with the independence of America or such-like?"

"No."

"A mechanical engine for winding clocks?"

"No."

"A tumour, or the lather in a cow's mouth, or those elastic articles that ladies wear?"

"Not them by a long chalk."

"Not an eastern musical instrument played by Arabs?"

He clapped his hands.

"Not that but very near it," he smiled, "something next door to it. You are a cordial intelligible man. A bulbul is a Persian nightingale. What do you think of that now?"

"It is seldom I am far out," I said dryly.

He looked at me in admiration and the two of us sat in silence for a while as if each was very pleased with himself and with the other and had good reason to be.

"You are a B.A. with little doubt?" he questioned.

I gave no direct answer but tried to look big and learned and far from simple in my little chair.

"I think you are a sempiternal man," he said slowly.

He sat for a while giving the floor a strict examination and then put his dark jaw over to me and began questioning me about my arrival in the parish.

"I do not want to be insidious," he said, "but would you inform me about your arrival in the parish? Surely you had a three-speed gear for the hills?"

"I had no three-speed gear," I responded rather sharply, "and no two-speed gear and it is also true that I had no bicycle and little or no pump and if I had a lamp itself it would not be necessary if I had no bicycle and there would be no bracket to hang it on."

"That may be," said MacCruiskeen, "but likely you were laughed at on the tricycle?"

"I had neither bicycle nor tricycle and I am not a dentist," I said with severe categorical thoroughness, "and I do not believe in the penny-farthing or the scooter, the velocipede or the tandem-tourer."

MacCruiskeen got white and shaky and gripped my arm and looked at me intensely.

"In my natural puff," he said at last, in a strained voice, "I have never encountered a more fantastic epilogue or a queerer story. Surely you are a queer far-fetched man. To my dying night I will not forget this today morning. Do not tell me that you are taking a hand at me?"

"No," I said.

"Well Great Crikes!"

He got up and brushed his hair with a flat hand back along his skull and looked out of the window for a long interval, his eyes popping and dancing and his face like an empty bag with no blood in it.

Then he walked around to put back the circulation and took a little spear from a place he had on the shelf.

"Put your hand out," he said.

I put it out idly enough and he held the spear at it. He kept putting it near me and nearer and when he had the bright point of it about half a foot away, I felt a prick and gave a short cry. There was a little bead of my red blood in the middle of my palm.

"Thank you very much," I said. I felt too surprised to be annoyed with him.

"That will make you think," he remarked in triumph, "unless I am an old Dutchman by profession and nationality."

He put his little spear back on the shelf and looked at me crookedly from a sidewise angle with a certain quantity of what may be called *roi-s'amuse*.

"Maybe you can explain that?" he said.

"That is the limit," I said wonderingly.

"It will take some analysis," he said, "intellectually."

"Why did your spear sting when the point was half a foot away from where it made me bleed?"

"That spear," he answered quietly, "is one of the first things I ever manufactured in my spare time. I think only a little of it now but the year I made it I was proud enough and would not get up in the morning for any sergeant. There is no other spear like it in the length and breadth of Ireland and there is only one thing like it in Amurikey but I have not heard what it is. But I cannot get over the no-bicycle. Great Crikes!"

"But the spear," I insisted, "give me the gist of it like a good man and I will tell no one."

"I will tell you because you are a confidential man," he said, "and a man that said something about bicycles that I never heard before. What you think is the point is not the point at all but only the beginning of the sharpness."

"Very wonderful," I said, "but I do not understand you."

"The point is seven inches long and it is so sharp and thin that you cannot see it with the old eye. The first half of the sharpness is thick and strong but you cannot see it either because the real sharpness runs into it and if you saw the one you could see the other or maybe you would notice the joint."

"I suppose it is far thinner than a match?" I asked.

"There *is* a difference," he said. "Now the proper sharp part is so thin that nobody could see it no matter what light is on it or what eye is looking. About an inch from the end it is so sharp that sometimes—late at night or on a soft bad day especially—you cannot think of it or try to make it the subject of a little idea because you will hurt your box with the excruciation of it."

I gave a frown and tried to make myself look like a wise person who was trying to comprehend something that called for all his wisdom.

"You cannot have fire without bricks," I said, nodding.

"Wisely said," MacCruiskeen answered.

"It was sharp sure enough," I conceded, "it drew a little bulb of the red blood but I did not feel the pricking hardly at all. It must be very sharp to work like that."

MacCruiskeen gave a laugh and sat down again at the table and started putting on his belt.

"You have not got the whole gist of it at all," he smiled. "Because what gave you the prick and brought the blood was not the point at all; it was the place I am talking about that is a good inch from the reputed point of the article under our discussion."

"And what is this inch that is left?" I asked. "What in heaven's name would you call that?"

"That is the real point," said MacCruiskeen, "but it is so thin that it could go into your hand and out in the other extremity externally and you would not feel a bit of it and you would see nothing and hear nothing. It is so thin that maybe it does not exist at all and you could spend half an hour trying to think about it and you could put no thought around it in the end. The beginning part of the inch is thicker than the last part and is nearly there for a fact but I don't think it is if it is my private opinion that you are anxious to enlist."

I fastened my fingers around my jaw and started to think with great concentration, calling into play parts of my brain that I rarely used. Nevertheless I made no progress at all as regards the question of the points. MacCruiskeen had been at the dresser a second time and was back at the table with a little black article like a leprechaun's piano with diminutive keys of white and black and brass pipes and circular revolving cogs like parts of a steam engine or the business end of a thrashing-mill. His white hands were moving all over it and feeling it as if they were trying to discover some tiny lump on it, and his face was looking up in the air in a spiritual attitude and he was paying no attention to my personal existence at all. There was an overpowering tremendous silence as if the roof of the room had come down half-way to the floor, he at his queer occupation with the instrument and myself still trying to comprehend the sharpness of the points and to get the accurate understanding of them.

After ten minutes he got up and put the thing away. He wrote for a time in his notebook and then lit his pipe.

"Well now," he remarked expansively.

"Those points," I said.

"Did I happen to ask you what a bulbul is?"

"You did," I responded, "but the question of those points is what takes me to the fair."

"It is not today or yesterday I started pointing spears," he said, "but maybe you would like to see something else that is a medium fair example of supreme art?"

"I would indeed," I answered.

"But I cannot get over what you confided in me privately sub-rosa about the no-bicycle, that is a story that would make your golden fortune if you wrote down in a book where people could pursue it literally."

He walked back to the dresser, opened the lower part of it, and took out a little chest till he put it on the table for my inspection. Never in my life did I inspect anything more ornamental and well-made. It was a brown chest like those owned by seafaring men or lascars from Singapore, but it was diminutive in a very perfect way as if you were looking at a full-size

one through the wrong end of a spy-glass. It was about a foot
in height, perfect in its proportion and without fault in work-
manship. There were indents and carving and fanciful excoria-
tions and designs on every side of it and there was a bend on
the lid that gave the article great distinction. At every corner
there was a shiny brass corner-piece and on the lid there were
brass corner-pieces beautifully wrought and curved impeccably
against the wood. The whole thing had the dignity and the
satisfying quality of true art.

"There now," said MacCruiskeen.

"It is nearly too nice," I said at last, "to talk about it."

"I spent two years manufacturing it when I was a lad," said
MacCruiskeen, "and it still takes me to the fair."

"It is unmentionable," I said.

"Very nearly," said MacCruiskeen.

The two of us then started looking at it and we looked at
it for five minutes so hard that it seemed to dance on the table
and look even smaller than it might be.

"I do not often look at boxes or chests," I said, simply, "but
this is the most beautiful box I have even seen and I will always remember it. There might be something inside it?"

"There might be," said MacCruiskeen.

He went to the table and put his hands around the article
in a fawning way as if he were caressing a sheepdog and he
opened the lid with a little key but shut it down again before
I could inspect the inside of it.

"I will tell you a story and give you a synopsis of the ramifica-
tion of the little plot," he said. "When I had the chest made
and finished, I tried to think what I would keep in it and what
I would use it for at all. First I thought of them letters from
Bridie, the ones on the blue paper with the strong smell but I
did not think it would be anything but a sacrilege in the end

because there was hot bits in them letters. Do you comprehend the trend of my observations?"

"I do," I answered.

"Then there was my studs and the enamel badge and my presentation iron-pencil with a screw on the end of it to push the point out, an intricate article full of machinery and a Present from Southport. All these things are what are called Examples of the Machine Age."

"They would be contrary to the spirit of the chest," I said.

"They would be indeed. Then there was my razor and the spare plate in case I was presented with an accidental bash on the gob in the execution of me duty . . ."

"But not them."

"Not them. Then there was my certificates and me cash and the picture of Peter the Hermit and the brass thing with straps that I found on the road one night near Matthew O'Carahan's. But not them either."

"It is a hard conundrum," I said.

"In the end I found there was only one thing to do to put myself right with my private conscience."

"It is a great thing that you found the right answer at all," I countered.

"I decided to myself," said MacCruiskeen, "that the only sole correct thing to contain in the chest was another chest of the same make but littler in cubic dimension."

"That was very competent masterwork," I said, endeavouring to speak his own language.

He went to the little chest and opened it up again and put his hands down sideways like flat plates or like the fins on a fish and took out of it a smaller chest but one resembling its mother-chest in every particular of appearance and dimension. It almost interfered with my breathing, it was so delightfully unmistakable. I went over and felt it and covered it with my hand to see how big its smallness was. Its brasswork had a shine like the sun on the sea and the colour of the wood was a rich deep richness like a colour deepened and toned only by the years. I got slightly weak from looking at it and sat down on a chair and for the purpose of pretending that I was not disturbed I whistled *The Old Man Twangs His Braces*.

MacCruiskeen gave me a smooth inhuman smile.

"You may have come on no bicycle," he said, "but that does not say that you know everything."

"Those chests," I said, "are so like one another that I do not believe they are there at all because that is a simpler thing to believe than the contrary. Nevertheless the two of them are the most wonderful two things I have ever seen."

"I was two years manufacturing it," MacCruiskeen said.

"What is in the little one?" I asked.

"What would you think now?"

"I am completely half afraid to think," I said, speaking truly enough.

"Wait now till I show you," said MacCruiskeen, "and give you an exhibition and a personal inspection individually."

He got two thin butter-spades from the shelf and put them down into the little chest and pulled out something that seemed to me remarkably like another chest. I went over to it and gave it a close examination with my hand, feeling the same identical wrinkles, the same proportions and the same completely perfect brasswork on a smaller scale. It was so faultless and delightful that it reminded me forcibly, strange and foolish as it may seem, of something I did not understand and had never even heard of.

"Say nothing," I said quickly to MacCruiskeen, "but go ahead with what you are doing and I will watch here and I will take care to be sitting down."

He gave me a nod in exchange for my remark and got two straight-handled teaspoons and put the handles into his last chest. What came out may well be guessed at. He opened this one and took another one out with the assistance of two knives. He worked knives, small knives and smaller knives, till he had twelve little chests on the table, the last of them an article half the size of a matchbox. It was so tiny that you would not quite see the brasswork at all only for the glitter of it in the light. I did not see whether it had the same identical carvings upon it because I was content to take a swift look at it and then turn away. But I knew in my soul that it was exactly the same as the others. I said no word at all because my mind was brimming with wonder at the skill of the policeman.

"That last one," said MacCruiskeen, putting away the knives, "took me three years to make and it took me another year to believe that I had made it. Have you got the convenience of a pin?"

I gave him my pin in silence. He opened the smallest of them all with a key like a piece of hair and worked with the pin till he had another little chest on the table, thirteen in all arranged in a row upon the table. Queerly enough they looked to me as if they were all the same size but invested with some crazy perspective. This idea surprised me so much that I got my voice back and said:

"These are the most surprising thirteen things I have ever seen together."

"Wait now, man," MacCruiskeen said.

All my senses were now strained so tensely watching the policeman's movements that I could almost hear my brain rattling in my head when I gave a shake as if it was drying up into a wrinkled pea. He was manipulating and prodding with his pin till he had twenty-eight little chests on the table and the last of them so small that it looked like a bug or a tiny piece of dirt except that there was a glitter from it. When I looked at it again I saw another thing beside it like something you would take out of a red eye on a windy dry day and I knew then that the strict computation was then twenty-nine.

"Here is your pin," said MacCruiskeen.

He put it into my stupid hand and went back to the table thoughtfully. He took a something from his pocket that was too small for me to see and started working with the tiny black thing on the table beside the bigger thing which was itself too small to be described.

At this point I became afraid. What he was doing was no longer wonderful but terrible. I shut my eyes and prayed that he would stop while still doing things that were at least possible for a man to do. When I looked again I was happy that there was nothing to see and that he had put no more of the chests prominently on the table but he was working to the left with the invisible thing in his hand on a bit of the table itself. When he felt my look he came over to me and gave me an enormous magnifying-glass which looked like a basin fixed to a handle. I felt the muscles around my heart tightening painfully as I took the instrument.

"Come over here to the table," he said, "and look there till you see what you see infra-ocularly."

When I saw the table it was bare only for the twenty-nine chest articles but through the agency of the glass I was in a position to report that he had two more out beside the last ones, the smallest of all being nearly half a size smaller than ordinary invisibility. I gave him back the glass instrument and took to the chair without a word. In order to reassure myself and make a loud human noise I whistled *The Corncrake Plays the Bigpipes*.

"There now," said MacCruiskeen.

He took two wrinkled cigarettes from his fob and lit the two at the same time and handed me one of them.

"Number Twenty-Two," he said, "I manufactured fifteen years ago and I have made another different one every year since with any amount of nightwork and overtime and piece-work and time-and-a-half incidentally."

"I understand you clearly," I said.

"Six years ago they began to get invisible, glass or no glass. Nobody has ever seen the last five I made because no glass is strong enough to make them big enough to be regarded truly as the smallest things ever made. Nobody can see me making them because my little tools are invisible into the same bargain. The one I am making now is nearly as small as nothing. Number One would hold a million of them at the same time and there would be room left for a pair of woman's horse-breeches if they were rolled up. The dear knows where it will stop and terminate."

"Such work must be very hard on the eyes," I said, determined to pretend that everybody was an ordinary person like myself.

"Some of these days," he answered, "I will have to buy spectacles with gold ear-claws. My eyes are crippled with the small print in the newspapers and in the offeecial forms."

"Before I go back to the day-room," I said, "would it be right to ask you what you were performing with that little small piano-instrument, the article with the knobs, and the brass pins?"

"That is my personal musical instrument," said Mac-Cruiskeen, "and I was playing my own tunes on it in order to extract private satisfaction from the sweetness of them."

"I was listening," I answered, "but I did not succeed in hearing you."

"That does not surprise me intuitively," said MacCruiskeen,

"because it is an indigenous patent of my own. The vibrations
of the true notes are so high in their fine frequencies that they
cannot be appreciated by the human earcup. Only myself has
the secret of the thing and the intimate way of it, the confidential knack of circumventing it. Now what do you think
of that?"

I climbed up to my legs to go back to the day-room, passing
a hand weakly about my brow.

"I think it is extremely acatalectic," I answered.

9 ◎ *Norman Mailer*

Metaphysician, poet, amateur boxer, film-maker, essayist, novelist, and
New York mayoral candidate Norman Mailer was born in Long Branch,
New Jersey, in 1923. He is one of the most stubborn and eloquent critics of the absurdities, contradictions, and terrors of contemporary life in
our Americanized world. His five novels include The Naked and the
Dead (1948), Barbary Shore (1951), The Deer Park (1955), An American Dream (1965) and Why Are We in Vietnam? (1967).

THE MAN WHO STUDIED YOGA

I

I would introduce myself if it were not useless. The name I
had last night will not be the same as the name I have tonight.
For the moment, then, let me say that I am thinking of Sam
Slovoda. Obligatorily, I study him, Sam Slovoda who is neither
ordinary nor extraordinary, who is not young nor yet old, not
tall nor short. He is sleeping, and it is fit to describe him now,
for like most humans he prefers sleeping to not sleeping. He
is a mild pleasant-looking man who has just turned forty. If
the crown of his head reveals a little bald spot, he has nour-
ished in compensation the vanity of a mustache. He has generally when he is awake an agreeable manner, at least with
strangers; he appears friendly, tolerant, and genial. The fact is

that like most of us, he is full of envy, full of spite, a gossip, a man who is pleased to find others are as unhappy as he, and yet—this is the worst to be said—he is a decent man. He is better than most. He would prefer to see a more equitable world, he scorns prejudice and privilege, he tries to hurt no one, he wishes to be liked. I will go even further. He has one serious virtue—he is not fond of himself, he wishes he were better. He would like to free himself of envy, of the annoying necessity to talk about his friends, he would like to love people more; specifically, he would like to love his wife more, and to love his two daughters without the tormenting if nonetheless irremediable vexation that they closet his life in the dusty web of domestic responsibilities and drudging for money.

How often he tells himself with contempt that he has the cruelty of a kind weak man.

May I state that I do not dislike Sam Slovoda; it is just that I am disappointed in him. He has tried too many things and never with a whole heart. He has wanted to be a serious novelist and now merely indulges the ambition; he wished to be of consequence in the world, and has ended, temporarily perhaps, as an overworked writer of continuity for comic magazines; when he was young he tried to be a bohemian and instead acquired a wife and family. Of his appetite for a variety of new experience I may say that it is matched only by his fear of new people and novel situations.

I will give an instance. Yesterday, Sam was walking along the street and a bum approached him for money. Sam did not see the man until too late; lost in some inconsequential thought, he looked up only in time to see a huge wretch of a fellow with a red twisted face and an outstretched hand. Sam is like so many; each time a derelict asks for a dime, he feels a coward if he pays the money, and is ashamed of himself if he doesn't. This once, Sam happened to think, I will not be bullied, and hurried past. But the bum was not to be lost so easily. "Have a heart, Jack," he called after in a whisky voice, "I need a drink bad." Sam stopped, Sam began to laugh. "Just so it isn't for coffee, here's a quarter," he said: and he laughed, and the bum laughed. "You're a man's man," the bum said. Sam went away pleased with himself, thinking about such things as the community which existed between all people. It was cheap of Sam. He should know better. He should know he was merely relieved the situation had turned out so well. Although he thinks he is sorry for bums, Sam really hates them. Who knows what violence they can offer?

At this time, there is a powerful interest in Sam's life, but many would ridicule it. He is in the process of being psychoanalyzed. Myself, I do not jeer. It has created the most unusual situation between Sam and me. I could go into details but they are perhaps premature. It would be better to watch San awaken.

His wife, Eleanor, has been up for an hour, and she has shut the window and neglected to turn off the radiator. The room is stifling. Sam groans in a stupor which is neither sleep nor refreshment, opens one eye, yawns, groans again, and lies twisted, strangled and trussed in pajamas which are too large for him. How painful it is for him to rise. Last night there was a party, and this morning, Sunday morning, he is awakening with a hangover. Invariably, he is depressed in the morning, and it is no different today. He finds himself in the flat and familiar dispirit of nearly all days.

It is snowing outside. Sam finally lurches to the window, and opens it for air. With the oxygen of a winter morning clearing his brain, he looks down six stories into the giant quadrangle of the Queens housing development in which he lives, staring morosely at the inch of slush which covers the monotonous artificial park that separates his apartment building from an identical structure not two hundred feet away. The walks are

black where the snow has melted, and in the children's playground, all but deserted, one swing oscillates back and forth,
pushed by an irritable little boy who plays by himself among
the empty benches, swaddled in galoshes, muffler, and overcoat.
The snow falls sluggishly, a wet snow which probably will turn
to rain. The little boy in the playground gives one last disgusted shove to the swing and trudges away gloomily, his over-
shoes leaving a small animal track behind him. Back of Sam,
in the four-room apartment he knows like a blind man, there
is only the sound of Eleanor making breakfast.

Well, thinks Sam, depression in the morning is a stage of
his analysis, Dr. Sergius has said.

This is the way Sam often phrases his thoughts. It is not
altogether his fault. Most of the people he knows think that
way and talk that way, and Sam is not the strongest of men.
His language is doomed to the fashion of the moment. I have
heard him remark mildly, almost apologetically, about his
daughters: "My relation with them still suffers because I
haven't worked through all my feminine identifications." The
saddest thing is that the sentence has meaning to Sam even if
it will not have meaning to you. A great many ruminations, dis-
coveries, and memories contribute their connotation to Sam.
It has the significance of a cherished line of poetry to him.

Although Eleanor is not being analyzed, she talks in a similar
way. I have heard her remark in company, "Oh, you know
Sam, he not only thinks I'm his mother, he blames me for
being born." Like most woman, Eleanor can be depended
upon to employ the idiom of her husband.

What amuses me is that Sam is critical of the way others
speak. At the party last night he was talking to a Hollywood
writer, a young man with a great deal of energy and enthusiasm. The young man spoke something like this: "You see, boy-
chick, I can spike any script with yaks, but the thing I can't

do is heartbreak. My wife says she's gonna give me heartbreak. The trouble is I've had a real solid-type life. I mean I've had my ups and downs like all of humanity, but there's never been a shriek in my life. I don't know how to write shrieks."

On the trip home. Sam had said to Eleanor, "It was disgraceful. A writer should have some respect for language."

Eleanor answered with a burlesque of Sam's indignation. "Listen, I'm a real artist-type. Culture is for comic-strip writers."

Generally, I find Eleanor attractive. In the ten years they have been married she has grown plump, and her dark hair which once was long is now cropped in a mannish cut of the prevailing mode. But, this is quibbling. She still possesses her best quality, a healthy exuberance which glows in her dark eyes and beams in her smile. She has beautiful teeth. She seems aware of her body and pleased with it. Sam tells himself he would do well to realize how much he needs her. Since he has been in analysis he has come to discover that he remains with Eleanor for more essential reasons than mere responsibility. Even if there were no children, he would probably cleave to her.

Unhappily, it is more complicated than that. She is always—to use their phrase—competing with him. At those times when I do not like Eleanor, I am irritated by her lack of honesty. She is too sharp-tongued, and she does not often give Sam what he needs most, a steady flow of uncritical encouragement to counteract the harshness with which he views himself. Like so many who are articulate on the subject, Eleanor will tell you that she resents being a woman. As Sam is disappointed in life, so is Eleanor. She feels Sam has cheated her from a proper development of her potentialities and talent, even as Sam feels cheated. I call her dishonest because she is not so ready as Sam to put the blame on herself.

Sam, of course, can say all this himself. It is just that he experiences it in a somewhat different way. Like most men who have been married for ten years, Eleanor is not quite real to him. Last night at the party, there were perhaps half a dozen people whom he met for the first time, and he talked animatedly with them, sensing their reactions, feeling their responses, aware of the life in them, as they were aware of the life in him. Eleanor, however, exists in his nerves. She is a rather vague embodiment, he thinks of her as "she" most of the time, someone to conceal things from. Invariably, he feels uneasy with her. It is too bad. No matter how inevitable, I am always sorry when love melts into that pomade of affection, resentment, boredom and occasional compassion which is the best we may expect of a man and woman who have lived together a long time. So often, it is worse, so often no more than hatred.

They are eating breakfast now, and Eleanor is chatting about the party. She is pretending to be jealous about a young girl in a strapless evening gown, and indeed, she does not have to pretend altogether. Sam, with liquor inside him, had been leaning over the girl; obviously he had coveted her. Yet, this morning, when Eleanor begins to talk about her, Sam tries to be puzzled.

"Which girl was it now?" he asks a second time.

"Oh, you know, the hysteric," Eleanor says, "the one who was parading her bazooms in your face." Eleanor has ways of impressing certain notions upon Sam. "She's Charlie's new girl."

"I didn't know that," Sam mutters. "He didn't seem to be near her all evening."

Eleanor spread marmalade over her toast and takes a bite with evident enjoyment. "Apparently, they're all involved. Charles was funny about it. He said he's come to the conclusion that the great affairs of history are between hysterical women and detached men."

"Charles hates women," Sam says smugly. "If you notice, almost everything he says about them is a discharge of aggression." Sam has the best of reasons for not liking Charles. It takes more than ordinary character for a middle-aged husband to approve of a friend who moves easily from woman to woman.

"At least Charles discharges his aggression," Eleanor remarks. "He's almost a classic example of the Don Juan complex. You notice how masochistic his women are?"

"I know a man or two who's just as masochistic."

Sam sips his coffee. "What made you say the girl was an hysteric?"

Eleanor shrugs. "She's an actress. And I could see she was a tease."

"You can't jump to conclusions," Sam lectures. "I had the impression she was a compulsive. Don't forget you've got to distinguish between the outer defenses, and the more deeply rooted conflicts."

I must confess that this conversation bores me. As a sample it is representative of the way Sam and Eleanor talk to each other. In Sam's defense I can say nothing; he has always been too partial to jargon.

I am often struck by how eager we are to reveal all sorts of supposedly ugly secrets about ourselves. We can explain the hatred we feel for our parents, we are rather pleased with the perversions to which we are prone. We seem determinedly proud to be superior to ourselves. No motive is too terrible for our inspection. Let someone hint, however, that we have bad table manners and we fly into a rage. Sam will agree to anything you may say about him, provided it is sufficiently serious —he will be the first to agree he has fantasies of murdering his wife. But tell him that he is afraid of waiters, or imply to Eleanor that she is a nag, and they will be quite annoyed.

Sam has noticed this himself. There are times when he can hear the jargon in his voice, and it offends him. Yet, he seems powerless to change his habits.

An example: He is sitting in an armchair now, brooding upon his breakfast, while Eleanor does the dishes. The two daughters are not home; they have gone to visit their grandmother for the week-end. Sam had encouraged the visit. He had looked forward to the liberty Eleanor and himself would enjoy. For the past few weeks the children had seemed to make the most impossible demands upon his attention. Yet now they are gone and he misses them, he even misses their noise. Sam, however, cannot accept the notion that many people are dissatisfied with the present, and either dream of the past or anticipate the future. Sam must call this "ambivalence over possessions." Once he even felt obliged to ask his analyst, Dr. Sergius, if ambivalence over possessions did not characterize him almost perfectly, and Sergius whom I always picture with the flat precision of a coin's head—bald skull and horn-rimmed glasses—answered in his German accent, "But, my dear Mr. Slovoda, as I have told you, it would make me happiest if you did not include in your reading, these psychoanalytical text-works."

At such rebukes, Sam can only wince. It is so right, he tells himself, he is exactly the sort of ambitious fool who uses big words when small ones would do.

I I

While Sam sits in the armchair, gray winter light is entering the windows, snow falls outside. He sits alone in a modern seat, staring at the gray, green, and beige décor of their living room. Eleanor was a painter before they were married, and she has arranged this room. It is very pleasant, but like many husbands, Sam resents it, resents the reproductions of modern painters upon the wall, the slender coffee table, a free-form poised like a spider on wire legs, its feet set onto a straw rug. In the corner, most odious of all, is the playmate of his children, a hippopotamus of a television-radio-and-phonograph cabinet with the blind monstrous snout of the video tube.

Eleanor has set the Sunday paper near his hand. Soon, Sam intends to go to work. For a year, he has been giving a day once or twice a month to a bit of thought and a little writing on a novel he hopes to begin sometime. Last night, he told himself he would work today. But he has little enthusiasm now. He is tired, he is too depressed. Writing for the comic strips seems to exhaust his imagination.

Sam reads the paper as if he were peeling an enormous banana. Flap after flap of newsprint is stripped away and cast upon the straw rug until only the Magazine Section is left. Sam glances through it with restless irritability. A biography of a political figure runs its flatulent prose into the giant crossword puzzle at the back. An account of a picturesque corner of the city becomes lost in statistics and exhortations on juvenile delinquency, finally to emerge with photographs about the new style of living which desert architecture provides. Sam looks at a wall of windows in rotogravure with a yucca tree framing the pool.

There is an article about a workingman. His wife and his family are described, his apartment, his salary and his budget. Sam reads a description of what the worker has every evening for dinner, and how he spends each night of the week. The essay makes its point; the typical American workingman must watch his pennies, but he is nonetheless secure and serene. He would not exchange his life for another.

Sam is indignant. A year ago he had written a similar article in an attempt to earn some extra money. Subtly, or so
he thought, he had suggested that the average workingman
was raddled with insecurity. Naturally, the article had been
rejected.

Sam throws the Magazine Section away. Moments of such
anger torment him frequently. Despite himself, Sam is enraged at editorial dishonesty, at the smooth strifeless world
which such articles present. How angry he is—how angry and
how helpless. "It is the actions of men and not their sentiments which make history," he thinks to himself, and smiles
wryly. In his living room he would go out to tilt the wind-
mills of a vast, powerful, and hypocritical society; in his week
of work he labors in an editorial cubicle to create spaceships,
violent death, women with golden tresses and wanton breasts,
men who act with their fists and speak with patriotic slogans.

I know what Sam feels. As he sits in the armchair, the
Sunday papers are strewn around him, carrying their war news,
their murders, their parleys, their entertainments, mummery
of a real world which no one can grasp. It is terribly frustrat-
ing. One does not know where to begin.

Today, Sam considers himself half a fool for having been
a radical. There is no longer much consolation in the thought
that the majority of men who succeed in a corrupt and ac-
quisitive socity are themselves obligatorily corrupt, and one's
failure is therefore the price of one's idealism. Sam cannot
recapture the pleasurable bitterness which resides in the notion that one has suffered for one's principles. Sergius is too
hard on him for that.

They have done a lot of work on the subject. Sergius feels
that Sam's concern with world affairs has always been spurious.
For example, they have uncovered in analysis that Sam wrote
his article about the worker in such a way as to make certain

it would be refused. Sam, after all, hates editors; to have such
a piece accepted would mean he is no better than they, that
he is a mediocrity. So long as he fails he is not obliged to
measure himself. Sam, therefore, is being unrealistic. He re-
jects the world with his intellect, and this enables him not
to face the more direct realities of his present life.

Sam will argue with Sergius but it is very difficult. He will
say, "Perhaps you sneer at radicals because it is more comfortable to ignore such ideas. Once you became interested it
might introduce certain unpleasant changes in your life."

"Why," says Sergius, "do you feel it so necessary to assume
that I am a bourgeois interested only in my comfort?"

"How can I discuss these things," says Sam, "if you insist
that my opinions are the expression of neurotic needs, and
your opinions are merely dispassionate medical advice?"

"You are so anxious to defeat me in an argument," Sergius
will reply. "Would you admit it is painful to relinquish the
sense of importance which intellectual discussion provides
you?"

I believe Sergius has his effect. Sam often has thoughts these
days which would have been repellent to him years ago. For
instance, at the moment, Sam is thinking it might be better
to live the life of a worker, a simple life, to be completely
absorbed with such necessities as food and money. Then one
could believe that to be happy it was necessary only to have
more money, more goods, less worries. It would be nice, Sam
thinks wistfully, to believe that the source of one's unhappi-
ness comes not from oneself, but from the fault of the boss,
or the world, or bad luck.

Sam has these casual daydreams frequently. He likes to
think about other lives he might have led, and he envies the
most astonishing variety of occupations. It is easy enough to
see why he should wish for the life of an executive with the

power and sense of command it may offer, but virtually from the same impulse Sam will wish himself a bohemian living in an unheated loft, his life a catch-as-catch-can from day to day. Once after reading an article, Sam even wished himself a priest. For about ten minutes it seemed beautiful to him to surrender his life to God. Such fancies are common, I know. It is just that I, far better than Sam, know how serious he really is, how fanciful, how elaborate, his imagination can be.

The phone is ringing. Sam can hear Eleanor shouting at him to answer. He picks up the receiver with a start. It is Marvin Rossman who is an old friend, and Marvin has an unusual request. They talk for several minutes, and Sam squirms a little in his seat. As he is about to hang up, he laughs. "Why, no, Marvin, it gives me a sense of adventure," he says.

Eleanor has come into the room toward the end of this conversation. "What is it all about?" she asks.

Sam is obviously a bit agitated. Whenever he attempts to be most casual, Eleanor can well suspect him. "It seems," he says slowly, "that Marvin has acquired a pornographic movie."

"From whom?" Eleanor asks.

"He said something about an old boy friend of Louise's."

Eleanor laughs. "I can't imagine Louise having an old boy friend with a dirty movie."

"Well, people are full of surprises," Sam says mildly.

"Look, here," says Eleanor suddenly. "Why did he call us?"

"It was about our projector."

"They want to use it?" Eleanor asks.

"That's right." Sam hesitates. "I invited them over."

"Did it ever occur to you I might want to spend my Sunday some other way?" Eleanor asks crossly.

"We're not doing anything." Sam mumbles. Like most

men, he feels obliged to act quite nonchalantly about pornography. "I'll tell you. I am sort of curious about the film. I've never seen one, you know."

"Try anything once, is that it?"

"Something of the sort." Sam is trying to conceal his excitement. The truth is that in common with most of us, he is fascinated by pornography. It is a minor preoccupation, but more from lack of opportunity than anything else. Once or twice, Sam has bought the sets of nude photographs which are sold in marginal bookstores, and with guilty excitement has hidden them in the apartment.

"Oh, this is silly," Eleanor says. "You were going to work today."

"I'm just not in the mood."

"I'll have to feed them," Eleanor complains. "Do we have enough liquor?"

"We can get beer," Sam pauses. "Alan Sperber and his wife are coming too."

"Sam, you're a child."

"Look, Eleanor," says Sam, controlling his voice, "if it's too much trouble, I can take the projector over there."

"I ought to make you do that."

"Am I such an idiot that I must consult you before I invite friends to the house?"

Eleanor has the intuition that Sam, if he allowed himself, could well drown in pornography. She is quite annoyed at him, but she would never dream of allowing Sam to take the projector over to Marvin Rossman's where he could view the movie without her—that seems indefinably dangerous. Besides she would like to see it, too. The mother in Eleanor is certain it cannot hurt her.

"All right, Sam," she says, "but you are a child."

More exactly, an adolescent, Sam decides. Ever since Marvin

phoned, Sam has felt the nervous glee of an adolescent locking himself in the bathroom. Anal fixation, Sam thinks automatically.

While Eleanor goes down to buy beer and cold cuts in a
delicatessen, Sam gets out the projector and begins to clean
it. He is far from methodical in this. He knows the machine
is all right, he has shown movies of Eleanor and his daughters
only a few weeks ago, but from the moment Eleanor left the
apartment, Sam has been consumed by an anxiety that the
projection bulb is burned out. Once he has examined it, he
begins to fret about the motor. He wonders if it needs oiling,
he blunders through a drawer of household tools looking for
an oilcan. It is ridiculous. Sam knows that what he is trying
to keep out of his mind are the reactions Sergius will have.
Sergius will want to "work through" all of Sam's reasons for
seeing the movie. Well, Sam tells himself, he knows in advance what will be discovered: detachment, not wanting to
accept Eleanor as a sexual partner, evasion of responsibility,
etc. etc. The devil with Sergius. Sam has never seen a dirty
movie, and he certainly wants to.

He feels obliged to laugh at himself. He could not be more
nervous, he knows, if he were about to make love to a woman
he had never touched before. It is really disgraceful.

When Eleanor comes back, Sam hovers about her. He is
uncomfortable with her silence. "I suppose they'll be here
soon," Sam says.

"Probably."

Sam does not know if he is angry at Eleanor or apprehensive that she is angry at him. Much to his surprise he catches
her by the waist and hears himself saying, "You know, maybe
tonight when they're gone . . . I mean, we do have the apartment, to ourselves." Eleanor moves neither toward him nor

away from him. "Darling, it's not because of the movie," Sam goes on, "I swear. Don't you think maybe we could . . ."

"Maybe," says Eleanor.

III

The company has arrived, and it may be well to say a word or two about them. Marvin Rossman who has brought the film is a dentist, although it might be more accurate to describe him as a frustrated doctor. Rossman is full of statistics and items of odd information about the malpractice of physicians, and he will tell these things in his habitually gloomy voice, a voice so slow, so sad, that it almost conceals the humor of his remarks. Or, perhaps, that is what creates his humor. In his spare time, he is a sculptor, and if Eleanor may be trusted, he is not without talent. I often picture him working in the studio loft he has rented, his tall bony frame the image of dejection. He will put a piece of clay to the armature, he will rub it sadly with his thumb, he will shrug, he does not believe that anything of merit could come from him. When he talked to Sam over the phone, he was pessimistic about the film they were to see. "It can't be any good," he said in his melancholy voice. "I know it'll be a disappointment." Like Sam, he has a mustache, but Rossman's will droop at the corners.

Alan Sperber who has come with Rossman is the subject of some curiosity for the Slovodas. He is not precisely womanish; in fact, he is a large plump man, but his voice is too soft, his manners too precise. He is genial, yet he is finicky; waspish, yet bland; he is fond of telling long rather affected stories, he is always prepared with a new one, but to general conversation he contributes little. As a lawyer, he seems miscast. One cannot imagine him inspiring a client to confidence. He is the sort of heavy florid man who seems boyish at forty, and the bow ties and gray flannel suits he wears do not make him appear more mature.

Roslyn Sperber, his wife, used to be a schoolteacher, and she is a quiet nervous woman who talks a great deal when she is drunk. She is normally quite pleasant, and has only one habit which is annoying to any degree. It is a little flaw, but social life is not unlike marriage in that habit determines far more than vice or virtue. This mannerism which has become so offensive to the friends of the Sperbers is Roslyn's social pretension. Perhaps I should say intellectual pretension. She entertains people as if she were conducting a salon, and in her birdlike voice is forever forcing her guests to accept still another intellectual canapé. "You must hear Sam's view of the world market," she will say, or "Has Louise told you her statistics on divorce?" It is quite pathetic for she is so eager to please. I have seen her eyes fill with tears at a sharp word from Alan.

Marvin Rossman's wife, Louise, is a touch grim and definite in her opinions. She is a social welfare worker, and will declare herself with force whenever conversation impinges on those matters where she is expert. She is quite opposed to psychoanalysis, and will say without quarter, "It's all very well for people in the upper-middle area"—she is referring to the upper middle class—"but, it takes more than a couch to solve the problems of . . ." and she will list narcotics, juvenile delinquency, psychosis, relief distribution, slum housing, and other descriptions of our period. She recites these categories with an odd anticipation. One would guess she was ordering a meal.

Sam is fond of Marvin but he cannot abide Louise. "You'd think she discovered poverty," he will complain to Eleanor.

The Slovodas do feel superior to the Rossmans and the

Sperbers. If pressed, they could not offer the most convincing explanation why. I suppose what it comes down to is that Sam and Eleanor do not think of themselves as really belonging to a class, and they feel that the Sperbers and Rossmans are petit-bourgeois. I find it hard to explain their attitude. Their company feels as much discomfort and will apologize as often as the Slovodas for the money they have, and the money they hope to earn. They are all of them equally concerned with progressive education and the methods of raising children to be well adjusted—indeed, they are discussing that now—they consider themselves relatively free of sexual taboo, or put more properly, Sam and Eleanor are no less possessive than the others. The Slovodas' culture is not more profound; I should be hard put to say that Sam is more widely read, more seriously informed, than Marvin or Alan, or for that matter, Louise. Probably, it comes to this: Sam, in his heart, thinks himself a rebel, and there are few rebels who do not claim an original mind. Eleanor has been a bohemian and considers herself more sophisticated than her friends who merely went to college and got married. Louise Rossman could express it most soundly. "Artists, writers, and people of the creative layer have in their occupational ideology the belief that they are classless."

One thing I might remark about the company. They are all being the most unconscionable hypocrites. They have rushed across half the city of New York to see a pornographic film, and they are not at all interested in each other at the moment. The women are giggling like tickled children at remarks which cannot possibly be so funny. Yet, they are all determined to talk for a respectable period of time. No less, it must be serious talk. Roslyn has said once, "I feel so funny at the thought of seeing such a movie," and the others have passed her statement by.

At the moment, Sam is talking about value. I might note that Sam loves conversation and thrives when he can expound an idea.

"What are our values today?" he asks. "It's really fantastic when you stop to think of it. Take any bright talented kid who's getting out of college now."

"My kid brother, for example," Marvin interposes morosely. He passes his bony hand over his sad mustache, and somehow the remark has become amusing, much as if Marvin had said, "Oh, yes, you have reminded me of the trials, the worries, and the cares which my fabulous younger brother heaps upon me."

"All right, take him," Sam says. "What does he want to be?"

"He doesn't want to be anything," says Marvin.

"That's my point," Sam says excitedly. "Rather than work at certain occupations, the best of these kids would rather do nothing at all."

"Alan has a cousin," Roslyn says, "who swears he'll wash dishes before he becomes a businessman."

"I wish that were true," Eleanor interrupts. "It seems to me everybody is conforming more and more these days."

They argue about this. Sam and Eleanor claim the country is suffering from hysteria; Alan Sperber disagrees and says it's merely a reflection of the headlines; Louise says no adequate criteria exist to measure hysteria; Marvin says he doesn't know anything at all.

"More solid liberal gains are being made in this period," says Alan, "than you would believe. Consider the Negro—"

"Is the Negro any less maladjusted?" Eleanor shouts with passion.

Sam maneuvers the conversation back to his thesis. "The values of the young today, and by the young I mean the cream of the kids, the ones with ideas, are a reaction of indifference to the culture crisis. It really is despair. All they know is what they don't want to do."

"That is easier," Alan says genially.

"It's not altogether unhealthy," Sam says. "It's a corrective for smugness and the false value of the past, but it has created new false value." He thinks it worth emphasizing. "False value seems always to beget further false value."

"Define your terms," says Louise, the scientist.

"No, look," Sam says, "there's no revolt, there's no acceptance. Kids today don't want to get married, and—"

Eleanor interrupts. "Why should a girl rush to get married? She loses all chance for developing herself."

Sam shrugs. They are all talking at once. "Kids don't want to get married," he repeats, "and they don't want not to get married. They merely drift."

"It's a problem we'll all have to face with our own kids in ten years," Alan says, "although I think you make too much of it, Sam."

"My daughter," Marvin states. "She's embarrassed I'm a dentist. Even more embarrassed than I am." They laugh.

Sam tells a story about his youngest. Carol Ann. It seems he had a fight with her, and she went to her room. Sam followed, he called through the door.

"No answer," Sam says. "I called her again, 'Carol Ann.' I was a little worried you understand, because she seemed so upset, so I said to her, 'Carol Ann, you know I love you.' What do you think she answered?"

"What?" asks Roslyn.

"She said, 'Daddie, why are you so anxious?' "

They all laugh again. There are murmurs about what a clever thing it was to say. In the silence which follows, Roslyn leans forward and says quickly in her high voice, "You must get Alan to tell you his wonderful story about the man who studied yogi."

"Yoga," Alan corrects. "It's too long to tell."

The company prevails on him.

"Well," says Alan, in his genial courtroom voice, "it concerns a friend of mine named Cassius O'Shaugnessy."

"You don't mean Jerry O'Shaugnessy, do you?" asks Sam.

Alan does not know Jerry O'Shaugnessy. "No, no, this is Cassius O'Shaugnessy," he says. "He's really quite an extraordinary fellow." Alan sits plumply in his chair, fingering his bow tie. They are all used to his stories, which are told in a formal style and exhibit the attempt to recapture a certain note of urbanity, wit, and élan which Alan has probably copied from someone else. Sam and Eleanor respect his ability to tell these stories, but they resent the fact that he talks at them.

"You'd think we were a jury of his inferiors," Eleanor has said. "I hate being talked down to." What she resents is Alan's quiet implication that his antecedents, his social position, in total his life outside the room is superior to the life within. Eleanor now takes the promise from Alan's story by remarking, "Yes, and lets see the movie when Alan has finished.

"Ssh," Roslyn says.

"Cassius was at college a good while before me," says Alan, "but I knew him while I was an undergraduate. He would drop in and visit from time to time. An absolutely extraordinary fellow. The most amazing career. You see, he's done about everything."

"I love the way Alan tells it," Roslyn pipes nervously.

"Cassius was in France with Dos Passos and Cummings, he was even arrested with e.e. After the war, he was one of the founders of the Dadaist school, and for a while I understand he was Fitzgerald's guide to the gold of the Côte d'Azur. He knew everybody, he did everything. Do you realize that before the twenties had ended. Cassius had managed his father's business and then entered a monastery? It is said he influenced T. S. Eliot."

"Today, we'd call Cassius a psychopath," Marvin observes.

"Cassius called himself a great dilettante," Alan answers, "although perhaps the nineteenth-century Russian conception of the great sinner would be more appropriate. What do you say if I tell you this was only the beginning of his career?"

"What's the point?" Louise asks.

"Not yet," says Alan, holding up a hand. His manner seems to say that if his audience cannot appreciate the story, he does not feel obliged to continue. "Cassius studied Marx in the monastery. He broke his vows, quit the Church, and became a Communist. All through the thirties he was a figure in the Party, going to Moscow, involved in all the Party struggles. He left only during the Moscow trials."

Alan's manner while he relates such stories is somewhat effeminate. He talks with little caresses of his hand, he mentions names and places with a lingering ease as if to suggest that his audience and he are aware, above all, of nuance. The story as Alan tells it is drawn overlong. Suffice it that the man about whom he is talking, Cassius O'Shaugnessy, becomes a Trotskyist, becomes an anarchist, is a pacifist during the second World War, and suffers it from a prison cell.

"I may say," Alan goes on, "that I worked for his defense, and was successful in getting him acquitted. Imagine my dolor when I learned that he had turned his back on his anarchist friends and was living with gangsters."

"This is weird," Eleanor says.

"Weird, it is," Alan agrees. "Cassius got into some scrape,

and disappeared. What could you do with him? I learned only recently that he had gone to India and was studying yoga. In fact, I learned it from Cassius himself. I asked him of his experiences at Brahna-puth-thar, and he told me the following story."

Now Alan's voice alters, he assumes the part of Cassius and speaks in a tone weary of experience, wise and sad in its knowledge. " 'I was sitting on my haunches contemplating my navel,' Cassius said to me, 'when of a sudden I discovered my navel under a different aspect. It seemed to me that if I were to give a counter-clockwise twist, my navel would unscrew.' "

Alan looks up, he surveys his audience which is now rapt and uneasy, not certain as yet whether a joke is to come. Alan's thumb and forefinger pluck at the middle of his ample belly, his feet are crossed upon the carpet in symbolic suggestion of Cassius upon his haunches.

" 'Taking a deep breath, I turned, and the abysses of Vishtarni loomed beneath. My navel had begun to unscrew. I knew I was about to accept the reward of three years of contemplation. So,' said Cassius, 'I turned again, and my navel unscrewed a little more. I turned and I turned,' " Alan's fingers now revolving upon his belly, " 'and after a period I knew that with one more turn my navel would unscrew itself forever. At the edge of revelation, I took one sweet breath, and turned my navel free.' "

Alan looks up at his audience.

" 'Damn,' said Cassius, 'if my ass didn't fall off.' "

IV

The story has left the audience in an exasperated mood. It has been a most untypical story for Alan to tell, a little out of place, not offensive exactly, but irritating and inconsequential. Sam is the only one to laugh with more than bewildered courtesy, and his mirth seems excessive to everyone but Alan, and of course, Roslyn, who feels as if she has been the producer. I suppose what it reduces to, is a lack of taste. Perhaps that is why Alan is not the lawyer one would expect. He does not have that appreciation—as necessary in his trade as for an actor—of what is desired at any moment, of that which will encourage as opposed to that which does not encourage a stimulating but smooth progression of logic and sentiment. Only a fool would tell so long a story when everyone is awaiting the movie.

Now, they are preparing. The men shift armchairs to correspond with the couch, the projector is set up, the screen is unfolded. Sam attempts to talk while he is threading the film, but no one listens. They seem to realize suddenly that a frightful demand has been placed upon them. One does not study pornography in a living room with a beer glass in one's hand, and friends at the elbow. It is the most unsatisfactory of compromises; one can draw neither the benefits of solitary contemplation nor of social exchange. There is, at bottom, the same exasperated fright which one experiences in turning the shower tap and receiving cold water when the flesh has been prepared for heat. Perhaps that is why they are laughing so much now that the movie is begun.

A title, *The Evil Act*, twitches on the screen, shot with scars, holes, and the dust lines of age. A man and woman are sitting on a couch, they are having coffee. They chat. What they say is conveyed by printed words upon an ornately flowered card, interjected between glimpses of their casual gestures, a cup to the mouth, a smile, a cigarette being lit. The man's name, it seems, is Frankie Idell; he is talking to his wife, Magnolia. Frankie is dark, he is sinister, he confides in Magnolia, his dark counterpart, with a grimace of his brows, black from make-up pencil.

This is what the titles read:

FRANKIE: She will be here soon.
MAGNOLIA: This time the little vixen will not escape.
FRANKIE: No, my dear, this time we are prepared.
(He looks at his watch.)
FRANKIE: Listen, she knocks!

There is a shot of a tall blond woman knocking on the door. She is probably over thirty, but by her short dress and rib-boned hat it is suggested that she is a girl of fifteen.

FRANKIE: Come in, Eleanor.

As may be expected, the audience laughs hysterically at this. It is so wonderful a coincidence. "How I remember Frankie," says Eleanor Slovoda, and Roslyn Sperber is the only one not amused. In the midst of the others' laughter, she says in a worried tone, obviously adrift upon her own concerns, "Do you think we'll have to stop the film in the middle to let the bulb cool off?" The others hoot, they giggle, they are weak from the combination of their own remarks and the action of the plot.

Frankie and Magnolia have sat down on either side of the heroine, Eleanor. A moment passes. Suddenly, stiffly, they attack. Magnolia from her side kisses Eleanor, and Frankie commits an indecent caress.

ELEANOR: How dare you? Stop!
MAGNOLIA: Scream, my little one. It will do you no good. The walls are soundproofed.

FRANKIE: We've fixed a way to make you come across.
ELEANOR: This is hideous. I am hitherto undefiled. Do not touch me!

The captions fade away. A new title takes their place. It says, *But There Is No Escape From The Determined Pair.* On the fade-in, we discover Eleanor in the most distressing situation. Her hands are tied to loops running from the ceiling, and she can only writhe in helpless perturbation before the deliberate and progressive advances of Frankie and Magnolia. Slowly they humiliate her, with relish they probe her.

The audience laughs no longer. A hush has come upon them. Eyes unblinking they devour the images upon Sam Slovoda's screen.

Eleanor is without clothing. As the last piece is pulled away, Frankie and Magnolia circle about her in a grotesque of pantomime, a leering of lips, limbs in a distortion of desire. Eleanor faints. Adroitly, Magnolia cuts her bonds. We see Frankie carrying her inert body.

Now, Eleanor is trussed to a bed, and the husband and wife are tormenting her with feathers. Bodies curl upon the bed in postures so complicated, in combinations so advanced, that the audience leans forward, Sperbers, Rossmans, and Slovodas, as if tempted to embrace the moving images. The hands trace abstract circles upon the screen, passes and recoveries upon a white background so illumined that hollows and swells, limb to belly and mouth to undescribables, tip of a nipple, orb of a navel, swim in giant magnification, flow and slide in a lurching yawing fall, blotting out the camera eye.

A little murmur, all unconscious, passes from their lips. The audience sways, each now finally lost in himself, communing hungrily with shadows, violated or violating, fantasy triumphant.

At picture's end, Eleanor the virgin whore is released from

the bed. She kisses Frankie, she kisses Magnolia. "You dears," she says, "let's do it again." The projector lamp burns empty light, the machine keeps turning, the tag of film goes slap-tap, slap-tap, slap-tap, slap-tap, slap-tap, sla-ta.

"Sam, turn it off," says Eleanor.

But when the room lights are on, they cannot look at one another. "Can we see it again?" someone mutters. So, again. Eleanor knocks on the door, is tied, defiled, ravished, and made rapturous. They watch it soberly now, the room hot with the heat of their bodies, the darkness a balm for orgiastic vision. To the Deer Park, Sam is thinking, to the Deer Park of Louis XV were brought the most beautiful maidens of France, and there they stayed, dressed in fabulous silks, perfumed and wigged, the mole drawn upon their cheek, ladies of pleasure awaiting the pleasure of the king. So Louis had stripped an empire, bankrupt a treasury, prepared a deluge, while in his garden on summer evenings the maidens performed their pageants, eighteenth-century tableaux of the evil act, beauteous instruments of one man's desire, lewd translation of a king's power. That century men sought wealth so they might use its fruits; this epoch men lusted for power in order to amass more power, a compounding of power into pyramids of abstraction whose yield are cannon and wire enclosure, pillars of statistics to the men who are the kings of this century and do no more in power's leisure time than go to church, claim to love their wives, and eat vegetables.

Is it possible, Sam wonders, that each of them here, two Rossmans, two Sperbers, two Slovodas, will cast off their clothes when the movie is done and perform the orgy which tickles at the heart of their desire? They will not, he knows, they will make jokes when the projector is put away, they will gorge the plate of delicatessen Eleanor provides, and swallow more beer, he among them. He will be the first to make jokes.

Sam is right. The movie has made him extraordinarily alive to the limits of them all. While they sit with red faces, eyes bugged, glutting sandwiches of ham, salami, and tongue, he begins the teasing.

"Roslyn," he calls out, "is the bulb cooled off yet?"

She cannot answer him. She chokes on beer, her face glazes, she is helpless with self-protecting laughter.

"Why are you so anxious, Daddie?" Eleanor says quickly.

They begin to discuss the film. As intelligent people they must dominate it. Someone wonders about the actors in the piece, and discussion begins afresh. "I fail to see," says Louise, "why they should be hard to classify. Pornography is a job to the criminal and prostitute element."

"No, you won't find an ordinary prostitute doing this," Sam insists. "It requires a particular kind of personality."

"They have to be exhibitionists," says Eleanor.

"It's all economic," Louise maintains.

"I wonder what those girls felt?" Roslyn asks. "I feel sorry for them."

"I'd like to be the cameraman," says Alan.

"I'd like to be Frankie," says Marvin sadly.

There is a limit to how long such a conversation may continue. The jokes lapse into silence. They are all busy eating. When they begin to talk again, it is of other things. Each dollop of food sops the agitation which the movie has spilled. They gossip about the party the night before, they discuss which single men were interested in which women, who got drunk, who got sick, who said the wrong thing, who went home with someone else's date. When this is exhausted, one of them mentions a play the others have not seen. Soon they are talking about books, a concert, a one-man show by an artist who is a friend. Dependably, conversation will voyage its orbit. While the men talk of politics, the women are discus-

sing fashions, progressive schools, and recipes they have attempted. Sam is uncomfortable with the division; he knows
Eleanor will resent it, he knows she will complain later of the
insularity of men and the basic contempt they feel for wom-
en's intelligence.

"But you collaborated," Sam will argue. "No one forced you
to be with the women."

"Was I to leave them alone?" Eleanor will answer.

"Well, why do the women always have to go off by themselves?"

"Because the men aren't interested in what we have to say."

Sam sighs. He has been talking with interest, but really he
is bored. These are nice pleasant people, he thinks, but they
are ordinary people, exactly the sort he has spent so many
years with, making little jokes, little gossip, living little everyday events, a close circle where everyone mothers the other
by his presence. The womb of middle-class life, Sam decides
heavily. He is in a bad mood indeed. Everything is laden with
dissatisfaction.

Alan has joined the women. He delights in preparing odd
dishes when friends visit the Sperbers, and he is describing to
Eleanor how he makes blueberry pancakes. Marvin draws
closer to Sam.

"I wanted to tell you," he says, "Alan's story reminded me.
I saw Jerry O'Shaugnessy the other day."

"Where was he?"

Marvin is hesitant. "It was a shock, Sam. He's on the
Bowery. I guess he's become a wino."

"He always drank a lot," says Sam.

"Yeah." Marvin cracks his bony knuckles. "What a stinking time this is, Sam."

"It's probably like the years after 1905 in Russia," Sam says.

"No revolutionary party will come out of this."

"No," Sam says, "nothing will come."

He is thinking of Jerry O'Shaugnessy. What did he look like? what did he say? Sam asks Marvin, and clucks his tongue at the dispiriting answer. It is a shock to him. He draws closer to Marvin, he feels a bond. They have, after all, been through some years together. In the thirties they have been in the Communist Party, they have quit together, they are both weary of politics today, still radicals out of habit, but without enthusiasm and without a cause. "Jerry was a hero to me," Sam says.

"To all of us," says Marvin.

The fabulous Jerry O'Shaugnessy, thinks Sam. In the old days, in the Party, they had made a legend of him. All of them with their middle-class origins and their desire to know a worker-hero.

I may say that I was never as fond of Jerry O'Shaugnessy as was Sam. I thought him a showman and too pleased with himself. Sam, however, with his timidity, his desire to travel, to have adventure and know many women, was obliged to adore O'Shaugnessy. At least he was enraptured with his career.

Poor Jerry who ends as a bum. He has been everything else. He has been a trapper in Alaska, a chauffeur for gangsters, an officer in the Foreign Legion, a labor organizer. His nose was broken, there were scars on his chin. When he would talk about his years at sea or his experiences in Spain, the stenographers and garment workers, the radio writers and unemployed actors would listen to his speeches as if he were the prophet of new romance, and their blood would be charged with the magic of revolutionary vision. A man with tremendous charm. In those days it had been easy to confuse his love for himself with his love for all underprivileged working-men.

"I thought he was still in the Party," Sam says.

"No," says Marvin, "I remember they kicked him out a couple of years ago. He was supposed to have piddled some funds, that's what they say."

"I wish he'd taken the treasury," Sam remarks bitterly. "The Party used him for years."

Marvin shrugs. "They used each other." His mustache droops. "Let me tell you about Sonderson. You know he's still in the Party. The most progressive dentist in New York." They laugh.

While Marvin tells the story, Sam is thinking of other things. Since he has quit Party work, he has studied a great deal. He can tell you about prison camps and the secret police, political murders, the Moscow trials, the exploitation of Soviet labor, the privileges of the bureaucracy, it is all painful to him. He is straddled between the loss of a country he has never seen, and his repudiation of the country in which he lives. "Doesn't the Party seem a horror now?" he bursts out.

Marvin nods. They are trying to comprehend the distance between Party members they have known, people by turn pathetic, likable, or annoying—people not unlike themselves —and in contrast the immensity of historic logic which deploys along statistics of the dead.

"It's all schizoid," Sam says. "Modern life is schizoid."

Marvin agrees. They have agreed on this many times, bored with the petulance of their small voices, yet needing the comfort of such compaints. Marvin asks Sam if he has given up his novel, and Sam says. "Temporarily." He cannot find a form, he explains. He does not want to write a realistic novel, because reality is no longer realistic. "I don't know what it is," says Sam. "To tell you the truth, I think I'm kidding myself. I'll never finish this book. I just like to entertain the idea I'll do something good some day." They sit there in friendly depression. Conversation has cooled. Alan and the women are no longer talking.

"Marvin," asks Louise, "what time is it?"

They are ready to go. Sam must say directly what he had hoped to approach by suggestion. "I was wondering," he whispers to Rossman, "would you mind if I held onto the film for a day or two?"

Marvin looks at him. "Oh, why of course, Sam," he says in his morose voice. "I know how it is." He pats Sam on the shoulder as if, symbolically, to convey the exchange of owner-ship. They are fellow conspirators.

"If you ever want to borrow the projector," Sam suggests.

"Nah," says Marvin, "I don't know that it would make much difference."

It has been, when all is said, a most annoying day. As Sam and Eleanor tidy the apartment, emptying ash trays and wash-ing the few dishes, they are fond neither of themselves nor each other. "What a waste today has been," Eleanor remarks, and Sam can only agree. He has done no writing, he has not been outdoors, and still it is late in the evening, and he has talked too much, eaten too much, is nervous from the movie they have seen. He knows that he will watch it again with Eleanor before they go to sleep; she has given her assent to that. But as is so often the case with Sam these days, he cannot await their embrace with any sure anticipation. Eleanor may be in the mood or Eleanor may not; there is no way he can control the issue. It is depressing; Sam knows that he circles about Eleanor at such times with the guilty maneuvers of a sad hound. Resent her as he must, be furious with himself as he will, there is not very much he can do about it. Often, after they have made love, they will lie beside each other in silence, each offended, each certain the other is to blame. At such times, memory tickles them with a cruel feather. Not

always has it been like this. When they were first married, and
indeed for the six months they lived together before marriage,
everything was quite different. Their affair was very exciting
to them; each told the other with some hyperbole but no real
mistruth that no one in the parst had ever been comparable
as lover.

I suppose I am a romantic. I always feel that this is the
best time in people's lives. There is, after all, so little we accomplish, and that short period when we are beloved and
triumph as lovers is sweet with power. Rarely are we concerned then with our lack of importance; we are too important. In Sam's case, disillusion means even more. Like so many
young men, he entertained the secret conceit that he was an
extraordinary lover. One cannot really believe this without
supporting at the same time the equally secret conviction that
one is fundamentally inept. It is—no matter what Sergius
would say—a more dramatic and therefore more attractive view
of oneself than the sober notion which Sam now accepts with
grudging wisdom, that the man as lover is dependent upon
the bounty of the woman. As I say, he accepts the notion, it
is one of the lineaments of maturity but there is a part of him
which, no matter how harried by analysis, cannot relinquish
the antagonism he feels that Eleanor has respected his private
talent so poorly, and has not allowed him to confer its benefits
upon more women. I mock Sam, but he would mock himself
on this. It hardly matters; mockery cannot accomplish everything, and Sam seethes with that most private and tender
pain: even worse than being unattractive to the world is to
be unattractive to one's mate; or, what is the same and describes Sam's case more accurately, never to know in advance
when he shall be undesirable to Eleanor.

I make perhaps too much of the subject, but that is only
because it is so important to Sam. Relations between Eleanor

and him are not really that bad—I know other couples who have much less or nothing at all. But comparisons are poor comfort to Sam; his standards are so high. So are Eleanor's. I am convinced the most unfortunate people are those who would make an art of love. It sours other effort. Of all artists, they are certainly the most wretched.

Shall I furnish a model? Sam and Eleanor are on the couch and the projector, adjusted to its slowest speed, is retracing the elaborate pantomime of the three principals. If one could allow these shadows a life . . . but indeed such life has been given them. Sam and Eleanor are no more than an itch, a smart, a threshold of satisfaction; the important share of themselves has steeped itself in Frankie-, Magnolia-, and Eleanor-of-the-film. Indeed the variations are beyond telling. It is the most outrageous orgy performed by five ghosts.

Self-critical Sam! He makes love in front of a movie, and one cannot say that it is unsatisfactory any more than one can say it is pleasant. It is dirty, downright porno dirty, it is a lewd slop-brush slapped through the middle of domestic exasperations and breakfast eggs. It is so dirty that only half of Sam—he is quite divisible into fractions—can be exercised at all. The part that is his brain worries along like a cuckolded burgher. He is taking the pulse of his anxiety. Will he last long enough to satisfy Eleanor? Will the children come back tonight? He cannot help it. In the midst of the circus, he is suddenly convinced the children will walk through the door. "Why are you so anxious, Daddie?"

So it goes. Sam the lover is conscious of exertion. One moment he is Frankie Idell, destroyer of virgins—take that! you whore!—the next, body moving, hands caressing, he is no more than some lines from a psychoanalytical text. He is thinking about the sensitivity of his scrotum. He has read that this is a portent of femininity in a male. How strong is his

latent homosexuality worries Sam, thrusting stiffly, warm sweat
running cold. Does he identify with Eleanor-of-the-film?

Technically, the climax is satisfactory. They lie together in
the dark, the film ended, the projector humming its lonely
revolutions in the quiet room. Sam gets up to turn it off; he
comes back and kisses Eleanor upon the mouth. Apparently,
she has enjoyed herself more than he; she is tender and
fondles the tip of his nose.

"You know, Sam," she says from her space beside him, "I
think I saw this picture before."

"When?"

"Oh, you know when. That time."

Sam thinks dully that women are always most loving when
they can reminisce about infidelity.

"That time!" he repeats.

"I think so."

Racing forward from memory like the approaching star which
begins as a point on the mind and swells to explode the eyeball
with its odious image, Sam remembers, and is weak in the
dark. It is ten years, eleven perhaps, before they were married,
yet after they were lovers. Eleanor has told him, but she has
always been vague about details. There had been two men it
seemed, and another girl, and all had been drunk. They had
seen movie after movie. With reluctant fascination, Sam can
conceive the rest. How it had pained him, how excited him.
It is years now since he has remembered, but he remembers.
In the darkness he wonders at the unreasonableness of jealous
pain. That night was impossible to imagine any longer—therefore it is more real; Eleanor his plump wife who presses a
pigeon's shape against her housecoat, forgotten heroine of
black orgies. It had been meaningless, Eleanor claimed; it was
Sam she loved, and the other had been no more than a fancy
of which she wished to rid herself. Would it be the same

today, thinks Sam, or had Eleanor been loved by Frankie, by
Frankie of the other movies, by Frankie of the two men she
never saw again on that night so long ago?

The pleasure I get from this pain, Sam thinks furiously.

It is not altogether perverse. If Eleanor causes him pain,
it means after all that she is alive for him. I have often observed that the reality of a person depends upon his ability
to hurt us; Eleanor as the vague accusing embodiment of the
wife is different, altogether different, from Eleanor who lies
warmly in Sam's bed, an attractive Eleanor who may wound
his flesh. Thus, brother to the pleasure of pain, is the sweeter
pleasure which follows pain. Sam, tired, lies in Eleanor's arms,
and they talk with the cozy trade words of old professionals,
agreeing that they will not make love again before a movie,
that it was exciting but also not without detachment, that all
in all it has been good but not quite right, that she had loved
this action he had done, and was uncertain about another. It
is their old familiar critique, a sign that they are intimate and
well disposed. They do not talk about the act when it has
failed to fire; then they go silently to sleep. But now, Eleanor's
enjoyment having mollified Sam's sense of no enjoyment, they
talk with the apologetics and encomiums of familiar mates.
Eleanor falls asleep, and Sam falls almost asleep, curling next
to her warm body, his hand over her round belly with the
satisfaction of a sculptor. He is drowsy, and he thinks drowsily
that these few moments of creature-pleasure, this brief compassion he can feel for the body that trusts itself to sleep beside him, his comfort in its warmth, is perhaps all the meaning
he may ask for his life. That out of disappointment, frustra-
tion, and the passage of dreary years come these few moments
when he is close to her, and their years together possess a connotation more rewarding than the sum of all which has gone
into them.

But then he thinks of the novel he wants to write, and he
is wide-awake again. Like the sleeping pill which fails to
work and leaves one warped in an exaggeration of the ills
which sought the drug, Sam passes through the promise of
sex-emptied sleep, and is left with nervous loins, swollen
jealousy of an act ten years dead, and sweating irritable resentment of the woman's body which hinders his limbs. He has
wasted the day, he tells himself, he has wasted the day as he
has wasted so many days of his life, and tomorrow in the
office he will be no more than his ten fingers typing plot and
words for Bramba the Venusian and Lee-Lee Deeds, Hollywood Star, while that huge work with which he has cheated
himself, holding it before him as a covenant of his worth, that
enormous novel which would lift him at a bound from the
impasse in which he stifles, whose dozens of characters would
develop a vision of life in bountiful complexity, lies foundered,
rotting on a beach of purposeless effort. Notes here, pages
there, it sprawls through a formless wreck of incidental ideas
and half-episodes, utterly without shape. He has not even a
hero for it.

One could not have a hero today, Sam thinks, a man of
action and contemplation, capable of sin, large enough for
good, a man immense. There is only a modern hero damned
by no more than the ugliness of wishes whose satisfaction he
will never know. One needs a man who could walk the stage,
someone who—no matter who, not himself. Someone, Sam
thinks, who reasonably could not exist.

The novelist, thinks Sam, perspiring beneath blankets, must
live in paranoia and seek to be one with the word; he must
be terrified of experience and hungry for it; he must think
himself nothing and believe he is superior to all. The feminine
in his nature cries for proof he is a man; he dreams of power
and is without capacity to gain it; he loves himself above all
and therefore despises all that he is.

He is that, thinks Sam, he is part of the perfect prescription, and yet he is not a novelist. He lacks energy and belief. It is left for him to write an article some day about the temperament of the ideal novelist.

In the darkness, memories rise, yeast-swells of apprehension. Out of bohemian days so long ago, comes the friend of Eleanor, a girl who had been sick and was committed to an institution. They visited her, Sam and Eleanor, they took the suburban train and sat on the lawn of the asylum grounds while patients circled about intoning a private litany, or shuddering in boob-blundering fright from an insect that crossed their skin. The friend had been silent. She had smiled, she had answered their questions with fewest words, and had returned again to her study of sunlight and blue sky. As they were about to leave, the girl had taken Sam aside. "They violate me," she said in a whisper. "Every night when the doors are locked, they come to my room and they make the movie. I am the heroine and am subjected to all variety of sexual viciousness. Tell them to leave me alone so I may enter the convent." And while she talked, in a horror of her body, one arm scrubbed the other. Poor tortured friend. They had seen her again, and she babbled, her face had coarsened into an idiot leer.

Sam sweats. There is so little he knows, and so much to know. Youth of the depression with its economic terms, what can he know of madness or religion? They are both so alien to him. He is the mongrel, Sam thinks, brought up without religion from a mother half Protestant and half Catholic, and a father half Catholic and half Jew. He is the quarter-Jew, and yet he is a Jew, or so he feels himself, knowing nothing of Gospel, tabernacle, or Mass, the Jew through accident, through state of mind. What . . . whatever did he know of penance? self-sacrifice? mortification of the flesh? the love of his fellow man? Am I concerned with my relation to God?

ponders Sam, and smiles sourly in the darkness. No, that has never concerned him, he thinks, not for better nor for worse. "They are making the movie," says the girl into the ear of memory, "and so I cannot enter the convent."

How hideous was the mental hospital. A concentration camp, decides Sam. Perhaps it would be the world some day, or was that only his projection of feelings of hopelessness? "Do not try to solve the problems of the world," he hears from Sergius, and pounds a lumpy pillow.

However could he organize his novel? What form to give it? It is so complex. Too loose, thinks Sam, too scattered. Will he ever fall asleep? Wearily, limbs tense, his stomach too keen, he plays again the game of putting himself to sleep. "I do not feel my toes," Sam says to himself, "my toes are dead, my calves are asleep, my calves are sleeping . . ."

In the middle from wakefulness to slumber, in the torpor which floats beneath blankets, I give an idea to Sam. "Destroy time, and chaos may be ordered," I say to him.

"Destroy time, and chaos may be ordered," he repeats after me, and in desperation to seek his coma, mutters back, "I do not feel my nose, my nose is numb, my eyes are heavy, my eyes are heavy."

So Sam enters the universe of sleep, a man who seeks to live in such a way as to avoid pain, and succeeds merely in avoiding pleasure. What a dreary compromise is life!

10 ☙ *Rudolph Wurlitzer*

Rudolph Wurlitzer's stories have appeared in the Atlantic Monthly *and the* Paris Review. Nog, *his first novel, was reviled and ignored by older, traditional critics and was received quite warmly in the underground press. His second novel,* Flats, *was published in* 1970.

FROM NOG

Yesterday afternoon a girl walked by the window and stopped for sea shells. I was wrenched out of two months of calm. Nothing more than that, certainly, nothing ecstatic or even interesting, but very silent and even, as those periods have become for me. I had been breathing in and out, out and in, calmly, grateful for once to do just that, staring at the waves plopping in, successful at thinking almost nothing, handling easily the three memories I have manufactured, when that girl stooped for sea shells. There was something about her large breasts under her faded blue tee shirt, the quick way she bent down, her firm legs in their rolled-up white jeans, her thin ankles—it was her feet, actually; they seemed for a brief, painful moment to be elegant. It was that thin-boned brittle movement with her feet that did it, that touched some spot that I had forgotten to smother. The way those thin feet remained planted, yet shifting slightly in the sand as she bent down quickly for a clam shell, sent my heart thumping, my mouth dry, no exaggeration, there was something gay and insane about that tiny gesture because it had nothing to do with her.

I went to Smitty's, a roadhouse a quarter of a mile down the beach. When I came back, she was gone. I could not sit in my room. The walls closed in on me. I could see the walls closing in on me, and my situation, if that is what it is, a situation, seemed suddenly so dull and hopeless; this cheap thrown-together guest house of imitation redwood on the California coast with its smell of mold and bad plumbing, the inane view from my window of driftwood and seaweed, flat predictable waves, corny writings in the sand, pot-bellied fishermen and bronzed godlike volleyball players. I had to pull out, I thought, I was beginning to notice things, lists were forming, comparisons were on the way. And now I don't have the octopus. I suppose that is what there is to tell about. Then I'll move on. Last night there was a storm, and I abandoned the octopus. I didn't really abandon the octopus, it's still in the bathysphere on the truck bed, and the truck bed is still up on blocks, but it's not the same any more. I'm going to move on alone.

I have money and I can make money. I want to say that now. I'm no reprobate, nor am I a drain on anyone. My great aunt left me two thousand a year, and I have, or had, an octopus and a truck. A man sold me the octopus and truck in Oregon. I met him in a bar in one of those logging towns on the Coast where the only attractive spot is the village dump, which at least has the advantage of facing the sea. Nog, he was apparently of Finnish extraction, was one of those semi-religious lunatics you see wandering around the Sierras

on bread and tea, or gulping down peyote in Nevada with the
Indians. He was dressed in black motorcycle boots, jeans and
an old army shirt with sergeant chevrons still on the sleeves.
His face was lean and hatchet-edged, with huge fuzzy eyes
sunk deep in his skull like bullet holes. He kept complaining
about a yellow light that had lately been streaming out of his
chest from a spot the size of a half dollar. We drank and
talked about the spot and the small burning sensation it gave
him early in the morning and about his octopus. He had become disillusioned about traveling with the octopus and had
begun having aggressive dreams about it. He wanted to sell it.
We bought a bottle and walked out beyond the town into
logged-off hills that looked like old battlefields. A low mist
hung over a struggling second growth of redwood and Douglas
fir. The tracks of giant caterpillar tractors wound everywhere.
Pits and ditches were scattered about like shell holes. Thousands of frogs croaked and salamanders hung suspended between lids of green slime and rotting logs. I felt vaguely elated,
like a witness to some ancient slaughter.

Nog lived in what had once been a water tank in the middle
of a rough field. The octopus was there, all right. It was sitting inside a bathysphere on a truck bed. Nog had built a
mold out of plaster of Paris for the tentacles and another
one for the obese body with its parrot-like beak and bulging
eyes. Then he had poured liquid latex rubber into the molds.
The bathysphere was carefully fashioned out of a large bu-
tane gas tank and stolen pieces of metal from a nearby
bridge. There were three portholes from which you could
watch the octopus move its eight tentacles around in the
bubbling water. Nog had been traveling to all the state and
county fairs through the West and Midwest, charging kids
a dime and adults a quarter. Most people believed the
octopus was real, but whenever there was a loud doubt Nog

would tell them the truth. He would never give money back, and occasionally there would be fights. In Bird City, Utah, the bathysphere had been tipped over by three men who had just been on a losing softball team. He was weary of the whole thing, he kept repeating. We sat down on a bench in front of his house, and he filled me in on octopus lore. The crowd appreciated the devilfish myth the most, and it was important to tell them how dangerous octopi are and how they can drown and mangle a human or sink a small boat. One should never tell them the truth, which is that octopi are quite friendly. I refused any more information. We sat quietly and it grew dark. Finally Nog said that he had stopped knowing how to entertain himself. He said he guessed that was my trouble, too, but that I should take a chance with the octopus. He suggested I transform it into a totem that I didn't mind seeing every day.

I bought the octopus, and for a year I traveled through the country with it.

Nog is not quite clear enough. I have to invent more. It always comes down to that. I never get a chance to rest. I have never been able, for instance, to understand the yellow light streaming from his chest. But now that the octopus has faded away, Nog might emerge into a clearer focus. Those were sentimental and fuzzy days, those trips through the West with the octopus, and sometimes I find myself wishing more of it were true. (I find, when I ruminate like this, that I invent a great deal of my memories—three now, to be exact—because otherwise I have trouble getting interested.) But I have gotten faster with myself and more even-tempered since I met Nog. Perhaps not even-tempered but certainly more dulcet. I think about trips, bits and pieces of trips, but I no longer try and put anything together (my mind has become blessedly slower), nor do I try as much to invent a suitable character who can handle the fragments. But I don't want to get into all that. There is always the danger that I might become impressed by what once was a misplaced decision for solitude.

I'm thinking about trying the East. I will go to New York and get a small room on the top of a hotel.

When I was on the road with the octopus I did a lot of reminiscing about New York. New York was, in fact, my favorite memory for four or five months, until it got out of hand and I had to drop it. I lived in a comfortable duplex apartment on top of an old hotel overlooking a small park and harbor. I was sort of an erotic spy on myself then, but managed to survive, at least for those four or five months, by keeping an alert and fastidious watch on the terrifying view outside. I watched ships glide and push into huge docks, and far below, through silvery leaves, the quiet violence in the park. At night I stayed up with the fantastic lights of cars and subways as they flowed over the concrete ramps that weaved around the hotel. I lived precariously in the center of brutal combinations of energy, and gradually, as I closed in on myself, the bridges transformed into massive spider webs imprisoning the subways as they rumbled like mechanical snakes across the black river. The subways shot off green and yellow sparks in defense, in specific relays of time, always getting through. I had to drop that memory. But now, with more miles and memories in control, I might attempt New York.

From my window I can see the beach. An old couple digs razorbacked clams, and a small boy writes "David Salte Hates the Slug" on the sand with a large knotted stick. It has never been enough for me to have a stick and some sand to draw in. I am not indifferent enough. I am too self-engrossed to play in the sand. But yesterday afternoon I was *trying* to at least get ready to play, trying to find the right approach, the right kind of silence, when the girl walked by. That touch of elegance ruined my confidence. It made me dwell on the time I have spent just getting by, made me hate the octopus and the kingdom of the octopus, the small towns, the long monotonous highways, the squalid fairgrounds. It made me take a walk on the beach.

It's a glorious beach, I suppose; usually empty, very wide and sandy. In back there are warm and green mountains, and most of the time the sea is well-behaved, although it was rough then and it had begun to rain. I began to think of beaches. I have been on eighty-seven beaches in the last fifteen years. Before that it is easier to be vague. Lately I have been reviewing each beach, although it isn't a satisfactory way of getting through the day. Too much of my life has been spent on beaches: Cannes, Far Rockaway, Stinson Beach, one beach in Ireland, two in Crete, Lido, Curaçao, Luquillo, Curadado, Malibu, Deya, Nice, Tangiers, Cob, the Virgin Islands—to name a few. I never run into the water. I am actually afraid of moving water. Nor do I get a suntan. I lie in one place, usually on my stomach, and do nothing. For me, beaches are profane.

So there I was, reaching the end of the beach, thinking about beaches, when I saw the girl again. She was standing near a black rock, a yellow shawl wrapped around her face, staring inanely at the sea. I walked up to her, and standing a little apart and to the rear of her, I too stared at the sea. The waves were rushing in and out, quite furious now, sucking at the stones. I looked at her. She seemed not to have noticed me, and for this I was grateful. I was happy enough just to stand there, next to her, for my former feelings about her foot were quite in control. In fact, I inspected her feet and it didn't seem possible that one of them should have acted as such a catalyst. Her feet were like her face, too broad

and splotchy, rather crude and used up. Her dull features reassured me so much that I thought I might be able to stay on
for another few months.

She turned towards me.

I have never been able to connect with strange women
except if they are in distress or in some way hung up. She
looked abysmally happy.

"You live in the boarding house, don't you?" she asked.
"Yes, I think you're the only one who is permanent there."

I wasn't able to answer, a common fault of mine.

"What do you do? I mean, we've all been wondering what
you do. You look frail and timid, like some great thinker or
something. That's what I think, anyway. My husband thinks
you're recovering from some romantic disease. Who's right,
him or me?"

She sat down on the black rock. The rain was drenching
us. I was unprepared for such a downpour, being dressed in
white seersucker pants, white paisley shirt and finely-woven
linen shoes. I stood near her, waiting, but resolved not to give
out with any information. If pressed, I might improvise on one
of my memories. One should have an electric mind, I decided
right there, not a tepid half-awake coping mind.

"Walk me down the beach," the girl said. "I'm so wet.
We're *both* so wet. You don't mind, do you? I'll tell you a
secret, we call you Dr. Angst because of the gloom on your
face. You don't mind, do you?"

I walked with her. I was, in fact, deeply offended, not by
being called Dr. Angst but by being noticed that much. Words
began to spill out of me, quite out of my control. "Why try
to know anything about a place? The customs, the size, the
suntan techniques, the games, the swimming. It is better to
stay indoors and not mess around with useless experiences.
A small room in a boarding house. Anonymous. Eat each meal

at a plastic counter. Smitty's will do. Do nothing, want nothing, if you feel like walking, walk; sleeping, sleep. Do you know how hard that is? No memories; if they start to intrude, invent them. Three is sufficient. I use only three. New York for adventure, beaches for relaxation, the octopus and Nog for speculation. No connections. Narrow all possibilities. Develop and love your limitations. No one knows you. Know no one. Natural rhythms, my dear. That's the ticket."

She had wandered off to pick up a mussel shell. She came skipping back. "I use them for collages. I paste them in; shells, colored pieces of glass, driftwood, anything." She giggled. "Did you know that today is the Fourth of July?"

"No."

"We're having a party. You're invited. Everyone is coming. Well, not everyone, but Timmons and Harry and the man who runs the gift shop and one or two others. My husband too, of course."

I put my arm around her. Her behavior seemed to allow for such an embrace as long as nothing called her attention to it. But she stepped away, giving me a quizzical glance. I am unable to cope with quizzical glances.

"I know you," I said decisively, trying to struggle away. "Ten years ago in New York; I don't remember your name, but I *might* have even slept with you. It scares me, stumbling onto a part of my past like that. You were more emaciated then, of course, with your hair very ratty. You were carrying a sign in some kind of demonstration when I met you, that's you, very political. Am I right?"

"I'm from Baltimore," she said with a quick glance down at her awful feet. "I've never seen a demonstration of any kind. We moved out here when Ollie got a job working with an agricultural firm. They transferred him. We like it fine."

"I won't press," I said. I have retained a certain amount of old-fashioned dignity. "Who you are and what you do are your problems."

We walked on in silence. The silence, in fact, was fierce. And, I was proud to think, not one piece of information had I given away. No history, therefore no bondage. I have known myself to give out with facts, numbers, names, stories. I am that nervous sometimes. But as I said before, I am faster now. It was a joy to walk beside her with only her self-conscious distrust of me to handle. She was thinking I was only a little weird, possibly diseased; she was too simple, too nice to think anything more. And I'm too haggard to produce sexual fears; my ears are too huge and my lips too thin and uncontrolled.

We pressed on in the rain. I was all for delaying the walk as much as possible, but she was too determined to get home. Just before the house she had proudly marked as hers, we passed an old man in a First World War hat, struggling with a heavy log. He was bent and puffing as he tried to shift the log on top of a low makeshift sea wall.

I stopped. He was remarkably ugly and defiant.

"Colonel Green," the girl said. "He lives in that big three-story house next to ours. He has a grandson in there and some kind of a woman, but they hardly ever show themselves. It's not a good policy to talk to him. He comes out in every storm. A maniac about the sea. He must be eighty, honest, and Ollie says that all that's keeping him alive is this crazy war he has going against the sea. Everyone thinks he's a blight on the community."

"Grab hold," Colonel Green ordered. He marched up and shouted in my ear. "Goddamn water rising at three hundred miles an hour. Too dumb to see it? Flood the whole town before anyone shifts ass to do anything about it. Fact. Lift her up."

I helped him lift the log onto the sea wall. He was dressed

in a yellow mackintosh and big fishing boots. His furiously weathered face was sunk deep into his neck, and his tiny blue eyes, like two pale robin's eggs, protruded into the night, unblinking and beautiful.

"People," he yelled again into my ear.

I helped him with another log. We labored and swore, but the log kept slipping back onto the sand. Finally the colonel ordered a halt and sat down on the sea wall, wheezing and kicking the wet sand with his boots. I could only pick out every third or fourth word the colonel said, the wind was so strong and his voice had sunk to such a rasp. "Hear . . . no retreat . . . only . . . bastard sea . . . kicking up higher . . . iron woman . . . What . . . ? What . . . ? What . . . ?"

I went up and yelled in his ear. "Right. A huge operation. Biggest operation in years. Massive. Mounting up out there. Ready to initiate general collapse. Anytime."

We yelled back and forth. Then he punched me amiably in the stomach, and we struggled with the log. This time we made it. After another rest, we walked down to the sea for a better evaluation. "Jeep," the colonel yelled, coming up to my ear again and grasping me by the neck so I wouldn't turn away. He only had, after all, so many words in him. "Good thick sand tires. Drag every piece of maverick wood to the stronghold. Dig in! Protect the road!"

I nodded and followed him up the beach to his house. Before very long, however, I took a sharp turn to the left and ducked out of his line of march. As it happened, I was unfortunate enough to be standing in front of the girl's large bay window. She was standing with several other people, looking gaily down at me. I didn't, of course, want to have anything to do with anyone. The evening had already been too much of a lark. It might possibly set me back for months. I wanted only to get to bed and pull the covers over my head.

A few sips of whiskey, that would do me fine. Just to listen
to the storm with a memory or two. To go over once again
a few details about the octopus. My clothes were drenched.
I had long ago taken off my shoes and shirt. I was suffering
from chills. They were waving. But I wasn't going anywhere.
I had done very well that night. I had talked far too much
but was rather amazed at how well I had managed. Nothing
had been said. It was all right.

A hand grabbed the upper part of my arm and escorted me
into the house.

"It's about time," a low, modulated, terrifically friendly
voice roared. "I'm Ollie, of course. Glad to have you aboard.
You're quite the stranger around here. I won't even ask what
you were doing with that old maniac out there. It looks like
we got to you just in time. What's that? Look here, Sarah,
this poor fella has had it. Get him some dry clothes. Better
still, get him into my terrycloth bathrobe. That's it. Get in
there now. That's the boy."

I followed Sarah into the bedroom. She smiled at me, and
I took off my clothes.

"Now wait," she said, very fast. "Listen. I don't know you.
That bathrobe. The bathrobe is hanging in the bathroom."

I went into the bathroom and stood, shivering, behind the
door. I too was a little ill at ease. After all, at first sight I've
been told I'm not exactly pleasing to look at. "I was a track
man," I yelled into the bedroom. "Four-forty under fifty-five
seconds. I assure you." There was no answer. There didn't
seem to be anything else to do but to give out with some
information. "Slipping out from New York, everything going
too fast. Left and wandered out to Coast. Met Nog and bought
octopus. Traveled to county and state fairs, developing wonderful aversion to people and trips in general but at the same
time a growing obsession with octopus. Hard to even talk

about it. Was afraid to let go, surrender it, walk away. Settled down here just to sit, you understand, wanting nothing at all. Waiting it out. Then thinking of beaches, developing that memory up to par with other two. Beaches, you understand, beaches where most of life has dribbled away, past beaches, future beaches and now right here a . . ."

I ventured a peek out the door, but she had left the bedroom. I preferred to think she hadn't heard me; that, indeed, she had never heard me. I could still slip out. The terrycloth bathrobe was hanging behind the door. I put it on and turned to investigate the bathroom. It was a beautiful bathroom. There was a huge green tile tub, a new toilet and washbowl. I opened the cabinet over the washbowl. I couldn't stop looking at the objects on the top two shelves: suntan oil, Anacins, cold cream, three pink hair curlers, two yellow toothbrushes, one of which was very dirty. Dramamine pills, Itolsol eye bath, Ban, Kolex cold capsules, Ammens Medicated Powder and a small box of Benzedrine pills. I stared at each object and then went over them again. A bottle of hydrogen peroxide fell from one of the lower shelves. I dumped the contents of every bottle in the cabinet into the bathtub except for the Benzedrine pills, which I put into the pocket of the terrycloth bathrobe. I turned the water on. It was a reviving thing to do. Then I turned the water off and stepped into the bedroom. The bedroom was painted a pale mauve. There was a king-sized bed, three small watercolors of clipper ships, a dresser, a sewing machine, two night tables and a television set. It was pleasant. I felt very relaxed. I got into bed and pulled the covers over my head.

I thought of Nog. He would be wandering over the Sierras probably, that yellow light streaming from his chest. I haven't been able to think too clearly about the octopus since I had come to the beach. I had given it a chance, it wasn't as if I had deserted it. I had driven through the Northwest, the

Southwest and the Midwest. Thousands of people had looked
at it, and many had even thought it was real. I had made
money. But once off the road I could never go out behind
the boarding house and look at it up on the truck bed. It was
the last thing to throw away. Lately I've imagined its eight
tentacles wrapped around my head, slowly smothering me.

I must have fallen asleep. A hand shook me. "Now look.
It's perfectly all right if you come in and use my terrycloth
bathrobe and even take a nap in the middle of my bed, but
why violate my bathroom?"

I slipped my head under the covers.

Ollie pulled the covers off the bed. I looked up at his face.

It wasn't too bad a face. It was broad and handsome in a
puffy way. Ollie was about to say something when Sarah took
him by the hand and led him to the doorway. They whispered
together. Finally Sarah came back and said, sweetly, "I'll bet
you would like to join the party. We're going to have fireworks. Please, it will be fun."

Between the two of them I was escorted to the edge of
the living-room rug. There were only five people. There might
have been more in other rooms, but I counted five. I took
care not to notice anything else. I sat down.

"The last time was in New York," I said.

"Is that right," a fat man said. He was eating an egg- and
shrimp-salad sandwich and drinking bourbon and water.

"New York is an active place. Not as much action as you
might have been led to believe, but still, an active place. I
lived in a sort of penthouse. Beautiful furniture. Turn-of-the-
century stuff.

"What exactly is your line?" I was asked.

"I'm a cultural impresario. Nog is the name. I'm investigating cephalopods or, as they say here, octopi or octopuses.
Timid creatures, really, much maligned."

The man excused himself and went into the next room.

The wind battered against the window. I remember that very well, the wind battering against the window and the hum of conversation. I pulled the curtain over the bay window to protect the room from the terrible racket of the storm.

There was boisterous talk about fireworks and drinking and last year's Fourth of July party.

Sarah advanced towards me, smiling bravely, "Having fun?" she asked.

"Of course I'm having fun," I replied.

"Would you mind telling me what you do?" she asked.

It was obvious that they were closing in on me. I was forced to throw out a series of delaying actions.

"You may ask," I said, being extremely polite. "Of course you may ask. I'm making a survey of the West Coast. Marine animals mostly. Did you know fossils of cephalopods have been found in rocks that are believed to be at least four hundred million years old? They are harmless. Most people don't want to know that, but they are harmless, even rather stupid . . . I am also making a survey of the Sierras and another, more general survey, on Los Angeles, Sacramento, Portland, Seattle, San Francisco, Oakland and Santa Barbara, to name a few. I am also, on the side, so to speak, investigating totems."

I remember dancing.

I remember sitting for a long stretch, looking at television.

I was able to become more anonymous. I ate roast beef and drank Seven-Up.

I remember no more until I was asked down to the game room by Ollie. "Now, Mr. Mysterious," he said, laughing and slapping me on the back. "You can tell me what you do."

"A survey of beaches," I replied quickly. "Taking ten to fifteen years. The best years of my life consumed in this project. All over the Western world. Marvelous and fantastic stories. Over eight beaches noted so far, actually eighty-seven.

To name a few: Far Rockaway, Montauk, Las Palmas, Harrison's Landing, Brighton, Antibes, Westhampton, Orient, Marblehead, Malibu, Coventry, Truro, the whole of the Ceylonese coast, Tangier, Tunis and Ceuta, that whole stretch, Ibiza and Formentera, Vancouver and two beaches in Rhodes and Hydra, three in Crete and only one in all of Ireland. The beach here, the present one, is calm, wide and sandy, few sharks, and a good class of swimmers. Weather mostly good. Except, of course, for tonight. Tonight there is a storm."

He handed me a Ping-Pong racket. We played Ping-Pong.

At first I just shoveled the ball back, trying to be polite. I managed to get the ball close to his racket. But then he grew angry and shouted at me to play ball. I put little twists on the ball and chopped back on the serve. He slammed back harder. Several times it appeared that he wanted to say something, but we were playing so hard there was no time to talk. I kept him hopping. There were backhand smashes for him to contend with, forehand chops, tricky cross-court serves, sleezy slices. Balls sprayed around the room, but he had a plentiful supply from a large wicker basket that hung from the ceiling on a wire chain. We played even harder, and I rolled up the sleeves of my terrycloth bathrobe. Finally, wheezing and perspiring, he stood still, squeezing a Ping-Pong ball in his hand. He appeared to be stuck in some way. There was nothing else to do but grab the basket of Ping-Pong balls and fling them at him. That started him off. He yelled. I threw my paddle, catching him in the throat. Then I tipped over the table. He was left sitting on the floor.

I walked out of the game room and into the storm.

Colonel Green was still working on the sea wall. He had managed to move one more log.

"Getting you down?" I yelled at him. "Worst storm in years. Watch battle fatigue. Absolutely all right."

The colonel surveyed the beach, his hands on his hips.

"Crashing . . . now . . . 1937 . . . the drift . . . up later
. . . no help . . . tatters . . . tatters . . ."

I grabbed the end of a log. "Where do you get these logs?"
I yelled "What do you do, push them back when the storm
is over?"

"Selfish . . . 1937 . . . four-door sedan . . . stand tall . . ."

We labored some more but couldn't move the log. I went
back to my room and went to bed.

What I should have done was get rid of the octopus, what
I have been trying to do is get rid of the octopus, what I am
beginning just now to remember was that I did get rid of
the octopus. I see it now for the first time. I either took it
back to the party and put it in the bathtub or danced with
it on the beach. No, I did bring it back to the beach but not
to dance with. I took off my terrycloth bathrobe and ran down
to the truck and got the octopus out of the bathysphere, its
tentacles waving all over me. Struggling in the rain and wind,
I dragged it back and pulled it up on the sea wall. Such a
spectator gave the colonel enough of a jolt to finish the sea
wall. Then together we threw it in the sea, and I went home
and went to bed. It was something like that, I can remember
something like that, a storm, a party and then the octopus.
There was an octopus, although I know deep down that the
octopus is still up on blocks. I know, too, that nothing happened and I haven't traveled with the octopus. But I shall
move on anyway, perhaps to New York. I remember great
things about New York.

· · ·

I ran down to the sea. I took off a shoe and shoved a foot
in. There was a quickness, certainly, a sudden delirium, as if

I were about to be sure of something. But it's out of my depth
to run down to the sea and make a report. The only clarity
is in the morning air. But as my foot grew colder, a warmth
appeared, a flush to the cheeks, and there is something to say,
right now, but my voice doesn't have the momentum. I am
too comfortable sitting on the sand, my foot drying now, not
knowing that I am about to move on. The storm wasn't invented. I'm sure of that. And the sea was cold and even wet.
That was two or three days ago. But there must be another
place, a replacement, one foot having the problem of following the other foot, to another place. Now that there are no
other feet to follow. I stood and sat again. I must be holding
back. I'm breathing easier, trying to watch or not to watch,
my suitcase next to me and my frozen foot withdrawing from
the sea and entering the sock and then the shoe. There is no
sound within, although I'm lighter. I haven't eaten in days.
The day is lighter than the day before. I might manage a bark.
But I have to watch that. I don't have to bark against the
sound of waves. I must be moving on. I turned my back to
the sea. I stood facing the road. Orange and black butterflies
glided through the eucalyptus trees. I was holding back, but
I knew I had moved on long before, years before, despite my
calm breathing in and out, my suitcase ready to be grasped—
and I did grasp it, and my foot, as if by itself, took a step and
I was moving on, up the beach, past the sea wall, to the edge
of the road.

I hitchhiked to San Francisco.

I was let off near a supermarket. It was dark. I was standing
comfortably enough, looking at the neon lights, but I needed
a direction, the hint of some discernible habit, a movement
of some kind. A place to stand but at the same time to appear busy. I have no memories, only vague symbols of separations: an overturned kitchen table, a ripped bed sheet, a

broken battleship abandoned at the bottom of a bathtub. I
went into the supermarket. The aisles were crowded with
evening shoppers. There was Muzak. I slid into the warm
colors and the clicks of the cash registers. I tried to remember
near the frozen foods, I am trying to remember, what it was
I had to remember, but I had forgotten what I had gone in
for, what it is exactly I have to go out for. I pushed the car
down the length of one aisle and halfway up another. I picked
up a can of beans. I must have picked up a can of beans because I can remember putting a can of beans back on the
shelf and picking up another, a bottle of beans. I put the
bottle of beans near cans of chop suey and vegetables and
Pet milk. Then, finally, I managed to hold two cans of tuna
fish. Something was evoked. A meal. Mayonnaise and onions
and tuna fish in London, New York or Palma. It doesn't
matter. I put the two cans of tuna fish in the cart and pushed
on, past plastic toys, light bulbs and electrical fixtures. A red
can opener held me for several minutes. I put it in the cart
and pushed on. I paused near the meat counter, my eyes
locked by a delicate set of fingers stuffing a package of lamb
chops into the large pocket of a yellow rain slicker. The slicker
was unbuttoned. Inside was a faded blue-flowered print dress.
Her thick blond hair flowed loosely to her waist. Her short legs
were awkward around the kneecaps, as if somehow splayed,
but her wide stance was vulnerable enough to be exciting. Red
plastic shoes with stubby tips covered her feet. I watched her
fingers calmly drop pork chops into a straw basket followed by
several pounds of spareribs. I delayed looking at her face. I
concentrated on the foods in my cart and pushed forward until
the cart came to rest against her thighs. She turned. There is
no focus to her face; her features are broad and healthy, no
doubt lovely, call them lovely, but I don't know where to start,
how to approach the small stubborn nose, the unparted lips,

the eyes are fading, looking at me but fading, and my own
eyes have become glazed. I started at a point between her
eyes. She didn't smile or show any surprise, perhaps because
there was no motion at all to my own face, or so I thought. I
have been wrong about that before. She moved to the side
slowly and deliberately, as if completing a step in a formal
dance. She stood in front of the cold cuts. I too made a move,
as if responding to the same conductor, to a position in front
of the fish, to her right. I picked up a flounder, holding it for
a moment so that it draped over my hand. Then I slipped the
flounder under my shirt. It was remarkably cold, but I remained
silent. She moved on and I have moved on, not knowing if I
am following or if she is following or perhaps if in some way
we are moving parallel to each other. I stopped for a bottle of
artichoke hearts, slipping them into my jacket pocket. When
I looked up, she had disappeared. The separation is not acute.
At least I managed to inhabit, for a brief moment, a friendly
and detached space in front of the meat counter. I was quiet,
but I have thought and been suspicious about silence a long
time. There are certain moments, after an estrangement, when
my cock shrivels up into my body. No, that's not it. It has
nothing to do with that. I'm grazing. I should have pinioned
her with the cart and slipped it into her as she was bending over
the meat counter. Never mind the rest. She might not have
noticed. She hasn't noticed. The neutrality must have been
the seduction. I pushed on, filling my cart with orange juice,
milk, eggs and cheese. Foods with no smell, cool to the touch.
Her eyes had been very blue, as if far-reaching, like the eyes
of Nog. (Eyes I have known.) But her eyes were dim, faded.
The memories will come, are coming, lists of separations,
arrivals. I don't have to rush it. Nog has not disappeared. Only
memory survives. Her obtuse eyes reflected a quest, if only for
meat, but even so, a quest. And Nog is on a quest of obsessive

walking and sleeping between dog-eaten blankets on splintered floors. I can't see farther than that. She had turned away, there is no mistaking that, but something happened or at least was noted. Not an understanding, I'm not frantic enough to suspect that, but perhaps a paranoia, a shared paralysis, a delicate and withdrawn . . . It doesn't matter. I found her again on another aisle. I noticed a head of lettuce in her cart and two avocados. I picked up a bottle of crab-meat cocktail, two cans of smoked oysters and a can of chicken salad that I had no particular interest in. I remember filling both pockets of my pants with tartar sauce, onion flakes and paprika. I was not altogether unaware that this might be a setup, that I might be fingered for some kind of a mark or a bust. I dumped everything in the nearest cart except two pads of butter, a container of milk and a small bottle of artichoke hearts. I kept the flounder inside my shirt. Dampness keeps me in tune, focused on the task at hand, on the possibility of a progression, on the hope that there is, in fact, a task. We moved towards the checkout counter. I was open, ready for her to reveal herself, to move forward or backward, to hunt or flee. I am still open, lying as if in wait for something or someone. But it was confusing, people became blurred, the aisles without end, almost circular, the food suddenly animate, fields of waving coffee cans, rows of sweating lemons and expanding lettuce, shifting piles of bananas and candy bars and the food in my own cart huddling together, as if for warmth, minuscule and afraid. I was at the checkout counter, moving through, pushing away a delirium tremens, and nothing was happening. I paid, gratefully, and she paid too, just in front of me, for the lettuce and two avocados, her pockets bulging, her straw basket full and the huge mirror overhead reflecting all. But then we were on the street. Everything eventually finds its way to the street. We walked. She stopped in the middle of an empty parking lot and let her limp hand drop into mine. Kissing the lobe of an ear, she confessed that just to keep in shape, so to speak, to keep herself in control, she turned occasional tricks with the managers of two supermarkets.

From my window, which extends to the floor, I can see a bridge and several round hills. The bridge looks familiar. I suspect that I'm in San Francisco. It was dark when Meridith led me away from the supermarket two or three days ago. I have been lying on my mattress, jerking off. The bridge in New York bound and twisted two shores together, making the ugly rush of water insistent and brutal. Bodies floated against the pilings. I've flirted with that memory before. It doesn't work as a catalyst. But I can remember how Meridith handed me the straw basket and I emptied my food into it, including the flounder. She wanted to touch each object, to feel its weight and size. She walked on. I followed, carrying the basket. I have left Barcelona and Kuwait without knowing I was leaving. I need a list of departures to keep suspended my own sense of arrival. But they fail, my head fails, my steps succeeded and we came to a three-story house in a commercial neighborhood: empty and abandoned stores, warehouses, a gas station on one corner, a Mexican bar on the other. A street light shone a front of the supermarket. I sat down on the last step as caved in. I remembered, stepping over the step, that I had left my suitcase on the side of the road. Either that or in front of the supermarket. I sat down on the last step as Meridith went inside. I took out each object in the basket and slowly put them back, one by one. I had a ride in a blue pickup truck. I kept my eyes on the mile gauge, touching the side of the door as each mile came and went. The night of the storm is returning. I haven't asked for that. I can remember the television set and the octopus and the heavy weight of its tentacles. The tentacles were too long. They drooped. They got in the way. Losing my clothes and shaving kit doesn't bother me. But the suitcase itself, with the stickers and dents on it, was a record, a map I could retrace and run my fingers over whenever I wanted to. Sitting on the front step, I was afraid to go inside, to enter a space alone without a change of underwear or stickers, a lid to snap open or close, a weight to complain about. But I had the straw basket. That was enough of a ticket. I looked through my wallet. There were three carefully folded chewing-gum wrappers, the Oregon driver's license made out to Orin Carmele, an address of a hitch-hiker from Cody, Wyoming, two white pills, half a snapshot of a small sailboat, an empty air-mail stamp book, a flat fold of tin foil and three ripped movie stubs. I put everything but the forty-eight dollars into the straw basket. Entrances are always hard, never moist or dewy enough. Once inside, there is hopefully enough natural movement, enough frenzied propulsion to find a way out. I have entered a swimming pool in Palm Springs, a small hand on my wrist, and gone straight to the bottom. I have entered without hesitation Radio City Music Hall in the morning and either Susan or Ann. I have not left anything behind except for the suitcase and possibly the octopus and truck. That might reveal itself to me by degrees. There is plenty of time for that. I don't want to rush anything. I want to forget more than I remember. Last night and the immediate nights before can be suspended, until I go limp enough not to notice myself, to lose control. I touched the side of the house. Flakes of yellow paint fell off in my fingers. I could enter the house because with the basket I would be unnoticed, like a delivery boy, and would fall out as fast as I fell in. I did go inside, carrying the basket in front of me with both hands. I tried to keep from whistling, but a sound emerged, a soft two-note in a minor key. The long hall smelled of cat sperm and was lighted by candles placed in holes chiseled in the wall.

There were posters of rock-'n'-roll groups and children's drawings on yellow lined paper. There appeared to be poems scotch-taped here and there, but I didn't want to look too closely. I walked straight to the end of the hall without stopping. I entered the kitchen. I lowered the basket next to the icebox and sat down at a large wooden table with initials and words carved deeply into it. The words were mostly one-syllabled: sky, wood, card, cunt, river, hat, bag, mountain, beach, fuck, town, sand, gun, soldier, sailor, Indian chief, car, boat, plane, walk, fire, plants, snake, skull, brother, sister, father, mother. I read every initial and word, at the same time noticing hands reach methodically into a huge wooden salad bowl and withdraw pieces of lettuce, tomatoes, avocados, artichoke hearts, boiled eggs, onions, scallions, carrots and anchovies. Five men and three women were seated at the table. Three of the men had shoulder-length hair, and four of them had thick mustaches turning downwards at the edge of their mouths. I made the count several times. Two wore small blue pinch-brim caps with glass beads on the top. The women wore simple print dresses and no make-up, and the men blue jeans and faded work shirts. Everyone wore medallions around their necks. One woman nursed a baby, while the other two slowly shelled peas into a metal bowl. The men sat silently, their eyes blank, reaching out to eat from the bowl. They seem young although it is hard to tell. I seem young although it is hard to tell. I ate a tomato and a carrot and, very quickly, a handful of lettuce and boiled egg. I was hungry. No one seemed to notice me, or if they did they offered no sign. I ate steadily. I felt once a need to say something, to make some gesture, however small. But I could only eat. There were moments when I forgot anyone else was around. The bowl empty, I managed a low hum, a sound that has often signified a need for attention or a diversion from attention. A man stood up, slowly stretched, said "Later" and left. Another carved a word or initial into the table with a bowie knife. The women discussed the large amount of laundry and the diminishing food supply in the pantry. Meridith came in. She put her hands on my shoulders and slowly massaged the back of my neck. My head sagged. I struggled against giving in, against dropping to the floor. Her arms circled my neck, her hands groping my face as if she were blind. Through her sweaty fingers I saw a man begin to draw circles on a piece of white paper with green and yellow crayons. Her arms remind me of tentacles. Her breath on my neck is warm—a faint beginning, a dry sirocco, a labored breathing, a caress. I must not remember places. I have no need for beaches, parks, luncheonettes, cities, rooms, corners, attics, streets or rivers now that I am in a place. I have pulled down the shade. I don't need a bridge, only her breath in and out against my rigid neck and the tide going in and out as once, at anchor, I indulged the tea treatment, off the coast of . . . no, that's no longer necessary. I read the manual. First tea, then a dash of cold water, then hot tea. Then cold water, squirting it in with my mouth, slowly. Slowly. Endless alterations. She loved it, moaning over and over: there's a mad joy to the son of a bitch. I was entertaining myself, I hadn't forgotten, spreading her legs on the bunk, the liquid streaming down her thighs, kneeling before her, the captain pacing on the deck overhead, squirting it into her, even rhythms, that's the ticket, shooting it in and one and two and hold it, darling, hear the tide changing, and three and four, we're coming around and one and two and I did have an effect, suddenly, that long ago. I don't remember any more. Meridith's hands rested on my shoulders. Perhaps, even now, she is thinking of me. There have been other services, given and rendered, three-day passes, other inventions and manuals and I must find something, now that the others are slipping, have perhaps slipped away.

I have said it all before: having come to this house, some time ago, but first having crossed the country, wandering around, for a year, two years or perhaps longer. Perhaps, having said it before, this is the end. Perhaps pulling down the shade is the end. How am I to know except by looking back if I am settled or not? I am not thinking about going on or not going on. There is no anguish, no confusion even though I don't remember what happened last night after leaving the kitchen. Is that where the anguish lies, caked near the stopper? I do remember. I took a bath. Somewhere in the distance between the twisted blue sock in the corner and the window sill I can remember. I am going too fast and not fast enough, past the sound of speed or past the movement of the earth and yet I'm not moving at all.

"Time to get pumpkins," a man said. "In the moonlight you can pick em out. They squat there by the hundreds. Should get us forty to fifty."

Everyone left except the girl nursing the baby and Meridith. Meridith went to the icebox and came back with a small jar of artichoke hearts. She sat down beside me. She made no sound when she chewed. For that I am grateful.

The girl nursing the baby sighed. She was very thin, almost skeletal, with long stringy black hair and large brown eyes. Underneath her yellow dress she wore black stockings. Her mouth was thin and set in an expression of subdued pain. Two men came in. They sat down. Then one of them left.

"I can't handle certain things," the girl said, looking at Meridith. "I should take something or just keep quiet for a few days. Maybe it's nursing. I don't know. I might have to leave. A flower came at me yesterday when I was lying in bed. It came down from the ceiling. A few feet from my face it turned into a black umbrella. The umbrella just stayed there, it wasn't even raining, but then it became a mushroom and the mushroom got closer and closer. I had to get up and walk

around. I didn't know where I was . . . This afternoon I was
bouncing on the trampoline. My body needs it and it's therapeutic. I was going higher and higher and suddenly there was
this enormous black bird, like a pelican, right over me, opening
its mouth. The mouth kept getting bigger and bigger. It was
very real. But I kept jumping up and down even though I
wanted to run inside. Henry joined me and started jumping
alongside me and I told him about the bird. He held my hand
and the bird flew up a few feet. But it was still there. Then he
put his finger inside me at the top of a jump and he kept it
in as we went down and then up again and on top of the
jump the bird wasn't there. We lay on the trampoline and he
made it with me. Then he did a backward somersault over the
side of the trampoline and I haven't seen him since. But I'm
afraid of closing my eyes. I see things when I close my eyes."

She removed the baby from her nipple and placed him on
his stomach on the table. Then she changed his diaper. She
didn't look at anyone. When she had finished with the diaper
she picked the baby up and left. The man had gone to the
stove and was making a stew.

Meridith paused, holding an artichoke between thumb and
forefinger. "Would you like a bath?" she asked. "You must be
tired. Or would you rather split? Someone is probably expecting you somewhere."

"I would just as soon stay on," I said.

She walked over to a loudspeaker on the side of the wall
near the icebox. She pushed a button and said into a small
phone next to the speaker, "One for the top floor." She pushed
another button, and the reply came: "Room twenty-six.
Name?"

Meridith looked at me.

"Nog," I said.

She repeated the name and then came over to me and took

me by the hand. We went down the hall. She stopped. "What kind of music would you like?" she asked.

"Chants are okay," I said. "Anything with not too many words."

We went back to the kitchen. She said into the phone, "Chants for the bath." We returned down the hall. I followed her down dark winding steps to a large cavernous room dimly lit by a kerosene lamp. There were three concrete tubs, about ten feet long and five feet wide, and two smaller, regular-sized tubs. The floor was concrete and covered with an inch of water. We took our clothes off and laid them on a wooden bench. It was very warm. A low Gregorian chant filled the room. Two heads were visible in one of the tubs, and a large foot resting on the edge. A man lay on his stomach on a wooden table. The air smelled of ammonia. Meridith turned a switch near the door. A soft liquid light on the ceiling flashed slowly around.

We stood, looking each over, I suppose, although the light, like the revolving beam on top of police cars, made her seem mysterious and unapproachable. Her breasts were small and firm and her hips large.

We climbed into the tub nearest the far wall.

If I had fewer limbs, if I had been in some way maimed on the road or a victim of an accident, I would be more prepared. As it is, I have to invent my way into situations. It never hurts to have a story prepared, a memory, any kind of wrong information; to be ready to go forward or backward at the least suspicious move. The more sympathy enlisted, the more easily one can receive service and relaxation. But I have a suntan and a spring to my step. No, I'm pale and emaciated, but my body felt tan, even resonant, as I climbed into the tub. There are times when the voice of the narrator or the presence of the narrator should almost sing out.

Meridith's neck and head were above the water. The water seemed to be perfumed. I sat opposite her, my back against the edge. My skin felt soft, like mother-of-pearl. I reached out a foot and touched her thigh. Memories can be vast and delicious. The touch of one, like a favorite stone or shell, can balance the worst of looks. I wasn't having any trouble creating a protective covering. I wanted to say something formal, to balance my hysterical foot rubbing against her ass. "On the last beach I was face to face with a minor discovery, but now I'm beginning to inhabit that discovery. It's not that nature went mad before man did, but it's that life's principle is to make shells."

Meridith slid an arm around my stomach. A leg touched mine. She seemed to be half kneeling before me, her head bent so that her thick wet hair looked for a moment like a dome. I felt as if I were being slowly encircled. I held on to one of her nipples. "Shells are bits of man and bits of woman," I said. "The beach is a boneyard."

She bit me on the neck.

I remembered the storm, or I can remember it now, how the wind suddenly changed and the octopus flapped on top of the sea wall. I lost something, and this is the beginning of something else. It will take its own time. Her arms and legs embraced me, her mouth sucked at mine and I remembered lying on the beach, the wind whipping at me, my clothes heavy with water. I threw the octopus into a wave, but it was picked up and swept back, curled over on the beach, its tentacles torn off, the round hump battered and disfigured. I heard a soft splash. Someone else was in the tub. The light continued to revolve and I watched it, my cock now expanded despite the hot water, but not knowing for sure if I was inside Meridith. Her tongue was active. There was another splash. A large foot placed itself in the center of my back. "Give me some of that," I heard a voice say. I was pinned by several sets of legs. The chanting had stopped, but someone was talking very specifically about a naval battle off the coast of Brazil. I sank deeper. Hands rubbed me, soaping my hair, my stomach, my balls, my feet. I felt as if I were burrowing into a center, or perhaps I was being mutilated in some way in preparation to being swallowed. But tentacles were all around me and I was being munched on. And suddenly I came alive, or I came and I was dead and I only heard a faint humming as if reaching me down miles and miles of spirals.

I managed to extract myself. I was finished anyway. No one seemed to notice me climb out. I picked up the first set of clothes I came to. A pair of blue jeans, a khaki shirt and black boots. They were all too big, but I climbed the stairs without any trouble.

I would like to stay, certainly, not to move on, to allow nothing to happen while waiting for something to happen, to lie in front of the window now that I have the shade pulled. And so far I haven't said who I was, where I was going. I haven't given out with any information. Or rather, I have. I goofed. It was Nog. Nog survived. I'm stuck with Nog. Days have gone by. I haven't been out of the room. There is a loudspeaker on the wall and music and sometimes voices. In the early morning, exercises come across: ho ho hram hrim hrum hrah. The room is empty except for my mattress and the night table where the tray of food is left. The walls are white and the window sills pale blue. If I had fewer limbs, but I said that. There are certain repetitions that don't work. I used to turn a corner and expect wherever I was staying to have disappeared, and I would split to defeat the expectation. I must dare not to be fathomed. I must not let myself be known, in order to know myself. There are variations. I like the sound of them all. I am not involved in the process of change, but it is important that I see someone, to share this change. It is not crucial to know with whom. But it's probably necessary to spend time with whoever it is, before moving on. Perhaps with Meridith or the man who brings the tray. The octopus has disintegrated. But I haven't thought of that since the bath. I am very clean.

The loudspeaker reports a meeting in the living room. It is the seventh meeting in the living room in the last few days. There have also been meetings, gatherings and mergings in the kitchen, dining room, pantry and hallway on the second floor.

Nog was as comfortable inside as he was outside. I might as well get on with him. He could stand as well as sit before nothing in particular. Despite what he said, he could entertain himself. It's necessary now not to believe the memory of him, in order to develop it further. There is no need to name streets or waterfalls. He doesn't notice them that way. Recently he has become easily lost. I have an urge to listen to the sound of his breathing, of my breathing and balance myself between the two, between the sock and the mattress and to notice the distance that has been covered. That is not alarming because I plan to move on, to erase the distances just covered, perhaps to the kitchen, perhaps down the hall. In any case, soon.

11 ❧ *Richard Brautigan*

Poet and novelist Richard Brautigan lives in San Francisco. His books include The Octopus Frontier, A Confederate General from Big Sur, In Watermelon Sugar, *and* Trout Fishing in America.

"A TROUT FISHING SAMPLER"
(FROM *TROUT FISHING IN AMERICA*)

KNOCK ON WOOD
PART ONE

As a child when did I first hear about trout fishing in America? From whom? I guess it was a stepfather of mine.

Summer of 1942.

The old drunk told me about trout fishing. When he could talk, he had a way of describing trout as if they were a precious and intelligent metal.

Silver is not a good adjective to describe what I felt when he told me about trout fishing.

I'd like to get it right.

Maybe trout steel. Steel made from trout. The clear snow-filled river acting as foundry and heat.

Imagine Pittsburgh.

A steel that comes from trout, used to make buildings, trains and tunnels.

The Andrew Carnegie of Trout!

The Reply of Trout Fishing in America:

I remember with particular amusement, people with three-cornered hats fishing in the dawn.

KNOCK ON WOOD
PART TWO

One spring afternoon as a child in the strange town of Portland, I walked down to a different street corner, and saw a row of old houses, huddled together like seals on a rock. Then there was a long field that came sloping down off a hill. The field was covered with green grass and bushes. On top of the hill there was a grove of tall, dark trees. At a distance I saw a waterfall come pouring down off the hill. It was long and white and I could almost feel its cold spray.

There must be a creek there, I thought, and it probably has trout in it.

Trout.

At last an opportunity to go trout fishing, to catch my first trout, to behold Pittsburgh.

It was growing dark. I didn't have time to go and look at the creek. I walked home past the glass whiskers of the houses, reflecting the downward rushing waterfalls of night.

The next day I would go trout fishing for the first time. I would get up early and eat my breakfast and go. I had heard that it was better to go trout fishing early in the morning. The trout were better for it. They had something extra in the morning. I went home to prepare for trout fishing in America.

I didn't have any fishing tackle, so I had to fall back on corny fishing tackle.

Like a joke.

Why did the chicken cross the road?

I bent a pin and tied it onto a piece of white string.

And slept.

The next morning I got up early and ate my breakfast. I took a slice of white bread to use for bait. I planned on making doughballs from the soft center of the bread and putting them on my vaudevillean hook.

I left the place and walked down to the different street corner. How beautiful the field looked and the creek that came pouring down in a waterfall off the hill.

But as I got closer to the creek I could see that something was wrong. The creek did not act right. There was a strangeness to it. There was a thing about its motion that was wrong. Finally I got close enough to see what the trouble was.

The waterfall was just a flight of white wooden stairs leading up to a house in the trees.

I stood there for a long time, looking up and looking down, following the stairs with my eyes, having trouble believing.

Then I knocked on my creek and heard the sound of wood.

I ended up by being my own trout and eating the slice of bread myself.

The Reply of Trout Fishing in America:

There was nothing I could do. I couldn't change a flight of stairs into a creek. The boy walked back to where he came from. The same thing once happened to me. I remember mistaking an old woman for a trout stream in Vermont, and I had to beg her pardon.

"Excuse me," I said. "I thought you were a trout stream."

"I'm not," she said.

RED LIP

Seventeen years later I sat down on a rock. It was under a
tree next to an old abandoned shack that had a sheriff's notice
nailed like a funeral wreath to the front door.

NO TRESPASSING
4/17 OF A HAIKU

Many rivers had flowed past those seventeen years, and thousands of trout, and now beside the highway and the sheriff's
notice flowed yet another river, the Klamath, and I was trying
to get thirty-five miles downstream to Steelhead, the place
where I was staying.

It was all very simple. No one would stop and pick me up
even though I was carrying fishing tackle. People usually stop
and pick up a fisherman. I had to wait three hours for a ride.

The sun was like a huge fifty-cent piece that someone had
poured kerosene on and then had lit with a match and said,
"Here, hold this while I go get a newspaper," and put the coin
in my hand, but never came back.

I had walked for miles and miles until I came to the rock
under the tree and sat down. Every time a car would come by,
about once every ten minutes, I would get up and stick out my
thumb as if it were a bunch of bananas and then sit back down
on the rock again.

The old shack had a tin roof colored reddish by years of
wear, like a hat worn under the guillotine. A corner of the
roof was loose and a hot wind blew down the river and the
loose corner clanged in the wind.

A car went by. An old couple. The car almost swerved off
the road and into the river. I guess they didn't see many

hitchhikers up there. The car went around the corner with both of them looking back at me.

I had nothing else to do, so I caught salmon flies in my landing net. I made up my own game. It went like this: I couldn't chase after them. I had to let them fly to me. It was something to do with my mind. I caught six.

A little ways up from the shack was an outhouse with its door flung violently open. The inside of the outhouse was exposed like a human face and the outhouse seemed to say, "The old guy who built me crapped in here 9,745 times and he's dead now and I don't want anyone else to touch me. He was a good guy. He built me with loving care. Leave me alone. I'm a monument now to a good ass gone under. There's no mystery here. That's why the door's open. If you have to crap, go in the bushes like the deer."

"Fuck you," I said to the outhouse. "All I want is a ride down the river."

TROUT FISHING IN AMERICA WITH THE FBI

Dear Trout Fishing in America,

last week walking along lower market on the way to work saw the pictures of the FBI's TEN MOST WANTED MEN in the window of a store. the dodger under one of the pictures was folded under at both sides and you couldn't read all of it. the picture showed a nice, clean-cut-looking guy with freckles and curly (red?) hair

WANTED FOR:

RICHARD LAWRENCE MARQUETTE

Aliases: Richard Lawrence Marquette, Richard Lourence Marquette

Description:
26, born Dec. 12, 1934, Portland, Oregon
170 to 180 pounds
muscular
light brown, cut short
blue
   Complexion: ruddy
   Race: white
   Nationality: American
   Occupations   auto body w
                                    recapper, s
                                    survey rod
arks: 6″ hernia scar; tattoo "Mom" in wreath on
ight forearm
ull upper denture, may also have lower denture.
                                    Reportedly frequents
s, and is an avid trout fisherman.

(this is how the dodger looked cut off on both sides and
you couldn't make out any more, even what he was
wanted for.)

                                    Your old buddy,
                                    Pard

Dear Pard,
   Your letter explains why I saw two FBI agents watching
a trout stream last week. They watched a path that came
down through the trees and then circled a large black
stump and led to a deep pool. Trout were rising in the
pool. The FBI agents watched the path, the trees, the
black stump, the pool and the trout as if they were all
holes punched in a card that had just come out of a computer. The afternoon sun kept changing everything as it

moved across the sky, and the FBI agents kept changing
with the sun. It appears to be part of their training.

Your friend,

Trout Fishing in America

THE CLEVELAND WRECKING
YARD

Until recently my knowledge about the Cleveland Wrecking
Yard had come from a couple of friends who'd bought things
there. One of them bought a huge window: the frame, glass
and everything for just a few dollars. It was a fine-looking
window.

Then he chopped a hole in the side of his house up on
Potrero Hill and put the window in. Now he has a panoramic
view of the San Francisco County Hospital.

He can practically look right down into the wards and see
old magazines eroded like the Grand Canyon from endless
readings. He can practically hear the patients thinking about
breakfast: I hate milk, and thinking about dinner; I hate peas,
and then he can watch the hospital slowly drown at night,
hopelessly entangled in huge bunches of brick seaweed.

He bought that window at the Cleveland Wrecking Yard.

My other friend bought an iron roof at the Cleveland
Wrecking Yard and took the roof down to Big Sur in an old
station wagon and then he carried the iron roof on his back
up the side of a mountain. He carried up half the roof on his
back. It was no picnic. Then he bought a mule, George, from
Pleasanton. George carried up the other half of the roof.

The mule didn't like what was happening at all. He lost a
lot of weight because of the tricks, and the smell of the wild-
cats up on the plateau made him too nervous to graze there.
My friend said jokingly that George had lost around two hun-

dred pounds. The good wine country around Pleasanton in the
Livermore Valley probably had looked a lot better to George
than the wild side of the Santa Lucia Mountains.

My friend's place was a shack right beside a huge fireplace
where there had once been a great mansion during the 1920s,
built by a famous movie actor. The mansion was built before
there was even a road down at Big Sur. The mansion had been
brought over the mountains on the backs of mules, strung out
like ants, bringing visions of the good life to the poison oak,
the ticks, and the salmon.

The mansion was on a promontory, high over the Pacific.
Money could see farther in the 1920s, and one could look out
and see whales and the Hawaiian Islands and the Kuomintang
in China.

The mansion burned down years ago.

The actor died.

His mules were made into soap.

His mistresses became bird nests of wrinkles.

Now only the fireplace remains as a sort of Carthaginian
homage to Hollywood.

I was down there a few weeks ago to see my friend's roof.
I wouldn't have passed up the chance for a million dollars, as
they say. The roof looked like a colander to me. If that roof
and the rain were running against each other at Bay Meadows,
I'd bet on the rain and plan to spend my winnings at the
World's Fair in Seattle.

My own experience with the Cleveland Wrecking Yard
began two days ago when I heard about a used trout stream
they had on sale out at the Yard. So I caught the Number 15
bus on Columbus Avenue and went out there for the first time.

There were two Negro boys sitting behind me on the bus.
They were talking about Chubby Checker and the Twist. They
thought that Chubby Checker was only fifteen years old be-

cause he didn't have a mustache. Then they talked about some other guy who did the twist forty-four hours in a row until he saw George Washington crossing the Delaware.

"Man, that's what I call twisting," one of the kids said.

"I don't think I could twist no forty-four hours in a row," the other kid said. "That's a lot of twisting."

I get off the bus right next to an abandoned Time Gasoline filling station and an abandoned fifty-cent self-service car wash. There was a long field on one side of the filling station. The field had once been covered with a housing project during the war, put there for the shipyard workers.

On the other side of the Time filling station was the Cleveland Wrecking Yard. I walked down there to have a look at the used trout stream. The Cleveland Wrecking Yard has a very long front window filled with signs and merchandise.

There was a sign in the window advertising a laundry marking machine for $65.00. The original cost of the machine was $175.00. Quite a saving.

There was another sign advertising new and used two and three ton hoists. I wondered how many hoists it would take to move a trout stream.

There was another sign that said:

THE FAMILY GIFT CENTER,
GIFT SUGGESTIONS FOR THE ENTIRE FAMILY

The window was filled with hundreds of items for the entire family. Daddy, do you know what I want for Christmas? What, son? A bathroom. Mommy, do you know what I want for Christmas? What, Patricia? Some roofing material.

There were jungle hammocks in the window for distant relatives and dollar-ten-cent gallons of earth-brown enamel paint for other loved ones.

There was also a big sign that said:

USED TROUT STREAM FOR SALE.

MUST BE SEEN TO BE APPRECIATED.

I went inside and looked at some ship's lanterns that were for sale next to the door. Then a salesman came up to me and said in a pleasant voice, "Can I help you?"

"Yes," I said. "I'm curious about the trout stream you have for sale. Can you tell me something about it? How are you selling it?"

"We're selling it by the foot length. You can buy as little as you want or you can buy all we've got left. A man came in here this morning and bought 563 feet. He's going to give it to his niece for a birthday present," the salesman said.

"We're selling the waterfalls separately of course, and the trees and birds, flowers, grass and ferns we're also selling extra. The insects we're giving away free with a minimum purchase of ten feet of stream."

"How much are you selling the stream for?" I asked.

"Six dollars and fifty-cents a foot," he said. "That's for the first hundred feet. After that it's five dollars a foot."

"How much are the birds?" I asked.

"Thirty-five cents apiece," he said. "But of course they're used. We can't guarantee anything."

"How wide is the stream?" I asked. "You said you were selling it by the length, didn't you?"

"Yes," he said. "We're selling it by the length. Its width runs between five and eleven feet. You don't have to pay anything extra for width. It's not a big stream, but it's very pleasant."

"What kinds of animals do you have?" I asked.

"We only have three deer left," he said.

"Oh . . . What about flowers?"

"By the dozen," he said.

"Is the stream clear?" I asked.

"Sir," the salesman said. "I wouldn't want you to think that we would ever sell a murky trout stream here. We always make sure they're running crystal clear before we even think about moving them."

"Where did the stream come from?" I asked.

"Colorado," he said. "We moved it with loving care. We've never damaged a trout stream yet. We treat them all as if they were china."

"You're probably asked this all the time, but how's fishing in the stream?" I asked.

"Very good," he said. "Mostly German browns, but there are a few rainbows."

"What do the trout cost?" I asked.

"They come with the stream," he said. "Of course it's all luck. You never know how many you're going to get or how big they are. But the fishing's very good, you might say it's excellent. Both bait and dry fly," he said smiling.

"Where's the stream at?" I asked. "I'd like to take a look at it."

"It's around in back," he said. "You go straight through that door and then turn right until you're outside. It's stacked in lengths. You can't miss it. The waterfalls are upstairs in the used plumbing department."

"What about the animals?"

"Well, what's left of the animals are straight back from the stream. You'll see a bunch of our trucks parked on a road by the railroad tracks. Turn right on the road and follow it down past the piles of lumber. The animal shed's right at the end of the lot."

"Thanks," I said. "I think I'll look at the waterfalls first.

You don't have to come with me. Just tell me how to get there and I'll find my own way."

"All right," he said. "Go up those stairs. You'll see a bunch of doors and windows, turn left and you'll find the used plumbing department. Here's my card if you need any help."

"Okay," I said. "You've been a great help already. Thanks a lot. I'll take a look around."

"Good luck," he said.

I went upstairs and there were thousands of doors there. I'd never seen so many doors before in my life. You could have built an entire city out of those doors. Doorstown. And there were enough windows up there to build a little suburb entirely out of windows. Windowville.

I turned left and went back and saw the faint glow of pearl-colored light. The light got stronger and stronger as I went farther back, and then I was in the used plumbing department, surrounded by hundreds of toilets.

The toilets were stacked on shelves. They were stacked five toilets high. There was a skylight above the toilets that made them glow like the Great Taboo Pearl of the South Sea movies.

Stacked over against the wall were the waterfalls. There were about a dozen of them, ranging from a drop of a few feet to a drop of ten or fifteen feet.

There was one waterfall that was over sixty feet long. There were tags on the pieces of the big fall describing the correct order for putting the falls back together again.

The waterfalls all had price tags on them. They were more expensive than the stream. The waterfalls were selling for $19.00 a foot.

I went into another room where there were piles of sweet-smelling lumber, glowing a soft yellow from a different color skylight above the lumber. In the shadows at the edge of the room under the sloping roof of the building were many sinks and urinals covered with dust, and there was also another waterfall about seventeen feet long, lying there in two lengths and already beginning to gather dust.

I had seen all I wanted of the waterfalls, and now I was very curious about the trout stream, so I followed the salesman's directions and ended up outside the building.

O I had never in my life seen anything like that trout stream. It was stacked in piles of various lengths: ten, fifteen, twenty feet, etc. There was one pile of hundred-foot lengths. There was also a box of scraps. The scraps were in odd sizes ranging from six inches to a couple of feet.

There was a loudspeaker on the side of the building and soft music was coming out. It was a cloudy day and seagulls were circling high overhead.

Behind the stream were big bundles of trees and bushes. They were covered with sheets of patched canvas. You could see the tops and roots sticking out the ends of the bundles.

I went up close and looked at the lengths of stream. I could see some trout in them. I saw one good fish. I saw some crawdads crawling around the rocks at the bottom.

It looked like a fine stream. I put my hand in the water. It was cold and felt good.

I decided to go around to the side and look at the animals. I saw where the trucks were parked beside the railroad tracks. I followed the road down past the piles of lumber, back to the shed where the animals were.

The salesman had been right. They were practically out of animals. About the only thing they had left in any abundance were mice. There were hundreds of mice.

Beside the shed was a huge wire birdcage, maybe fifty feet high, filled with many kinds of birds. The top of the cage had a piece of canvas over it, so the birds wouldn't get wet when it rained. There were woodpeckers and wild canaries and sparrows.

On my way back to where the trout stream was piled, I
found the insects. They were inside a prefabricated steel building that was selling for eighty-cents a square foot. There was
a sign over the door. It said

INSECTS

DATE DUE

MAR 22 2011	

BACKGROUND OF
THE NEWFOUNDLAND

Many canines have been singled out in literature, but none better immortalized than Boatswain, the beloved Newfoundland owned by nineteenth-century British romantic poet Lord Byron in the poem "Epitaph to a Dog."

The ancient people dubbed it "the hero dog" because of its renowned and selfless feats of bravery. Poets extolled it for its loyal and loving nature, while artists immortalized it as a gentle giant whose bond with its human companions was irrevocable. It is one of the only breeds that has ever been honored by having its picture on a postage stamp. This is the Newfoundland, a large, strong, heavy-coated dog whose versatility on land and in water is unparalleled; a faithful companion who has found its way into more legends than even the most conscientious historian can recount; an imposing figure who impresses the eye with its great dignity and pride. In motion, the Newfoundland gives the impression of effortless

The Newf is a strong, imposing dog, equally adaptable to land and water.

power. It is, both literally and figuratively, a dog for all seasons.

Origins and History of the Breed

The "Newf" or "Newfy" as it is affectionately called, has had at least a passing acquaintance with more canine species in its evolution than practically any other breed in existence today. Various reports trace its origins to no less than three different continents: Asia, Europe, and North America. Ask any fancier of the breed and you're bound to be flooded with a flurry of tales, part whimsical, part factual, about how this great dog found its way into the history books. One of the earliest and more colorful legends relates that the original ancestor of this loyal and stately breed first appeared on

The Newfoundland made its way to the American continent even before the Vikings.

NEWF SOUNDBYTES

During the American colonial period, two famous Newfs belonged to our first president, George Washington, and to statesman Benjamin Franklin.

the North American continent at about 1000 A.D. aboard an ancient Viking ship. This formidable black "bear dog" named Oolam supposedly served as a trusty mate beside its master, Norse explorer Leif Erikson.

Still another narrative puts a Newf at the front lines of a campaign led by Napoleon I,

Due to its gentle personality and innate intelligence, the Newf served as a "nanny" to children in ancient times.

where the dog is said to have rescued the "Little General" from drowning. Even Napoleon's arch enemy, Admiral Lord Nelson, kept a Newf beside him in battle.

Another account relates the daring deeds of one QueQue, an American Newf owned by the colonist, Samuel Adams. The story goes that while the redcoats blockaded Boston Harbor, this great black dog did its patriotic best by being such an unrelenting pest and prankster

that the British soldiers were only too happy to accept defeat and return home.

In 1802 another American Newfoundland named Scannon gained its place in history by accompanying the explorers Lewis and Clark on their Northwest expedition. According to reports, Scannon was kidnapped by a group of Indians who apparently had him earmarked for a tribal banquet. But Lewis and Clark were so incensed about losing their valuable teammate

Black and Landseer are color variations of the Newfoundland.

that they sent out a search-and-rescue party to bring the dog back. When faced with such a formidable show of force, Scannon's captors put their dinner plans on hold and handed the great dog over.

An Ancient Breed

Though there are no early written records of the breed, it is generally accepted that the Newfoundland is one of the oldest species of dogs in existence. It is probably a combination of several different canines, including the Great Pyrenees, Basque spaniels, different varieties of sheepdogs, the Tibetan Mastiff, and the Norse bear dog. However, even before the Viking explorers landed on the North American continent, skeletal remains of giant dogs dating back to the fifth century A.D. were found in Indian gravesites. They had triangular-shaped heads, pointy, somewhat elongated muzzles, erect ears, and curled tails.

By the sixteenth century, French, English, Basque, Spanish, and Portuguese fishermen established settlements in Newfoundland, and it's reasonable to assume they brought their dogs with them and that these dogs bred with the native population. This may account for the two different color strains that developed in

The Landseer got its name from the English artist, Sir Edwin Landseer (1802–1873), who featured them in many of his paintings.

the breed: the self-colored Newfoundland, which is an all-black, brown, or gray dog, occasionally with a white blaze, and the Landseer, a predominately white dog with black markings. Today, the two are simply considered color variations of the same breed.

How Did the Newf Get Its Name

The breed as we know it probably originated in the easternmost Canadian province of Newfoundland, from which it derives its name. From an etching, we know that the dogs of this period had elongated muzzles, triangular heads,

and sparse furnishings. It wasn't until 1775 that the breed was officially named by George Cartwright, a native Newfoundlander who ascribed the name of his island to his pet dog. Ironically, five years later the Newf was in serious danger of extinction after a government proclamation limited the ownership of the giant dogs to one per household—all others were slated to be destroyed or exported. Because of its great size and strength, however, the Newf already occupied an intrinsic place in the daily flow of commerce, so most people ignored the ordinance. It's fairly easy to understand why.

One of the Newf's trademarks is its massive head.

Duties: The Newf pulled heavy loads, helped to haul in fishing nets and wood from the forest, powered the blacksmith's bellows, and was even known to serve as a nanny for children! When hitched to a cart, it was able to navigate its load through narrow streets a horse and buggy could not. In short, the Newf was such a fine laborer and worked so well at the side of its human charges that it was far too valuable to do without.

The Breed Yesterday and Today

The dog we now recognize as the Newfoundland was largely developed in both England and America in the nineteenth century. The first recorded showing of the Newfoundland was at a dog show in Birmingham, England, in 1860. Soon after, an all-black Newf named Nero, owned by the Prince of Wales, became the first Newfoundland to gain prominence in the show ring. By the late eighteenth century the Newf had made its way south from Canada to the United States. The first American champion was Sam in 1883. Thirty years later Major II won his championship. In 1908 Graydon's New Jersey Big Boy, a Landseer who was imported from England, became the third Newf to attain an American championship. Though the breed became very popular in the United States, it wasn't granted official AKC (American Kennel Club) status until 1914.

Setbacks: Besides the eighteenth-century proclamation, the breed had two other major setbacks in its development. During World War I, because of food rationing and the amount of food they required, Newfs nearly disappeared from England; the same occurred during World War II. But due to the dedication of a few breeders, the stock, though depleted, remained strong and of high quality. In fact, in the 1920s American and Canadian breeders began importing English stock to fortify their own. In this endeavor, one dog stands out above the rest: English Champion Siki, also known as the "father of champions."

Above all others, the Siki line laid the foundation for most of the successful breeding programs in the United States and Canada. Though not a spectacular specimen of the breed, Ch. Siki was nonetheless one of the most prepotent sires in the history of the breed, producing progeny of extraordinary quality. Most kennels

The Newfoundland has a sweet disposition and is a devoted companion.

operating today can trace their lines back to this all-important Siki bloodline.

Thanks to the efforts of a small number of dedicated breeders, this great dog thrives and prospers in breeding programs today.

Black Versus Landseer

Although it is now accepted among fanciers of the breed that the black Newfoundland and the Landseer are one and the same breed, some historians have pointed out that the two were initially separated geographically and may have a combination of different breeds in their ancestry.

The Landseer was named after the English artist, Sir Edwin Landseer, who painted many black-and-white Newfoundlands. In fact, the first English Newfoundland champion was a Landseer named Dick, who had a black head with a white blaze and saddle, black rump, and a white tail. It is also interesting to note that the black-and-white Landseer must be bred back to black Newfoundland stock at a fairly regular interval in order to maintain type. Otherwise, the Landseer becomes more refined looking with an elongated muzzle and narrower body and head, like its early ancestors.

UNDERSTANDING THE NEWFOUNDLAND

When someone comes face to face with a full-grown Newfoundland for the first time, it can be a daunting experience. But even those who may be initially intimidated by the Newf's formidable proportions, its awesome musculature, and dignified bearing are soon won over by its amazing gentleness and sweet disposition.

While the Newf is classified as a "giant" breed, it is not an overly active dog, but it does require regular exercise to keep fit and healthy. The Newf loves to play and is equally at home on land or in water. Its unique swimming ability and webbed feet make it the quintessential water dog. The Newf is also one of the most versatile breeds. Its double, water-resistant coat insulates it from extremes in temperatures, making it easily adaptable to either hot or cold weather. More than anything else, the most striking characteristic of the Newf is its desire to be with humans. The Newfoundland is definitely a "people" dog.

The Newf is a bit of a "ham," and loves to be noticed.

Man's Best Friend— the Newfoundland

Perhaps more than any other breed, the Newfoundland's very existence depended upon its ability to interact in a meaningful and productive manner with its human masters. Farmers, fishermen, tradesmen depended on the Newf as a working partner, while families counted on it to literally "carry" its load of responsibilities. This close proximity to humans would not have been possible if the Newf had not been a willing and eager participant endowed with a sweet, gentle disposition and an innate intelligence. More than most breeds, it has a need to bond with people and to give and receive affection. The Newf is also very protective of its human family and will go to any lengths to ensure the family's safety.

Showing your Newf is a rewarding and bonding experience for owner and pet.

Championships

To date, only two Newfoundlands have been awarded an OTCH. The first was OTCH Barbara Allen's Jessie, WD in 1982 and the second was OTCH Sweetbay's Gretl, TD. Gretl was also the first Newf to ever achieve a perfect score of 200! When Gretl retired from competition in 1991, she was given a special award for outstanding achievement.

The Newfoundland Club of America now offers a VN (Versatile Newfoundland) award to members dogs who earn:
- an AKC Championship
- an AKC Companion Dog (CD) obedience title
- an NCA (Junior) Water Dog title
- an NCA (Senior) Water Rescue title
- an NCA Draft Dog Title

Every year, these VN's are honored at the National Specialty.

Though not a barker, the Newf will alert its family to any situation that deviates from normal. Despite its large size, the Newf is extremely gentle and for that reason makes a wonderful companion for children.

Attention seeker: The Newf is also an attention seeker and a bit of a ham—in its quest to be noticed, it can be a downright pest at times! Many Newfoundland owners will tell amusing stories about how their Newfs compete for affection. This loyal and loving dog is happiest when sitting at the foot of its owner receiving an affectionate pat on the head. Even though the Newfoundland loves people, it is not a one-man dog, but it will tend to play favorites within a family, and spend the most time with the person who gives it the most attention.

As with any other breed, to ensure that the Newfoundland reaches its full potential as a companion dog, early training is essential and since the Newf is a working breed, it is particularly adaptable to instruction and takes pride in a task well done.

The Newfoundland in Obedience Trials

Working with your Newfy in obedience is probably one of the most rewarding activities both dog and owner will do together. Since it is a working breed, obedience is one of its key functions and consequently comes second nature to it. Although as a large breed the Newfy is not as quick or as agile as some of its smaller canine counterparts, it can still excel in obedience trials when trained and paced properly.

The American Kennel Club first established obedience trials in the 1930's. The purpose of the competition, which has three levels or classes of increasing difficulty, is to determine the dog's ability to obey a set of commands while accomplishing a set of tasks. There are four different obedience titles awarded when the dog has successfully completed a class.:

1. The CD title (Companion Dog) is awarded to a dog in the novice class.

2. The CDX (Companion Dog Excellent) is awarded to a dog in the open class.

3. The UD (Utility Dog) is awarded to a dog in the utility class.

4. The OTCH (Obedience Trial Championship) is the highest obedience title a dog can win.

If you intend to show your Newf, learn the breed standard before purchasing your dog.

TIP

Before Showing

Before showing your Newf, first have it evaluated by several people who are knowledgeable about the breed. Even though you may have bought a "show" puppy at nine weeks, by the time it's six months (the earliest you can enter it in conformation), it may not be the perfect specimen you bargained for. While breeders try to determine with reasonable accuracy which puppies will be show-quality, often the difference between a show and a pet pup is so slight that it may not become apparent until the puppy starts to mature. Another reason to have your puppy evaluated before showing it is to learn its faults. No dog is perfect and a professional with a good eye will be able to guide you on the best way to minimize its faults and accentuate its better features.

✔ Next, attend several dog shows and learn ring procedures. You can handle your own dog in the ring or hire a professional handler. Many people who have shown their own dogs to a championship will tell you that there is nothing more exciting than going in the ring and winning those points together. Most dog clubs offer regular conformation classes for owners who wish to compete with their dogs.

✔ In the United States, in order to become a champion of record, your dog must win 15 points. Two sets must be major points (three-, four-, or five-point blocks) and must be won under two different judges.

In order to become a champion of record, your Newf must win fifteen points in AKC confirmation shows.

The competitions consist of high and broad jumps, retrieving articles, scent discrimination, and a series of *stays* and *sits*.

Showing Your Newfoundland

Before buying your Newfoundland, one of the things you will have to decide is whether to pick a show- or a pet-quality puppy/dog. If you want to show your dog in conformation, you must pick a Newf that most closely typifies the standard for the breed. As a working breed, the Newfoundland is particularly well suited to performing tasks of any kind, and for that reason the Newf is a natural in the show ring. But unlike obedience or water trials, which require specific skills, the only mandate for competing

Best in Show

As a breed, the Newfoundland has fared very well in the show ring. In 1984 Am. Can. Ch. Seaward's Blackbeard, ROM, the most winning Newfoundland in the history of the breed, became the first Newf ever to win Best in Show at the most prestigious dog show of them all: The Westminster Kennel Club. Exactly 20 years later, in 2004, another Newf took top honors at Westminister: Ch. Darbydale's All Rise Pouch Cove, call name, "Josh." This awesome four-year-old is owned by Peggy Helming and Carol Bernard Bergmann.

in conformation is that your dog looks good in the ring. Simply put, it's a beauty contest—but like any activity you and your Newf do together, it's fun, rewarding, and if you've got a good dog, it can lead to a championship.

Newfoundland Standard

General Appearance

The Newfoundland is a large, heavily coated dog. It is well balanced and deep bodied with heavy bone and powerful musculature. Standing over 26 inches (63.5 cm) at the shoulder, its weight reaches about 150 pounds (68 kg).

Size: The average adult dog stands 28 inches (71 cm) high at the shoulder while adult bitches stand 24 (61 cm) inches high. A full-grown dog can weigh between 130 and 150 pounds (59–68 kg); a full-grown bitch, 100–120 pounds (45–54 kg). The Newfoundland is slightly longer than it is tall from the point of the shoulder to the point of the buttocks and from the withers to the ground. It has considerable substance, which is determined by the spring of its rib, strong muscles, and heavy bone.

Head: The Newfoundland has a massive head with a broad skull, slightly arched crown, and strongly developed occipital bone. Its cheeks are well developed. The eyes are dark brown (browns and grays may have lighter eyes), relatively small, deep set, and spaced wide apart. Eyelids fit closely with no inversion. The ears are relatively small and triangular with rounded tips. They are set on the skull level with or slightly above the brow, and lie close to the head. When the ear is brought forward, it reaches to the inner corner of the eye on the same side. The expression is soft and reflects the characteristics of the breed: benevolence, intelligence, and dignity.

The forehead and face are smooth and free of wrinkles. The slope of the stop is moderate, the muzzle clean-cut, broad throughout its length, and deep. Depth and lengths are approximately equal. The top of the muzzle is rounded. The bridge in profile is straight or only slightly arched. Teeth meet in a level or scissor bite.

Neck, Topline, Body: The neck is strong and well set on the shoulders and long enough for proud head carriage. The back is strong, broad, and muscular and is level from just behind the withers to the croup. The chest is full and deep with the brisket reaching at least down to the elbows. Ribs are well-sprung, with the anterior third of the rib cage tapered to allow clearance. The flank is deep. The croup is broad and slopes slightly. The tail set follows the natural line of the croup. The tail is broad at the base and strong. It has no kinks and the distal bone reaches the hock. When the dog is standing relaxed, its tail hangs straight or with a slight curve at the end. When the dog is in motion,

An adult Newf dog stands 28 inches (71 cm) high at the shoulder and weighs approximately 130 pounds (59 kg).

the tail is carried out, but it does not curl over the back.

Forequarters: The shoulders are muscular and well laid back. Elbows lie directly below the highest point of the withers. Forelegs are muscular, heavily boned, straight, and parallel to each

If you show your Newf, you will have to learn how to "stack" or set up its front and rear for judging: Left: too wide; Center: correct; Right: too close.

Once you have your Newf's front stacked, work on its rear: Left: cow-hocked; Center: correct; Right: too close (toeing-in).

other. The elbows point directly to the rear. The distance from the elbow to the ground equals about half the dog's height. Pasterns are strong and slightly sloping. Feet are proportionate to the body size, webbed and cat-foot in type. Dewclaws may be removed.

Hindquarters: The rear assembly is powerful, muscular, and heavily boned. Viewed from the rear, the legs are straight and parallel. Viewed from the side, the thighs are broad and fairly long. Stifles and hocks are well bent and the line from hock to ground is perpendicular. Hocks are well let down. Hind feet are similar to the front feet. Dewclaws should be removed.

Coat: The adult Newfoundland has a flat water-resistant double coat that tends to fall back into place when rubbed against the nap. The outer coat is coarse, moderately long, and full, whether straight or with a wave. The undercoat is soft and dense, although it is often less dense during the summer months or in warmer climates. Hair on the face and muzzle is short and fine. The backs of the legs are feathered all the way down. The tail is covered with long, dense hair. Excess hair may be trimmed for neatness. Whiskers need not be trimmed.

Color: Color is secondary to type, structure, and soundness. Recognized Newfoundland colors are black, brown, and gray with some white, or a white base coat with black markings (landseer).

Solids: Blacks, browns, and grays may appear as solid colors or solid colors with white at any, some, or all of the following locations: chin, chest, toes, and tip of tail. Any amount of white found at these locations is typical and is not penalized. Also typical are a tinge of bronze on a black or a gray coat and lighter furnishings on a brown or gray coat.

Landseer: White base coat with black markings. Typically the head is solid black, or black with white on the muzzle, with or without a blaze. There is a separate black saddle and black on the rump extending onto a white tail.

Note: Markings on either solid colors or Landseers might deviate considerably from those described and should be penalized only to the extent of the deviation. Clear white or white with minimal ticking is preferred.

Beauty of markings should be considered only when comparing dogs of otherwise comparable quality and never at the expense of type, structure, and soundness.

Gait

The Newfoundland in motion has good reach and strong drive; it gives the impression of effortless power. Its gait is smooth and rhythmic, covering the maximum amount of ground with the minimum number of steps. Forelegs and hind legs travel straight forward. As the dog's speed increases, the legs tend toward single tracking. When moving, a slight roll of the skin is characteristic of the breed. Essential to good movement is the balance of correct front and rear assemblies.

Need an extra pair of hands?

Temperament

Sweetness of temperament is the hallmark of the Newfoundland. This is the single most important characteristic of the breed. A multipurpose dog, at work it is tireless and eager to please and at home it is a fun-loving and devoted companion. It is equally at home on land or in water and possesses natural life-saving abilities.

The Newfoundland as a Working Dog

One of the characteristics that sets the Newf apart from other breeds is its prowess as a working dog. In today's computer age, we don't think much about a dog having a specific task to perform, except perhaps for those canines trained as guide dogs for the blind. Yet in earlier times, as we've already mentioned, a dog's worth was judged specifically by its ability to be a working member of the household. In short, it had to pull its own weight. That's why the Newf, due to its great size and placid disposition, gained acceptance as a working member of the family.

In contemporary society, we don't ask our canine companions to do much more than fetch a newspaper or roll over. But the Newf is still occasionally called upon by its human master to assist in some of the labors of daily living. In fact, teams of Newfs were running mail to remote outposts in their native Newfoundland until the 1940s. Today, however, Newfs also provide valuable assistance as search-and-rescue dogs. Since most Newf owners want to preserve the breed's working characteristics, they allow their dogs to compete in water, rescue, tracking, and draft trials as developed by the Newfoundland Club of America. These events not only provide the dog an opportunity to do what it was bred to do, but also give Newf owners a chance to socialize and enjoy fun family activities with their dogs.

Getting Your Newf in Shape

Before starting your Newf on a program of activities, you'll have to get it in top condition. Swimming is the best way to get your dog in shape. Swimming is not only great fun for the Newf, but it will also build up its muscles better than any other type of exercise. Jogging on a soft surface is also an excellent endurance exercise and something you can do with your pet so you can both stay in shape. Although many people like to exercise their dogs while they ride a bicycle, this is not advisable. The dog could easily pull the wrong way or go too fast and you could be seriously injured. Plus, you could inadvertently topple into the path of an oncoming car. Roadworking, or attaching your Newf with a lead to the back bumper of your car is also dangerous! For one thing, it's very difficult to maintain a slow speed for a long, steady inter-

All hands on deck! The Newf is happiest when it is performing a task.

val; imagine having to hit the brake suddenly and having your Newf come crashing into the rear end of the car, or under it!

Water Trials

The Newfoundland's natural swimming ability and stamina in the water make it the ideal water rescue dog. In fact, you could call it a canine lifeguard. The Newf's instinct is to jump into the water and aid anyone or anything in distress. Thus, the object of the water trial is to team up owner and dog in a number of exercises to demonstrate obedience and ability to perform the task of retrieve and rescue.

Before you take your Newf to any of the dozen water trials across the country sanctioned by The Newfoundland Club of America each year, you'll have to train it in basic obedience and then introduce it to the water. The Newf will adapt to both easily and will excel. Start it on both as a puppy.

✔ One of the first commands it will have to learn is to come on command. When you and your Newf participate in water trials, you do so as a team. You are the team leader; therefore, you must be in complete control of your dog.

NEWF SOUNDBYTES

Brumis, the big black Newfy that was the devoted companion of the late Robert F. Kennedy while Kennedy served as U.S. Attorney General, was often seen scampering along the halls of the Justice Department, just like one of the guys.

Swimming together is a great way to get your Newf and you in shape!

✔ Your Newf will have to learn things such as *retrieve* and *delivery*.

✔ It will have to learn to hold and then give, to pull and carry, all of which are designed to teach it to rescue.

Training your Newf to take part in water trials is hard, but rewarding work for both of you. Dogs that qualify in the Junior Division of the water trial are awarded the title WD (Water Dog). Those successfully competing in the Senior Division are awarded the title WRD (Water Rescue Dog).

The NCA now offers a WRDX, Water Dog Excellent title. This is open to those exceptional Newfoundlands that are instinctive lifesavers as well as strong, athletic swimmers capable of lifting a capsized raft and saving multiple victims.

Carting and Hauling

When you see a full-grown adult Newf, it is easy to understand why it was worth its weight in gold as a carting and hauling dog. The Newf's size plus its massive musculature made it perfect for hauling heavy loads. At the turn of the century, Newfs commonly worked in harness for their masters. Today, a Newf's activities may be restricted to pulling a wagon full of toddlers around a playground,

Here I come, ready or not!

Carting and Hauling Preparation

Before you harness up your Newf to the family sled, it'll have to be obedience-trained. As in water training, carting and hauling demands a dog that is under its master's control at all times. Introduce your Newf to a harness slowly; otherwise, it may resist, panic, and what could have been a fun activity for all will be permanently ruined. Don't begin to harness-train your Newf until it is physically mature. Young puppies have not had enough time to develop and could injure themselves if harnessed too soon. Carting and hauling requires great stamina and conditioning, so you will have to gradually start extending your dog's exercise periods for longer intervals to build up its muscles and its endurance.

taking the children for a sleigh ride after the first snowfall or dragging a freshly cut Christmas tree into the house. Nonetheless, a properly trained Newf performs all these activities with willingness and enthusiasm.

Competition: If you do decide to train your Newf for hauling and carting, you can have lots of fun by entering draft test competitions. The purpose of these competitions is to demonstrate the Newf's ability to perform these skills in real work situations. There are two different draft titles your dog can earn: Draft Dog (DD), which is awarded to dogs competing individually, or Team Draft Dog (TDD), awarded to teams of two or more dogs working together.

In order to qualify, your Newf must show a willingness to be harnessed and hitched and then demonstrate obedience to commands while it successfully maneuvers a cart. Finally, it must pull a load over a course of at least 1 mile (2 km).

While preparing your Newf for draft competition isn't easy, like the water trials, it is a rewarding experience and one that will strengthen the bond between you and your dog.

Tracking

If you've ever seen an old movie where the local lawmen were skirting through the swamps with a bunch of bloodhounds in tow, you get the basic idea of what tracking is all about. Tracking, which is an AKC-recognized sport, requires the dog to track a human scent over a specific course. In this type of event, both dog and owner work as a team to locate a specific human scent left by a "tracklayer."

Going my way? Carting is another one of the Newf's favorite activities.

A track is mapped out over a course of approximately 500 yards (457 m) and divided into two sections with corners. The tracklayer plants a flag into the ground at the beginning of the course and then begins walking it through as specified by the judge. At the 30-yard (27-m) mark, he plants another flag and continues to the end of the course. When he reaches the end, he drops an object that he has been carrying on his person throughout the course—a glove, a wallet, a shoe. It's then up to the dog to navigate the course and find the object containing the scent. The handler will start his dog, who is harnessed to a 30- to 40-foot (9–12-m) lead, at the first flag. He indicates the spot so the dog can pick up the scent. The dog, nose to ground, then moves forward, following the scent path. If the dog makes it to the second flag, the handler will know the dog has the scent and will continue to follow wherever the dog leads until the object is found. If your Newf finds the object, it passes the test and earns the title of Tracking Dog (TD).

Note: It's interesting to point out that in Tracking, your Newf will really be on its own. You, the handler, simply hold onto the lead and follow where it takes you. You cannot correct your dog or use any of the other obedience commands that were essential in all of the other activities. Tracking requires the dog to operate on an instinctual level.

Whew, I need a rest!

Backpacking

One of the most fun activities you can enjoy with your Newf is backpacking. There's nothing like a hike in the woods or a camping trip when all of nature is in bloom. And no one will enjoy accompanying you more than your Newf. Not only will it help haul your gear, but will be at your side at all times. However, before you take your Newf out on the trail, it must be trained to obey your commands. There are many distractions out in the woods, from other animals to fellow travelers, and an unruly dog will prove a menace to itself and anyone else in its path.

When you get ready to hit the trails with your Newf, be sure its backpack is well balanced. Even though the Newf is a working dog and loves to be challenged with a task, it shouldn't be weighted down with too much of a load. Use common sense and prepare to have a great time.

CONSIDERATIONS BEFORE YOU BUY

There is nothing more appealing than a litter of cuddly Newfoundland puppies. They are sure to tickle your funny bone and warm your heart. But wait!—before you get ready to scoop one up and take it home, be sure you know what you're getting into.

An eight-week-old puppy may be a joy to behold, but take a look at its parents before you make a final decision. It's important to be realistic and honest with yourself before anticipating the purchase of a Newf.

Owning a Giant Breed

Are you physically and psychologically ready to assume the care for a giant breed dog? That cute little 15-pound (7 kg) puppy will be tipping the scales at about 130 pounds (59 kg) by the time it's a year old. Can you handle that? Even though you've probably read several books about the breed and have decided the Newf is the dog for you, it's one thing to be intellectually aware of what's involved with owning a Newf, but it's quite another thing

Wow, am I really going to be as big as you, Mom?

to see a full-grown adult in the flesh. If you're not intimidated, then you've definitely settled on one of the most loyal and loving breeds out there.

Under no circumstances should you buy a Newf for a child and make him or her responsible for the dog's care. We've all heard a parent tell a child, "you can have the dog as long as you take care of it." This is absolutely the wrong reason to buy a Newf—or any dog, for that matter. Not only is this attitude unfair to the dog, but it also sets a terrible example for the child who will come to believe that all living things are disposable. Unless you are prepared to make your Newf a member of the family and be responsible for it for the rest of its life, resist the impulse to buy—get a stuffed animal instead. If more people gave serious thought to dog ownership and its responsibilities, there would be far fewer dogs euthanized in shelters across the country each year. Think

CHECKLIST

Questions

Before buying a Newf, ask yourself the following questions:

✔ Can your lifestyle accommodate your Newf's needs as it grows and matures? If you live in an apartment, the Newf is not the right dog for you.

✔ Do you have a reasonably large, fenced-in yard for your Newf to romp in?

✔ Can you spend the time and money required to care for a giant breed like the Newf? Remember, it will have daily grooming requirements.

✔ Do you have the time to train your Newf while it's still a puppy so that when it reaches adulthood, you won't have an unruly giant dog on your hands?

✔ Will other members of the family be responsible for your Newf's care? If so, be certain they know what role they will play in its growth and development.

about that before you purchase your Newf or any other pet.

If you've met every possible objection to owning a Newf and you still want to go full steam ahead, then you're ready to get serious.

Where to Find a Newf Puppy

Attending dog shows is a great way to familiarize yourself with different Newfoundland breeders and get a chance to see their dogs in action. If one breeder doesn't have dogs available, he or she will usually recommend another

breeder. By talking to several breeders, you will soon get a feeling for what you want in your dog. Try to visit breeders who impressed you. You'll be able to judge a well-kept kennel from a poorly maintained one fairly quickly. A kennel doesn't have to be elaborate, but it should be spotlessly clean. All resident dogs should look well cared for and well groomed. Kennels should be free of odors and be big enough for a giant dog such as the Newf to be comfortable.

If you can't visit Newfoundland breeders, you can go online and get a list of breeders from the Newfoundland Club of America. Many breeders have Web sites with pictures of their dogs and descriptions of their breeding programs and bloodlines. Good breeders are proud of their reputations and are happy to supply the prospective buyer with references. Once you decide on a dog, you can pick it up in person or, if you live too far away, the breeder will arrange to ship it to you on a commercial airline.

Puppy Versus Older Dog

Once you have made up your mind that the Newfoundland is the right breed for you, the next thing you'll want to consider is whether to get a puppy or an older dog. There are pros and cons to each, but ultimately, your decision may depend on your lifestyle.

Puppies

Puppies are cute and cuddly but they are also a lot of work. If you decide on a puppy, you will need to spend much more time with it than you would with an older dog that is already house-trained and probably obedience-trained. Here's where your lifestyle comes into play. In a two-career household, where Mom and Dad go out to work every day and the kids go to school, a puppy may not fit into that busy equation. However, a well-behaved Newf that is two or three years old might be perfect. This doesn't mean that older dogs don't need time and attention, too. They do. However, they are more adaptable to your needs than a puppy would be. An adult Newf won't need to go out as often as a puppy and won't require as many play periods.

Availability: One of the problems prospective owners face if they want an older dog is their availability. Most well-bred, well-trained adult Newfs are not for sale. Occasionally, however, breeders will have adult dogs for sale to good homes. Usually, a breeder will keep several puppies from a given litter with the intention of showing them in conformation and/or obedience. Sometimes, all the dogs don't mature into the great show specimens the breeder had hoped for. At that point, the dogs usually become available for sale as pets. This is often a good way to buy a fine older dog with excellent bloodlines.

Adults

Adult Newfs may be sold or put up for adoption through ads in the newspapers, though unless you really get a good picture of the dog's history from the present owner, this isn't the

Never entrust the care of a puppy to a young child.

best way to get an adult dog. Many times, people want to dispose of an animal because it has some kind of problem, either behavioral or physical. On the other hand, the dog could be perfectly fine, but the owners either didn't know how to deal with it or were not equipped to handle a dog with the Newf's needs. If you do buy an adult dog from someone other than from a reputable breeder, ask to see its health certificates and check with the veterinarian who has been taking care of it. Then you can go ahead with the purchase with more confidence that you've made the right choice.

Showing: Some people get into dogs because they want to show them. If that's the case, you're usually better off with a puppy that you can train yourself. Even if you have no intention of getting into the sport of dogs, you may still prefer a puppy. It is certainly one of the greatest experiences to bring a nine-week-old

NEWF SOUNDBYTES

Movie buffs are most familiar with a great bronze-colored Newfy named "Kodiak" who played the dog named "Lou" in the comedy, *Police Academy 2*. The dog also has the honor of being the most titled Newf in the history of the breed.

puppy into your life and have the pleasure of raising it, bonding with it, and loving it throughout its life. If you have the time, the space, and the patience, go for it! It's an experience you'll treasure forever.

Whether you decide on a puppy or an older dog, your responsibility as an owner remains the same. Once you have taken charge of this innocent and trusting living creature, you owe it the best you can give. In return, you will be rewarded a thousandfold with uncompromising devotion, absolute love, and perfect loyalty.

Male Versus Female

The decision to get a male or a female is usually a matter of personal choice or experience. Both make excellent pets. However, if you want to show your Newf, a male might be the better choice. If you purchase a show bitch (female), she cannot be spayed and you will have to contend with heat periods throughout her show

career. If you are not interested in showing and simply want a loving pet, the decision might come down to which puppy has the best chemistry with you, regardless of sex. Most important: Unless you plan to show and breed your puppy it should be spayed or neutered!

Unneutered males: An unneutered male can become a neighborhood nuisance. Males do tend to roam, especially if there is a female dog in heat. They also have a greater incidence of prostate cancer as they become advanced in years. Neutering, however, won't keep any male dog from going out on the town if it is not properly trained and confined to a fenced-in yard. Size may also dictate your choice. Male Newfs are larger and stronger and weigh more than females, so if that variation in size is a consideration, you might be better off with a female.

Spaying: As with the males, if the female is not to be shown, she should be spayed. This will not only free you from the worry of unwanted puppies, but it will be healthier for your bitch in the long run. Spayed females have less risk of mammary tumors and reproductive system diseases than nonspayed females.

To sum up, unless you have specific plans for breeding and showing your Newf, you should pick the best possible puppy you can find. You can arrive at this decision only after doing lots of homework and talking to many breeders and Newf owners. At that point, when you've narrowed down your choice to two or three dogs, the best choice will be the one that strikes your fancy the most. Male or female, you'll know you've chosen the best dog for you.

Choosing an older Newf over a puppy has certain advantages.

Pet- Versus Show-Quality

One thing must be stressed from the top. "Pet"-quality is not synonymous with "inferior" quality. The difference between a "show" Newf and a "pet" Newf can be so minor that only a highly trained eye can pick it out.

Show-quality: The official AKC standard for the breed describes the ideal Newf. Those dogs that most closely resemble the standard are considered show stock, those that fall a little short are sold as pets. Pet Newfs are neither unattractive nor unhealthy. They simply have some feature and/or features (such as a shorter muzzle, less chest depth, narrower skull) that makes them undesirable in the show ring. Interestingly, in any given litter of say, 12 puppies, even from the very best breeder, usually no more than two or three puppies will be evaluated as top show prospects. Beware of the breeder who boasts that all of his or her puppies are show-quality. It doesn't happen that way. A breeder is lucky to get *one* top show prospect from a litter; two or three is a rare gift.

Pet-quality: If you are not going to show your Newf, definitely purchase a pet dog. Even if you would like to do obedience work or compete in water or tracking sports with your Newf, a pet dog is a good choice. You can still spay/neuter your Newf and compete in these areas.

Conformation: If you plan to show your Newf in conformation classes (AKC-sanctioned dog shows), you will want to pick the best show specimen possible. Remember, in order to compete in conformation classes, your dog cannot be altered.

The best way to decide on a show Newf is to attend all the dog shows you can prior to your selection. Even within show dogs, there is great variation. In Newfs, for example, some bloodlines

Watching your Newf grow from puppyhood to adulthood can be one of life's most rewarding experiences.

carry a larger, heavier head and muzzle than others. There is also variation in color and, to a lesser degree, in size, from breeder to breeder. Some dogs move better than others. Some look better in a "stack" (standing in place in a position that best shows its conformation to the AKC standard for the breed) position. You must decide which characteristics you like best and then contact the breeders whose dogs appear to exemplify what you're looking for in your show Newf.

Be aware that, if you are purchasing a puppy, a breeder can, at best, make only an educated guess about its potential as a show dog. Most reputable breeders will allow you to return the puppy if it doesn't measure up to your expecta-

What to Choose

If you've decided on a show Newf, choose one with a good head and topline, superior movement, and a sweet disposition. As it matures, you can expect to see some changes. At about 10 to 14 months, it will appear too short for its legs and ears. Don't worry—your puppy is just going through the "uglies," as many breeders refer to this awkward stage. In most cases, the puppy will mature into a beautiful dog.

tion in the conformation ring. However, if you'd rather not go through the pain of disappointment, wait and get an older puppy or a young adult dog. Usually, by the time the dog is between six and eight months of age, a breeder

can tell you which ones are going to be the best show prospects.

Price

Generally, show puppies will command a higher price than pet puppies. But don't go bargain hunting—buy the best possible dog you can afford. Reputable breeders won't go into a bidding war with prospective owners. Breeders want their dogs to go to the best homes and most will be very wary of selling to someone who has come to haggle. As a prospective owner, you should also be very suspicious of the breeder who tries to push a "sale" puppy on you. Often, this is a puppy that the breeder has not been able to sell for one reason or another. That doesn't mean it isn't a good dog; it just means you should be extra cautious.

Sometimes a breeder will reduce the prices of a perfectly fine group of puppies because they are older and he or she hasn't had any buyers. Again, this doesn't mean they're inferior dogs. By and large, there are always far more dogs of any breed available than there are buyers. Many times, you can get a very good dog at a much lower price because the puppy is a little older and thus less desirable to the majority of buyers. The rule of thumb is to use common sense and exercise reasonable caution. Ask questions, talk to other breeders and Newf owners, then make an informed decision based on what you've learned.

Getting a Rescue Dog

Most breeds now have very active clubs that "rescue" abandoned animals. The purpose of the

Hey, I'm still a puppy! How am I supposed to know what I want to be when I grow up?

Unless you are planning to show your Newf in confirmation, purchasing a pet-quality Newf is a good choice.

rescue effort in any breed is to keep track of dogs that have become homeless for one reason or another and relocate them into good, loving homes. The Newfoundland Club of America and its many regional clubs have an active breed rescue program. The rescue clubs maintain a list, by state, of Newfs available for adoption. If you don't intend to show or breed your Newf, you may want to consider getting a dog from a rescue club.

NEWF SOUNDBYTES

In 1989 a young Newfy bitch, Dirigo's Magnificent Villa, CD, received a special presidential award for heroism after jumping the 6-foot (1.8-m) fence in its kennel to respond to the cries of a child trapped under a snowdrift. The courageous Newf tracked the child in the blinding storm, pulled her out, and carried her home to safety.

Why Rescue Is Needed

As we have discussed, people will sometimes buy a Newf without truly understanding what ownership of a giant breed entails. In such cases, the dog is either given to a local shelter, or worse, allowed to roam and become lost. In such situations, the rescue club intercedes by taking the dog, placing it in foster care, and getting it into good condition while it awaits a permanent home.

If you plan to show your Newf, look for a good head and topline when you select your puppy.

Occasionally, rescue dogs are in poor condition when they're taken in because the former owners weren't willing or able to keep up with the dog's regular maintenance requirements. Some-times, rescue dogs have temperament problems because they've been abused. In any case, the rescue volunteer who serves as a foster home honestly assesses the dog and works with it to make it adoptable. When it's ready to go to a home, the rescue club attempts to match the personality of the dog to its new owners.

If you decide you'd like to look into the possibility of getting a Newf from a rescue club, be prepared to answer a detailed questionnaire. The object of the club is to insure that the dog goes to the right home and is never again abandoned or given away.

Getting a dog from rescue can be a very rewarding and emotionally uplifting experience. Not only are you getting a wonderful friend and companion, but you'll also have the satisfaction

NCA Web Page

The Newfoundland Club of America, Inc. has a Web site that will answer any remaining questions you may have about the breed. There you will also find the NCA Breeders List, which lists breeders in every part of the country.

Be careful about relying on personal Web sites. Any type of breeder, good or bad, can have one of these and some information garnered there could be misleading.

of knowing you probably saved the dog's life. If you decide to open your heart to a rescue Newf, you will have to sign a spay/neuter contract. No matter what the quality of the dog—pet or show—the rescue club will not place it unless you agree to have it altered by an appointed time. Sometimes rescue dogs are already altered. There is a fee for adopting a rescue dog that goes back into the fund to help save other unfortunate Newfs.

The Newfoundland with Children

If, like most of us, you grew up enchanted by "Nana," the beloved, worry-wart Newf nanny of Wendy, Michael, and John in J. M. Barrie's *Peter Pan*, then you already have a good idea about the relationship between Newfs and children. The Newf is such a loyal companion and protector that in earlier times many families actually used the dogs to mind their small children. The Newf's devotion to youngsters is indeed legendary. Daring rescues have been recorded throughout the breed's history. Of all canines, the Newf is undoubtedly one of the best pets to have around children. Its natural protective instinct is a quality parents everywhere will appreciate. Despite its great size, the full-grown Newf is extremely gentle and nonaggressive with children. The two form an immediate bond and become fast friends and playmates for life. However, when bringing a Newf puppy into the house, as with any young dog, exercise care if there are children around. An energetic puppy will want to chase, play rough, and chew. Don't let your child become your new puppy's favorite toy—or vice

Newfs usually get along well with other dogs.

versa. Both puppy and child must be taught respect for each other. That way, by the time your Newf is a year old, it'll do just about everything but change your human baby's diapers!

The Newfoundland with Other Pets

The Newf is as loving and protective of other pets in the household as it is of its owners. A Newf raised with other pets has no problem adjusting. If you introduce another pet into the house once your Newf is older, it will probably be the other pet that will need to do the adjusting. Even to another dog, the Newf's great size can be intimidating. When bringing in another pet, introduce it to your Newf slowly. The Newf is a nonaggressive dog that accepts people and other pets with grace and generosity.

Despite its large size, it is very gentle with small pets. Many Newf owners with kittens report that their Newf takes over like a big

We eat a lot, but we're worth it!

"mama." As long as it doesn't perceive the new-comer as a threat to its loving family, the Newf will welcome a new arrival with open paws!

The Cost of Keeping a Newfoundland

Contrary to popular belief, it doesn't cost appreciably more money to own a Newf than, for example, an Irish setter. The largest financial investment you will make is the purchase price of your dog, which is comparable with most purebreds. You can expect to spend between $400 and $600 for a good pet-quality dog, somewhat more for a show dog. Other expenses are feeding, health care, and general mainte-nance. This will be the same for any dog you purchase, regardless of the breed.

True, a Newf will eat more than a Chihuahua, but just because the Newf weighs more than 120 pounds (54 kg) as an adult, it doesn't mean it needs to eat tons of food. In fact, your Newf will eat appreciably less as it gets older. If you keep it on a high-quality, premium dog food, you will save money on veterinarian bills in the long run. Realistically, its monthly feeding bill will probably average about $100–$150 for a new pet Newf and $150–$200 for a show Newf, depending on what supplements you add to its basic feed.

Regular veterinarian care should run about $1,000 per year, if the dog is healthy. One of the things you may want to look into is pet insurance. There are several companies that cover pets, as well as some companies that specialize in pet insurance. For a small premium per year, you can rest easy that, should your Newf require an expensive medical procedure, it will be covered.

Holiday Puppies

When the holidays roll around, it's often hard to resist the impulse to buy a puppy, tie a big bow around its neck, and put it under the Christmas tree. Word of advice? RESIST! You'll be glad you did. Again, use your common sense. The traditional portrait of Christmas, Hanukkah, and Easter may be tranquil, soothing, and benign, but the reality of any holiday never makes the cover of a greeting card. Holidays, while happy, festive times, are also chaotic, disruptive, and anything but orderly and quiet.

Imagine bringing a new puppy into the house on the same day that all 25 long-lost relatives of all ages and sizes descend upon the house for some holiday cheer! Puppy, who has just arrived from the security and tranquillity of its breeder's kennel, is sure to suffer immediate culture shock. The normal excitement of the occasion will throw the new puppy for a loop. All of the things you need when introducing a puppy into the house—consistency, patience, time—are out the window in a flash. How can you possibly see to your Newf's house-training if you have to keep running into the kitchen to replenish drinks, make sure the kids aren't getting into the dessert, and check that the turkey isn't burning to a crisp? Do you really want your Newf to be a part of this picture? Do everyone a favor: WAIT. Get your puppy *after*

Getting a Newf from a rescue club is one of the most rewarding experiences of pet ownership.

the holidays when you'll have enough time to spend acclimating it to its new environment.

If you do purchase the puppy before the holidays, make sure you bring it home at least several weeks in advance. That way, it'll have its routine down and you'll have yours.

Note: Incidentally, it's never a good idea to give a child a puppy for Christmas or any other occasion. While owning a dog can bring new meaning into the life of a child and create a bond of friendship that supercedes all others, a new puppy is just that—a new addition to the household. It is not an object to be given and taken away like a windup toy, but rather, a member of the family to be loved, respected, and cherished by all.

LIVING WITH YOUR NEWFOUNDLAND

Before you bring your Newf home, you'll have to prepare in advance for its arrival. Make no mistake— bringing a new dog into the house is very similar to bringing home a new baby. So put on your thinking cap and get to work!

Before You Bring Your Newfoundland Home

First, you must realize that your new pet will need a period of adjustment to get used to its new surroundings. This is especially true if you bought an older dog. So expect a certain amount of apprehension and stress on its part for the first few days. The best way to make its transition easier is to have everything ready for it in its new home.

Food and Dishes

Before you pick up your Newf, your breeder will give you an idea of some basic supplies you'll need to have on hand. The first, of course, is food. Find a good, full-service pet supply

The mild-mannered Newfoundland is the ultimate "people" dog.

store in your area and get ready to stock up. Make sure the store carries the same brand of dog food your breeder has been using. Even if you decide to change the brand at a later date, it's wise to continue the diet the dog is used to for the first few months. While you're at the pet store, there are some other essential items you'll need to pick up, such as dishes for food and water. Good heavy plastic or weighted stainless steel bowls are preferable because they won't slide around the floor.

You may also want to purchase a raised stand for your Newf's bowls. There are many breeders who feel the dog accumulates less gas in its intestinal tract when it eats from a raised position.

Collar and Leash

Next, you'll need a collar and leash or lead. It's best to purchase one permanent collar, either

Keeping your Newf's diet well-balanced and consistent will help to keep your pet healthy.

leather or nylon, which your Newf will wear all of the time with its identification tag attached.

You should also purchase a choke or a "slip" collar for use when your walk your Newf on the leash. Don't be upset by the word *choke*. When used properly, the collar does not choke the dog, but only gives its neck enough of a tug to get its attention. Never leave a choke collar on your dog when not on a leash. Because of the *slip* nature of the choke collar, it can easily become hooked onto another object and cause serious injury to your dog. The choke allows you to correct your dog instantly when it pulls or lunges.

If you have a puppy, remember it will soon grow out of the collar. To maximize your investment, choose one with ample room for

expansion as the pup's neck grows. Next, pick a sturdy 6-foot (2-m) leash in either nylon or leather. (Nylon tends to wear better.) Your pet store will also have several types of identification tags available. You can fill out an order form with your pet's name and your address and phone number. In approximately one to two weeks, you'll receive the tag in the mail.

Toys

If you're like most new pet owners, you'll also want to have some toys ready for your new pet to play with. If you have a puppy, remember it will need to satisfy its chewing urge, so purchase toys with that in mind. There are many good, sturdy nylon toys available that will not only keep it from teething on the leg of your dining room table, but will give the dog hours of pleasure as well. These toys have the added benefit of massaging the gums and, consequently, will make the puppy feel good, too. Various types of rawhide chews are also satisfactory.

Newf-Proofing Your Home

Once you have all the supplies your Newf will need, the next thing you'll have to do is get your house ready for its arrival.

✔ If you have cabinets in your kitchen or elsewhere in the house, you should "child-proof" them with appropriate locks. Your veterinarian can advise you on the best choices. Puppies, like babies, have a genius for getting into forbidden places.

Use a metal or nylon choke collar for training. Once the training session is over, remove the choker and replace it with a buckle or snap collar.

Hey, share some of the toys!

✔ If you have stairs in your home, you may want to section them off from your puppy with a gate.

✔ Make sure decks and balconies are also closed off.

✔ Remove all objects and bric-a-brac from tables or counters that are accessible to the puppy.

✔ Remove all electrical cords from any area your Newf will have access to. While your puppy is teething, it will seize on almost anything to satisfy its chewing urge. Chewing on an electrical cord could shock or even kill it.

✔ Remove any toxic plants from your home and yard. Your veterinarian and/or local nursery can provide you with a list of poisonous house and yard plants.

✔ Section off a portion of a room, usually the kitchen, for your Newf until it is acclimated to its new surroundings and is completely house-trained. Having its own space will give the dog more confidence and you fewer headaches.

Outdoors

If you want to keep your Newf outdoors part of the time, you should have a fenced-in yard or kennel area. If you plan to leave it out for any amount of time, be sure it has shelter from the elements. You can purchase an all-weather dog-house at your pet store for this purpose or build one yourself. If you do construct your own house, make sure it is big enough to accommodate a full-sized Newf and that it is properly insulated. Your pet store also sells various types of pet doors that can be attached to the door of the house, allowing your Newf to let itself in and out at will. However, if you use a pet door,

I'm so good, I won't even eat Mom's daisies.

Book me for a week at the lake.

it should always lead into a completely fenced yard or kennel area. Never let your pet door lead out to an open area or street.

Meet with Your Family

The day before you bring your Newf home, it's a good idea to gather family members together and have a conference about the do's and don'ts once your Newf arrives. Make sure everyone knows what is expected of them. The best way to be sure that your Newf will acclimate to its new surroundings is for everyone to help out and make the transition a happy one.

Your Newfoundland's First Night in Your Home

The moment you've been waiting for has arrived—you finally have your beautiful Newf

home with you. A puppy will be naturally excited and active in its new surroundings. It will want to play and do lots of exploring. If you have already pet-proofed your home, there's no danger that your Newf will get into trouble. If there are children in the family, be sure they know their responsibility where the new puppy is concerned. Don't allow children to manhandle the puppy, pulling at its tail or ears. They should respect it as they would any member of the household.

Special Spots

Once your puppy has had a few minutes of play and introduction to the rest of the family, take it outside to the special spot you have designated and allow it to relieve itself. Remember, puppies will need to go out after they play or become excited. Don't let your Newf become overexcited on its first day home.

After it has had its play session and you've taken it out, put it in its special area, whether that's a crate or a portion of a room you've sectioned off, and allow the dog to take a nap. Puppies need their sleep. Your Newf will also need to know it has a spot all its own where it can go and have some quiet time. It should have its own bed or mat and several toys such as nylon bones that it can chew on when it awakens.

Don't be upset if it cries or whimpers when it's left alone. This is normal. Until the puppy gets used to having its own space, it will cry to be with you. Don't give into its pitiful wails by constantly going over to soothe it or, worse, by allowing it to be with you. If you do, you will be laying the groundwork for unwanted behavior in the future, teaching it that every time it cries, you'll come running. Be gentle but firm, and above all, consistent.

After you've taken your Newf out for the last time in the evening, put it in its special spot to sleep. Be sure to leave some newspapers spread out in case it needs to relieve itself during the night. Again, it may cry, but don't worry—it will soon calm down and fall asleep. If it really seems upset, you can try leaving on a radio or a cassette tape playing soft music. Usually, the sound of voices or soft melodies will soon lull it to sleep. Remember, don't give in to its whin-

Can I get a treat now?

ing, no matter how pitiful it sounds. It goes without saying that you should be able to distinguish between whining for attention and a serious distress cry or yelp. Let common sense be your best guide.

House-training Your Newfoundland

When you bring your Newf home, the first thing you'll want to take care of is house-training. Once you begin your regular training exercises, you'll realize your puppy will be anxious to please you. The same goes for getting the hang of house-training.

✔ Let your puppy know *where* you want it to eliminate and *when*. But remember, a puppy has to relieve itself much more often than an adult dog, so be patient.

✔ Take your puppy out as soon as it awakens from a nap and after each meal or exercise period.

Put several layers of clean newspaper down in your puppy's pen or section of the house, in case it needs to eliminate when you are not at home.

✔ Take it out again just before you go to bed. Soon it will associate going out with the pleasurable experience of relieving itself.

✔ When it does eliminate in the proper place, praise it profusely. Remember, however, that accidents will happen no matter how consistent you try to be. Patience is essential.

✔ *Never* rub your puppy's nose in its excrement or use a rolled-up newspaper to correct it. Simply clean up the mess and bring it to the place where you want it to eliminate and praise it. It'll soon get the idea.

Home Alone

If the puppy is alone all or part of the day, don't give it the run of the house. A puppy needs boundaries or its life will seem very confusing. Some people like to section off a part of a room, preferably the kitchen or laundry room.

✔ Leave clean newspapers down each time you go out, and let your Newf become accustomed to eliminating on the papers when you're not there to take it outside.

✔ Some owners prefer to use a crate to keep their puppy in line while they are away from the house. If you do use a crate, consider purchasing the largest size available. That way, you will be able to use it later when your Newf is full grown, should you need to confine it for brief periods.

✔ If you have a large enough crate, section off a part of it for the puppy's elimination needs. However, never leave it in a crate for more than four or five hours at a time.

✔ A puppy pen is another good way to keep your Newf out of trouble and still give it some space. Puppy pens can be purchased at pet stores or from wholesale pet catalogs. You can also make one yourself.

Note: Be aware that your Newf will need lots of exercise, but don't overdo it. Puppies tend to run out of gas fast. Always follow up play/exercise sessions with a quick trip outside so the puppy can relieve itself. Then put it down for a nap.

Boarding Your Newfoundland

When it comes time for you to take a few days off or a family vacation, you'll have to decide what arrangements you will make for your Newf.

If you're like most people, you'll probably want to send your Newf on a vacation of its own while you take yours. There are many reputable boarding kennels where your Newf can stay while you're on your holiday. If they are accredited with the American Boarding Kennel Association (ABKA), all the better; however, many non-ABKA kennels are also excellent. Check out the facilities in your area and plan to visit several

I'm here to meet girls—how about you?

Diet While Boarding

When you leave your Newf at the kennel for its "holiday," remember to bring along its food; otherwise, the kennel staff will feed it whatever brand of feed they use. Since this will be an initially stressful time for your pet, the best way to avoid stressing its system further, is to keep its diet consistent. Leave written instructions regarding when to feed, the amount to feed and any supplements or medications that need to be given as well.

Be sure to bring some of your Newf's favorite toys so it will feel almost right at home.

of them beforehand. When choosing a boarding kennel, look for the following:

1. Make sure the establishment has large indoor and outdoor runs that are kept meticulously clean and odor-free.

2. The kennel should also have a large, common exercise area where your Newf can have its playtime each day.

3. Be sure your pet will get individualized attention and that the kennel has a good ratio of professional attendants to the number of animals being boarded.

4. Make sure the kennel has a veterinarian on call 24 hours a day, in the event of an emergency.

5. Make sure the kennel is equipped with an automatic sprinkler system and that there is someone in attendance 24 hours a day.

Don't be shy about asking all of these questions. The only way for your Newf to be safe and happy while you're away is for you to insure it. A reputable kennel will be proud of its reputation and happy to answer any questions or reservations you may have.

If you prefer not to put your Newf in a kennel while you're away, you might want to consider a pet-sitting service. Your veterinarian may be able to recommend people who either take pets into their homes and watch them while the owner is away or pet-sitters who will stay with your pet in your home. If you answer an ad in the newspaper for a pet-sitter, be sure to interview the person beforehand and demand to see references and then call the people on the list.

Of course, all of the above may be unnecessary if you have a willing friend or relative who will watch your Newf while you're on vacation. This is another reason to have a set of good "doggy" friends who all pitch in to help each other in times just like this.

Car Travel

Some owners decide to take their pets with them on trips. If you do, make your plans well in advance. If traveling by car, you'll need a safe place for your Newf to stay while you do the driving. A crate is very helpful in this situation; it's safer for the dog and for you. An unrestrained animal in a moving vehicle is an accident waiting to happen. Place a blanket or sheet under the crate for easy cleanup in case of motion sickness or toilet accidents. If you don't want to use a crate, you can also purchase a suitable pet gate that can effectively section off the back seat of the car from the front.

If you have the car windows open, don't allow your dog to stick its head out. Flying debris from the road can hit it and cause damage, especially to its eyes.

Warning: Remember never to leave your pet in the car in warm weather. Even if you open the windows, the inside of the car can become like an inferno in direct sunlight in just a few minutes.

Motels

Before you start out, find out which motels allow pets. Most major hotel/motel chains publish booklets, listing their various locations all over the country along with a note advising whether pets are allowed at a particular spot. Auto clubs and travel guides can also be of assistance.

In addition, there are a number of web sites that offer listings of pet-friendly hotels. The following are just a few of the resources available online:

www.dogfriendlydirectory.com
This site offers nationwide listings of pet-friendly hotels, motels, and other lodging options.

www.petswelcome.com
A searchable database of hotels, motels, inns, and bed and breakfasts that accept pets.

www.traveldog.com
A resource for people who travel with their dogs. Find accommodations, travel tips, and other pet services.

www.1clickpethotels.com
Free online directory of pet-friendly hotels with a pet size and pet fee guide.

Bear in mind that many motels and hotels require a

If you travel with your Newfoundland, be sure to have a crate of appropriate size on hand. As a safety precaution, a dog should always be crated when traveling in a car.

YOUR NEWFOUNDLAND

deposit, often nonrefundable. Some limit travelers to small dogs.

When staying at a hotel with your dog, it is a good idea to bring along a couple of sheets to protect motel beds from dog hair and dirty paws. Be sure to also bring toilet clean-up supplies, and a supply of food, treats, and water bowls.

Air Travel

✔ If you travel by plane with your pet, find out the rules and regulations regarding pets for the airline you will be using. Airlines require an approved carrier as well as health certificates for your pet. Be sure your Newf is up-to-date on all of its vaccinations.

✔ Always travel on the same flight as your pet to avoid its being accidentally shipped to another destination. On the day of departure, arrive at the airport with lots of time to spare so you can see that your Newf is handled properly and not rushed through the boarding process.

✔ Make sure it has been allowed to relieve itself before it's loaded onto the plane. Your pet will have to ride in a specially pressurized section of the baggage compartment that is fully air-conditioned.

✔ When you board the plane, it's a good idea to remind the flight attendant that your Newf is traveling with you, and ask him or her to inform the pilot. The flight crew is told before takeoff when there are pets on board, but it doesn't hurt to remind them, just for safety's sake.

✔ Don't put your Newf into its carrier with a choke chain around its neck. In fact, it's best to remove all collars and tape its identification information on the outside of the carrier along

When flying with your Newf, always remove its collar before locking it in an airline carrier. Be sure its identification and destination are clearly written on the outside of the carrier.

with your name, destination, phone and flight number.

✔ Also stick "Live Animal" decals in a prominent place on the carrier.

✔ Don't put any food inside, but do attach the airline conversion kit that comes with the airline carrier. This will permit your dog to have water available. Make certain the door of the carrier is fastened correctly and locked.

✔ If your pet is a good traveler, it should have no ill effects on the trip. However, some animals experience motion sickness or are just very nervous travelers. Ask your veterinarian's advice before you leave. He or she may want to prescribe motion sickness medicine or a mild tranquilizer to make the pet's trip less stressful.

Finally, before leaving, double-check if the hotel or motel where you will be staying is expecting your pet. There is generally a daily minimal charge.

If you're visiting friends or family members, advise them you are bringing your Newf along and make sure they are agreeable.

TRAINING YOUR NEWFOUNDLAND

In order to appreciate the whole concept of training, it's important to understand the order of the canine world. Like its fellow canine, the wolf, the dog is essentially a pack animal.

The Basic Premise of Training

In the dog's world, there is a clearly defined hierarchy that determines its actions from puppyhood. In the wild, a dog's place in the pack is determined by its strength. The top or "alpha" dog is the strongest and most aggressive male. It sets the rules and doles out the punishment whenever another dog gets out of line. It is the leader until it is displaced by another, stronger male.

Though our domestic dogs are far removed from their ancestral packs, they instinctively understand the pack order. When a puppy is born, its mother acts as top dog. She rewards its good behavior and corrects its bad behavior.

The Newfoundland excels in all types of training.

Once the puppy leaves its mother, you will have to assume the role of "top dog." Your Newf expects you to establish order in its world. The way to do that is by training it to please you. Far from being harsh or cruel, training your dog is the best thing you can do for it. It will make its world and yours a much happier and tranquil place.

Why Train?

Getting your mind-set into the training mode isn't easy. How can it be when all you can see in front of you is a cute, cuddly Newfy puppy? Everything it does, including jumping on you for love and attention and nibbling at your arms and feet with its razor-sharp milk teeth, is too endearing to stop. In fact, it's so adorable, you simply can't say "*No*" to it. Think again and project a year into the future when your bouncing 15-pounder (6.8 kg) is tipping the scales at well over 100 pounds (45 kg)! How cute will it be then when it wants your attention and ends up knocking you down and sending you straight to the local chiropractor? As the old adage goes, an ounce of prevention is worth a pound of cure. Simple translation: Learn to say "*No*" from Day One, and a year later you'll have a well-adjusted, happy dog that is a pleasure to live with. Far from being a negative expression, the training process is very positive and something you and your Newf can enjoy together. It will serve as the basis of your teamwork and mutual cooperation throughout your lives together. So pick up that collar and leash and prepare to have some fun.

Getting Started

The first rule of training is consistency. Remember the mother dog. When the puppy got too sassy, Mother corrected it immediately, every time, not just now and then. So don't reprimand your Newf three times for jumping on the couch and then let it get away with it the fourth time. Be consistent, just like the mother dog. That way, your puppy will understand what you expect of it. Use your tone of voice to tell it which behavior is permitted and which is not. When it jumps on the couch, assuming you don't want it on the furniture, say "*No*" firmly, then scoop it into a sitting position on the floor and praise it immediately. *Always* follow a correction with praise for the desired behavior. This will not confuse your Newf; instead, your tone of voice will let it know what you want of it. However, don't expect it to get it right the first time—training requires *repetition* and *patience*.

Crate Training

There are pros and cons to using a crate. Certainly no dog should be kept exclusively in a crate; however, when used properly, you'll find the crate has several advantages. First and foremost, it will keep your puppy from getting into things such as kitchen cabinets and drawers whenever you're out of the house. Not only is it annoying to come home and find the house a shambles, but your puppy can also injure itself. If it is trained to stay in a crate while you're away, it will soon come to regard the space as its den and will actually look forward to its "private" time inside the crate. It will even retreat there during the day when it wants its own space.

Size: The size of the crate depends on the size of the dog. Since the Newf will grow to a formidable stature, you may want to start off with a crate it will be able to use throughout its life. A dog should always be able to stand to its full height and be able to turn and change position in a crate. Never use the crate as a punishment for unacceptable behavior. Your puppy should feel that its crate is its refuge from the rough-and-tumble of daily life.

Acclimating: Acclimate your puppy to the crate as soon as it arrives in its new home. Most puppies come with crate experience, since breeders almost always keep their litters crated. If your puppy has been crated before, that will make your job all the easier.

If your Newf is not accustomed to being in a crate, introduce it slowly, with gradually longer periods of time. After play, put it in its crate for a nap. You may want to put down a mat or towel on the bottom of the crate and include one or two of its toys, just to make it feel at home. When it awakens, take it outside to

Early collar and leash training are essential.

relieve itself. Play with your Newf for a few moments and then put it back into its crate while you go about your household chores. If it barks or cries, look it straight in the eye and firmly tell it "*No.*"

Traveling: When you travel with your pet, the crate will also come in handy. If you own a van or station wagon, simply set up the crate in the rear area, lock your Newf in, and buckle up your seat belts—you're ready to roll. The crate is a safety device for your pet whenever it travels with you in the car. It will also prevent it from jumping all over you and distracting you, possibly causing an accident while you're trying to drive.

Collar and Leash Training

Get your Newf used to a collar and leash as soon as you pick it up from the breeder. For its own safety and the safety of others, a dog should never be allowed to roam freely so start developing good habits from the outset. Initially, your puppy may resist both collar and leash, unless the breeder has already accustomed it to accept one or both. In any case, it will soon get the hang of it.

✔ For everyday wear, your Newf should have a snap-on or buckle-down collar with its identification and rabies tags attached.

✔ For training purposes, use a thin metal or nylon choke collar. Remove it immediately after

Basic obedience training will make your life and your Newf's life more manageable and enjoyable.

the training session is complete. Use a 6-foot (2-m) leash or lead of approximately ¾ inch–1 inch (2–2.5 cm) wide.

✔ Take some time to get your Newf used to both the collar and the lead so it won't be afraid of it. Let it wear the collar and drag the lead for a few minutes so it can get the feel of it.

✔ When you pick up the other end of the lead, the puppy will tug and resist. Don't allow yourself to be pulled in the direction it wants to go. Simply stand still as it pulls and tugs. Say *"No,"* then give your lead a quick jerk, bringing the puppy to your side.

✔ Sit it down and praise it. Now you're ready for basic obedience.

Basic Obedience Training

Besides love and affection, one of the most important things you will impart to your precious Newf is basic obedience training—it could save its life and make yours a lot easier. Since the Newf is a working dog, it instinctively adapts well to obedience training.

Puppy Kindergarten

Many schools and communities offer formal obedience classes in various levels of difficulty. Generally, dogs under six months of age are not accepted. An alternative for the young puppy is something called "puppy kindergarten," the canine version of nursery school for your baby. Basically, puppy kindergarten is a means of

Left drawing: the correct position for a choke collar. Right drawing: the wrong position for a choke collar.

socializing your puppy and getting it started on some basic commands, but you can start it on basic commands yourself. Even if you enroll it in puppy kindergarten, you should also work with it every day yourself to reinforce what it has learned. Puppies have short attention spans and learn by constant repetition. Remember, there are two cardinal rules in obedience training: Be consistent and make it fun. Okay, let's get started!

Sitting on Command

Anyone who has ever had a dog that leaps and jumps and twirls when visitors arrive, can appreciate the need to have Thunder sit on command.
✔ Begin by slipping on his choke collar and leash.
✔ Bring him to a standing position with you on his right side. He will be on your left side. Always begin training sessions by assuming this starting position.
✔ Holding the leash in your right hand, pull back slightly. Simultaneously, press the backs of your Newf's legs behind the knee area with your left hand. This will make his legs buckle and he will ease into a *sit* position.
✔ At the same time, say, *"Thunder, sit."*
✔ As soon as your Newf is sitting, praise him.

Repeat the exercise about five times at each session. If you work with him every day, after a few days your Newf will understand what you want and will be sitting on command. The better he gets, the more praise you should lavish on him.

If Thunder is resistant, try using a treat. Instead of using the leash and choker, simply hold a treat in front and above his head with your right hand and press into the backs of his legs as before while saying, *"Thunder, sit."* When he obeys, give him the treat instantly, while praising him—*"Good boy!"* When he masters the exercise, remove the treat and get him used to sitting on command just for the praise that follows.

The Sit/Stay Command

Once your Newf has mastered the art of the *sit* command, it's time to get him to *stay* in that position until you tell him otherwise.

To teach your Newf to sit, hold the leash securely in your right hand and press gently on the backs of its legs with the left hand, repeating the command "sit."

Once your puppy is in a sit position, pass your left hand across its face and tell it to stay. Then step in front and face your Newf. If it gets up, return it to the sit position and repeat the command "Stay."

✔ Begin this exercise by repeating the *sit* exercise above. Remember, you are holding the lead in your right hand.

✔ Once the dog sits, quickly pass your left palm in front of his nose and say, "*Thunder, stay.*"

✔ Then, still holding the lead, step in front of him. If he gets up, quickly return him to the *sit* position, pass your left palm in front of his nose, and repeat, "*Stay.*"

✔ After several repetitions, he'll figure out what you want him to do.

✔ Once your Newf stays on command, walk around his right side and return to the starting position on his left side. Then bend down and praise him. If at any time he breaks the *stay*, simply return him to the sitting position and repeat the *stay* command until he gets it right and you are able to return to the starting position.

Coming on Command

One of the biggest frustrations in a dog owner's life is having a pet ignore you when you ask it to come. Here's how to rectify that.

✔ Using your choke collar and lead, allow your Newf to go to the full length of the lead, then call him—"*Thunder, come.*"

✔ As you do so, give a tug on the lead and begin reeling him in toward you, as if you were reeling in a fish on a line.

✔ When your Newf approaches you, quickly praise him.

✔ After four or five sessions, he should come without your having to reel him in. Then add another step to the exercise.

✔ When your Newf comes on command, tell him to *sit* when he approaches you. As in the basic *sit* command, if your puppy is resistant, you can also try the treat method. When the dog comes successfully, reward him with an enthusiastic "*Good Boy*" and a treat. Then add the *sit* command as above.

When your Newf obeys a command, praise him or her.

The Down Command

Now that you're beginning to feel good about the progress you're making, let's add another command to your Newf's basic repertoire. Lying down is a fairly natural position for a dog, but it's probably one of the hardest things to get your pet to do, especially if you've waited until he's an adult to get started with obedience work. If you get your Newf as a puppy, teach him the *down* and *down/stay* exercise early on. You won't regret your efforts.

✔ Begin with your Newf on your left side. Command him to sit. If you need to press on the backs of his legs with your left hand, do so.

✔ Then with the lead in your right hand, gently tug straight down while saying, "*Thunder, down.*"

✔ If this doesn't work, try the treat method. Once Thunder is sitting, hold the treat below his nose and say, "*Thunder, down,*" while lowering the treat to floor level, until the dog must get down on all fours to get it. When he does, praise him.

Once your Newf has mastered these four basic commands inside the house, it's time to try them outdoors where there will be many more distractions. Remember, be patient, be consistent, and you will succeed!

Obedience Classes

Enrolling your Newf in a formal group obedience class is a rewarding and challenging experience for both dog and owner. Many local dog clubs run classes several times a year. The purpose of the classes is not only to train your dog but to train you as well. Getting together once a week with other dog owners will boost your confidence and give you a chance to share and

Catching a few rays.

compare your experiences. If you've been working with your Newf religiously on his basic obedience, you'll probably be the star of the class! Remember, if you plan to enjoy other Newfy activities such as backpacking, water trials, and tracking, obedience training is essential. You and your Newf must learn to work as a team, and enrolling in a novice obedience class is the best way to start.

There are also private classes that are given by professional trainers, but, generally speaking, a group class is preferable because it gets your dog and you used to distractions and other dogs. The group class is also a great way to socialize a shy puppy and work on problem areas with an overly enthusiastic Newf. You may find that you and your Newf enjoy obedience work so much that you'll decide to continue and pursue an obedience title.

Jogging

We've all seen hapless owners holding onto a lead for dear life while their pet lunges and pushes ahead, literally taking *them* for a jog. Imagine this scenario with an adult Newf that weighs over 100 pounds (45 kg)! It's not only bad behavior, but it's also dangerous for you and your dog. Think about the possible repercussions: You could fall and be injured (especially in icy, slippery conditions), or your dog could break away, get hit by a car, or attack another dog or pedestrian. Not a pretty picture, by any stretch of the imagination. Teaching

When you stop walking, put your Newf into a sit position immediately. Then tell it to stay. After you complete the exercise, begin it again.

To teach your Newf to heel, stand on its right side and put it into a sit position. Gently tug on the slack in the leash and say heel and begin walking.

your Newf to walk beside you will make your daily outings a pleasure for the both of you.

Choke Collar and Lead

✔ Begin by putting the choke collar and lead on your dog. By now Thunder already associates this practice with his training sessions and hopefully with having fun because he is pleasing you.

✔ Assume your regular starting position with your Newf on your left side.

✔ Hold the loop end of your lead in the right hand and begin walking. Your Newf will probably forge ahead.

✔ When he comes to the end of his lead space, stop walking. This will bring him to an abrupt stop as well. Now begin walking again.

✔ The same pattern will undoubtedly repeat itself. Your Newf will look at you, confused—"What did I do wrong?" Tell your dog to sit and then walk up to him, coming to a halt when he is on your left side.

✔ Pick up the slack of the lead in your left hand and with a short tug of the left hand say, "*Thunder, heel.*"

✔ Immediately take a step with your left foot. Your Newf

When your Newf has successfully completed the exercise, praise it lavishly.

If you are having trouble getting your Newf to heel, trying coaxing it with a treat.

should get up and follow. If he does not, tug on the lead again. Now you're holding the lead in both hands, the looped end in the right, the slack in the left.

✔ When he tries to get ahead of you, use the left hand to tug on the lead, repeating, *"Thunder, heel."*

✔ Don't stop walking; simply repeat the correction and command each time he tries to pull ahead. The object is to have his head in line with your left leg. Once you have him heeling, stop and tell him to sit.

✔ Praise him and repeat the exercise again. As Thunder becomes more familiar with the exercise, he will learn to sit automatically each time you come to a stop.

Objective

The ultimate objective of the *heeling* exercise is to train your Newf to *heel* off the lead. If you decide to pursue an obedience championship with your Newf, he will have to complete all the above exercises off lead. However, for everyday purposes, the *heeling* command is helpful to keep your Newf in line when you take him on his daily walks on the lead.

FEEDING YOUR NEWFOUNDLAND

There are few subjects that invite as heated a debate as the type of food to feed your dog. Everyone seems to have an opinion on what to feed, how much, and how often; but the bottom line is a simple one: Feed your Newf a balanced diet.

A Balanced Diet

Your Newf should have a diet that is rich in high-quality protein, carbohydrates, fats, vitamins, and minerals. This will help build strong bones and muscles and generally keep it in good, healthy condition.

Most premium dog foods supply all the daily requirements your Newf will need. Choosing the one you use will depend on your preference and any particular requirements your dog may have. For example, many dogs do not do well on foods that contain soy; others may have a bad reaction to wheat or corn. But these are individual needs and even the dog with the most sensitive digestive system can find a premium dog food on the market that

will satisfy. Beware the person who boasts that he feeds his dog an all-meat diet. Although that might sound good, it's anything but well rounded.

Besides protein and fat (the chief components of an all meat diet), your Newf also needs the following:
• Carbohydrates to give it energy. These are found in grain products.
• Vitamins and minerals, such as calcium, potassium, phosphorus, sodium, and iron, which are supplied in a good premium dog food.

Once your Newf has that solid base, it will need little, if any supplementation to its diet. Don't arbitrarily feed additional vitamins or minerals without consulting your veterinarian first. Remember one of the cardinal rules of feeding—more is not better.

A healthy Newf is a happy Newf.

Feeding the Newfoundland Puppy

Obesity

Giant puppy equals giant meals, right? Wrong! In fact, one of the biggest mistakes puppy owners make, regardless of the breed, is overfeeding their new baby. A fat, pudgy Newf puppy does not a healthy Newf adult make. Why? Think about it in human terms. We've all read stories about how obese people are at a greater risk for serious health problems than their slender counterparts. It's exactly the same in the canine world. A fat dog has no stamina. It's lazy. It doesn't move around much. The fatter it gets, the worse its situation becomes. Soon its breathing is affected; then its heart and other organs begin to fail. In a growing puppy, any extra weight is especially dangerous. The added pounds put extra pressure on its skeletal structure, thereby causing improper development of its bones and joints.

A healthy puppy is a lean puppy—but don't go to the opposite extreme. It shouldn't look emaciated either! To ascertain if your Newf puppy is in good weight, put your palms against its ribs. They should not poke out, but by exerting just the slightest pressure, you should clearly be able to feel each rib. Puppies gain and drop weight very quickly, so you'll have to be vigilant about your Newf's diet. Weigh it each week and keep a record. It should gain weight at a slow and steady rate as the rest of its body grows.

Amount to Feed

The amount to feed your Newf puppy is based on its nutritional needs at a specific time in its

Puppy Feeding Plan

8–12 weeks: 4 meals a day
Morning: ½ cup of dry puppy food mixed with a little warm water.
Noon: ½ cup of dry puppy food.
Evening: ½ cup of dry puppy food mixed with a little warm water.
Bedtime: ½ cup of dry puppy food.

10–12 weeks: 3 meals a day
Morning: 1½ cups of puppy food mixed with a little water and any supplement recommended by your breeder.
Noon: 1½ cups of dry puppy food.
Evening: 1½ cups of puppy food mixed with a little water.

3–5 months: 2 meals a day
Morning: 2–3 cups of dry puppy food mixed with a little water and any supplement recommended by your breeder.
Evening: 2–3 cups of dry puppy food.

5 months–1 year: 2 meals a day
Morning: 3 cups of adult dry dog food with a protein level of 24%–26%, and any supplement recommended by your breeder.
Evening: 3–4 cups of adult dry dog food mixed with water.

The water-to-dry-food ratio should be approximately ¼ cup of water per 2 cups of dry food. Remember to keep fresh water available at all times. Each puppy is different and the above guidelines may have to be adjusted to your particular dog. Don't allow your puppy to get fat.

Feeding Regimen

Before you bring your Newf home, the breeder or former owner should acquaint you with its feeding regimen. If he or she doesn't volunteer, ask! It's extremely important to know what the dog was being fed and how often. Many guarantees require that the breeder's diet be fed or that the breeder must be made aware of any changes made to the diet after you pick up your puppy. Even if you do decide to change the feed, it should never be done abruptly, but gradually over a week or two.

life. The dog food you choose will have suggested daily amounts to feed the puppy on the back of the bag. But these are only suggested quantities that you may have to adjust for your particular Newf. A young puppy of seven weeks, for example, needs three or four meals a day. Since its stomach is still small, it needs to eat more frequently.

Generally, it's wise to feed the puppy three times a day: breakfast, lunch, and dinner. As it grows and begins to show no interest in lunch, it is telling you it's time to cut back on the amounts. Once you adjust the puppy's new ration, you can divide it into two or three meals per day.

Starting out: Start your Newf on a kibbled puppy food that is generally between 26 and 31 percent protein. There is a difference of opinion among Newf breeders regarding the amount of protein needed in the growing

puppy's diet. Some breeders insist that diets high in protein cause muscles and tissue to develop more rapidly than bone and skeletal structure, causing extra stress to be put on the developing bones and skeleton, resulting in abnormalities. The quality is more important than the quantity of protein since, as already noted, the Newf puppy grows rapidly between the ages of three and eighteen months.

Some breeders prefer their puppies to be kept on puppy ration until one year old. However, if you begin to notice scabs on its rear and the dog doesn't have an allergy, suspect too much protein as the culprit and switch it to an adult dog food with between 21 and 25 percent protein. The condition should clear up in a few weeks.

Calories and protein: As we've already said, too many calories can be disastrous for the growing Newf. But too much protein over a long period of time can also be very damaging

Consult your breeder before making any changes to your new puppy's diet.

Puppies need regularly scheduled feeding times.

Is it dinnertime yet?

to its general health. Although most bone and joint problems are thought to be genetic in origin, many are caused by improper diets. This is especially true in the giant breeds such as the Newfoundland. By changing your puppy to a lower protein food, you may be preventing orthopedic problems that could occur in later life.

Feeding the Adult Newfoundland

As your bouncing puppy approaches adulthood, you will notice that, along with its increase in size, it has had a marked decrease in activity level. Your Newf is no longer the tireless ball of fire that tears through the day at lightning speed, seeming never to become fatigued. It's normal for your Newf to settle down as it gets older. That doesn't mean it is or should become a couch potato by any means; it is just more selective about the times it wants to exercise and play. For this reason, an adult Newf does not need nearly as much food as its size would appear to dictate. That's why most nutritionists will warn you to be very wary of the feeding guidelines printed on the bag of dog food for a dog of your Newf's size. As it gets older, its metabolic rate decreases and thus cannot handle the huge quantities listed, so let your own common sense be the guide. And don't forget the "rib" test—if you can't feel them underneath all that coat, your Newf is too fat!

Feeding the Older Newfoundland

As your Newf approaches old age, its nutritional requirements will change again. When it reaches about seven or eight, you'll notice it starting to slow down a bit. It will have less energy and will need fewer calories, and less protein, carbohydrates, and fat than it did as a puppy and an adult dog. At that point in its life, it's best to think of switching the dog to one of the "senior" dog food diets on the market. If you continue to feed it the same food and quantities that you did when it was younger, it will soon become overweight. It's especially important to keep the older Newf fit and trim in order to keep its heart and other vital organs functioning at optimum effectiveness. If you are unsure about what type of food to switch to or when, consult your veterinarian.

Types of Dog Food

Now that you have a fairly good handle on what constitutes a balanced diet for your Newf, the question arises as to which type of food to choose. There are three basic types of dog food commercially available: dry, moist, and semimoist.

As your puppy matures into adulthood, his or her activity level will settle down.

Dry Food

By far, the most popular food is a high-quality dry food. It's also the most economical. There are several other advantages to feeding a premium dry food. Not only is it nutritionally complete, supplying your Newf with all its caloric, vitamin, and mineral requirements, but it can be stored for months in an airtight container without refrigeration. Because of the crunchy substance of dry food, it's also better for your dog's teeth and it will help to keep its teeth and gums in good shape. Even though dry dog food may not look or smell particularly mouthwatering to you,

An older Newf still requires exercise to stay healthy.

it's extremely tasty to your dog. You will also find that when you choose a high-quality premium food, you will actually feed your dog much less than you would if it were on some of the other commercially prepared foods.

Moist Food

Moist foods come in cans. They are very tasty and most dogs will gobble them up in a flash. However, for a dog the size of a Newf, feeding an all-moist food is very expensive and there is no nutritional benefit. In fact, canned foods, which usually contain more salt and sugar derivatives than other types of food, can cause your Newf to put on unwanted pounds very quickly. What many owners choose to do instead is to mix a very small portion of moist with a basic dry food diet to make it more palatable.

Semimoist Food

The most eye-appealing dog foods are the semimoist types that commonly come in burger,

nugget, or chunk shapes that look exactly like real meat. Like dry food, semimoist is fairly convenient and easy to feed. It's highly palatable, so most dogs like it without coaxing. Generally, it is more expensive to feed your Newf a semimoist food. Remember too, that the soft consistency of the food will not give its teeth and gums the same benefits as a dry food will.

Homemade Diets

There is some debate about how nutritionally complete any commercial dog food is, given the processing that is involved. Some owners feel that the only way their pets will receive 100 percent sound and completely balanced food is if they make it themselves. Certainly, homemade diets are another alternative to feeding commercial foods, but if that's the route you choose to go, you'll need to follow strict nutritional guidelines. It's not enough to "set an extra place" at the table and simply give your

Newf exactly what you eat. That's the best way to rob it of essential nutrients. So, unless you are well schooled in diet and nutrition, don't attempt to be your Newf's dietitian. If you are adamant about feeding your Newf a homemade diet, however, ask your veterinarian to give you a recipe to follow.

If your Newf has special dietary requirements because of allergies or other digestive problems, you may also want to consider the homemade diet alternative. However, there are specially prepared prescription diets available for just those problems. Remember, choosing to feed your dog a homemade diet will require diligence, added expense, and lots of added time.

Changing Foods

Once you have settled on a type and brand of dog food, stay with it unless your Newf has a bad reaction or your veterinarian recommends another feed. In order for your dog to get the most out of its diet, the diet must be consistent. Changes in your dog's food, when made at all, should be made slowly; otherwise, its stools could become loose and it may experience other digestive disorders.

A good rule when changing to another feed is to do it over a week's time, gradually adding the new food to the ration of old food. This way, your Newf's digestive system won't be unduly stressed.

Treats and Table Scraps

If you're like most dog owners, you won't be able to resist it when your Newf gives you that sad-eyed look while you're munching your lunchtime sandwich. Try anyway. Once you start feeding your Newf from the table, it's the beginning of the end. Throwing a 15-pound (7 kg) puppy a crust or two of your sandwich might seem cute, but several months down the line, when the 120-pound (54 kg) "Junior" bounds up for his share of your tuna on rye, it'll be a "horse of a different color." If you don't want your Newf to be a pest at your mealtimes, don't feed it from the table. If you want to give it some table scraps, do so in moderation, and then add them to its food at the appointed time.

Rewards

Often you'll want to reward your Newf for a task well done. At that time, dog biscuits fit the bill nicely. Like commercial dog food, they are nutritionally balanced and can help to keep your Newf's teeth and gums clean. There are many varieties of dog treats on the market, but

A dog biscuit makes an excellent treat to reward your Newf for a job well done.

I'm just working up an appetite, Mom!

don't overdo it—treats can be very fattening. Use them judiciously.

You may also want to give your Newf one of the many types of rawhide chews available in pet stores. For the most part, they satisfy its

Is somebody baking me cookies?

need to chew and can prevent the puppy from getting into trouble by chewing things such as furniture instead. They can also keep your Newf from getting bored when you're out of the house. However, some dogs have problems digesting the rawhide and if that's the case, discontinue giving them to your pet.

Nonedible products: There are nonedible products on the market such as nylon bones, which will also satisfy your puppie's need to chew without incurring the risk of a possible digestive upset. However, be advised that other commercially available chew toys, such as dried cow hooves, have been known to cause many a chipped tooth that can result in the need for extensive dental work. A good alternative for the young puppy that will cause no damage and satisfy its chewing need is to take a rag or small towel, wet it down completely, knot it at each end, and stick it in the freezer. In 15 minutes your puppy will have a treat it can have fun with for hours with no dangerous repercussions!

Somebody needs a bath!

GROOMING YOUR NEWFOUNDLAND

When you first decided to buy a Newf, you already knew that daily grooming would likely be a part of both your lives. True, but not a problem because, despite the Newfoundland's ample double coat, it's surprisingly simple to keep it looking at its best.

The amount of coat your Newf carries will depend on its bloodlines. Some dogs carry heavier coats than others. That's another reason it's always preferable to see the parents before purchasing a puppy. The Newfoundland has a somewhat oily double coat—a topcoat and an undercoat, which keeps it from getting wet down to the skin when it's in the water. Generally, Newfs that are kept in outdoor kennels have more undercoat than Newfs that live primarily in the house. Your Newf will shed more in the spring and fall, but daily brushing will keep it looking tip-top all year round.

Time for a haircut!

Start Early

It's important to get your Newf accustomed to being groomed as soon as you bring it home. Don't attempt anything too ambitious at first— a few seconds of brushing at a time, just to get it used to the idea, will suffice. It's doubly important to start grooming your Newf from puppyhood. Regular grooming not only makes your dog look terrific, but it will also help keep its skin and coat clean and healthy. Another reason to start your grooming sessions early on is purely practical. It's far easier to get a 20-pound (9-kg) Newf puppy accustomed to standing still for grooming than a 120-pound (54-kg) young adult! Start your grooming early. Your back will thank you!

Grooming Equipment

To groom your Newf, you'll need a place to do it and some basic tools.

The Grooming Table

The first investment you may want to make is in a grooming table. While it isn't necessary to groom your Newf on a table, it is easier for the groomer to stand while doing the job. For that reason, having a table on which the dog can either stand or lie is helpful. Extra-large grooming tables are available through pet supply stores for giant breeds such as the Newf.

Size: The grooming table should be very sturdy with a 24-inch (61-cm)-wide top and a length of at least 36 inches (91 cm). The tabletop should also have rubber matting to keep your Newf's feet from slipping. The height of most tables is approximately 30 inches (76 cm), but you can also buy an adjustable one.

"Arm": Be sure to purchase an "arm" with your table. This device, which looks like an inverted letter "L," is screwed into the corner of the table and is adjustable to the height of your dog. At the end, there is a noose that you slip over your Newf's neck during the grooming session. This will help you keep your dog standing still and in one position while you groom.

=== **T I P** ===

Grooming Sessions

If you want your puppy to enjoy being groomed, remember to keep the grooming sessions short at first, gradually increasing the time. The puppy won't need major grooming until it's about six months old. But if you've made its early grooming experience fun, then your Newf will not only be an old pro when the time comes for serious grooming, but it will also look forward to these daily sessions as quality time you spend together.

Never leave a dog unattended on a grooming table with its head in a noose—if your Newf were to jump off the table, it could injure itself. Such an experience would also make the dog loathe to ever want to get on a grooming table again.

Other Equipment

There are literally hundreds of grooming tools on the market. When you go to your favorite pet store, or look at a wholesale dog catalog, don't go crazy—you really need only six basic tools to get the job done.

Slicker brush: One of the most important tools you'll use is a *slicker brush*. This is the best tool to use to get your puppy accustomed to grooming because it feels so wonderful on its body. The slicker brush is also invaluable for removing loose hair and any debris from its coat.

To keep your Newfoundland looking good, you will need some basic grooming tools.

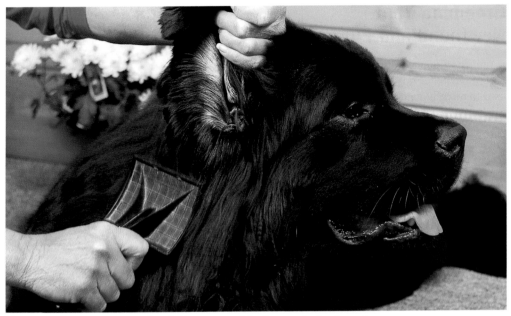

Get your puppy accustomed to being groomed in frequent, short sessions.

Coarse-toothed comb and rake: Once its adult coat starts to come in, you'll also need a *coarse-toothed comb* to get down deep to its skin and a *rake* for getting rid of all that excess dead hair.

Toenail clipper: Another essential item is the *toenail clipper*. Don't try to use human toenail clippers on your Newf. Choose one designed for big dogs. Make sure the model has replacement blades available since tough Newf nails wear out blades rather quickly. Most owners shy away from clipping nails, but once you accustom your Newf to the procedure it's very simple and painless.

Thinning shears: You'll also need *thinning shears*. It's wise to invest in a good pair with fine teeth, as these will give your Newf the best, most professional look.

Blunt-edged shears: A pair of *blunt-edged shears* is also very handy, especially when you want to strip all the hair that collects between your Newf's toes.

Be very gentle and careful when cleaning around your Newf's eye area.

Grooming Your Newfoundland Puppy

Your Newf puppy will not require a great deal of grooming, but it's a good idea to get it used to being groomed at a young age so you won't have problems keeping it looking good once it's older and needs more elaborate grooming.

✔ Lift your puppy onto its grooming table. Let it sit or lie down. Remember, make it fun. Be touchy and playful with the puppy as it rolls around on the table, then get down to the business at hand.

✔ First, tackle the toenails. Hold the toenail clippers and starting gently, pull one leg toward you. Make sure you have a firm grip and clip only the hooked part of the nail. If you cut more, you run the risk of cutting into the *quick*, which contains the nerve and vessels. If cut, it will cause bleeding from the vein. If that happens, have a styptic pencil or coagulant powder on hand. In puppies with white toenails, you can see the quick as a pinkish area. In dogs with black nails, make sliverlike cuts until you see a blackish, moist-looking center. That's the quick. Don't go any further.

When grooming your Newf for show, a thinning shears will come in handy to shape the hair behind its ears.

✔ Next, proceed to brush your Newf for a few seconds. If it starts to get impatient, don't let it jump off the table, as injury can result. Instead, settle it down and then lift it from the table.

Bathing

At some point, you'll want to give your dog its first bath. Since Newfs love water, this should be fairly easy, but introduce it gently. While it's a puppy, you can easily pick it up and put it into your bathtub.

✔ Start with only a few inches of water and throw in some of its toys. Get it used to splashing around and having fun in the tub. When it's ready for its first real bath, it'll already have a familiarity with the tub and will accept being there.

✔ Wet it down with a sponge, while praising it for its good behavior.

✔ Use either a commercial baby shampoo or one of the special dog shampoos on the market.

Regular brushing will keep your Newf looking neat and clean.

✔ Don't use an insecticide product unless the puppy has fleas or ticks (see pages 79 and 80). Be sure not to get the shampoo in its eyes or ears.

✔ Once you've soaped the puppy down, use either the spray attachment or a bucket with clean water and a sponge to rinse it. You can also pour water gently over the Newf until it is rinsed. Don't leave any shampoo on its coat.

✔ After your Newf is completely rinsed, have a big, bulky towel ready and begin to dry it. Most dogs love the sensation of being dried with a towel. If you have a dog blow dryer, use that. Once your Newf gets used to the sound, it'll love it. Don't use your human hair dryer, however, unless it has a "No Heat" setting. The heat setting on human hair dryers is much too hot for your puppy.

Unless you show your Newf or it gets into a lot of grime and dirt outside, you probably won't have to bathe it more than every few months—or longer, depending on how clean you keep its coat with brushings and combings in between.

Grooming Your Adult Newfoundland

As your Newf gets older, your grooming sessions will get longer and more ambitious. Your main objective is to keep the dog looking neat and clean at all times and free of mats, which can cause skin problems. Regular combing and brushing, along with infrequent baths will accomplish that. However, there are also a few other areas you'll want to attend to.

✔ Besides clipping its toenails and brushing its coat, you'll also need to remove the excess hair between its toes and keep the area around its

Left: Groomed toes and nails
Right: Toes and nails before grooming.

ears and neck shaped with the thinning shears and the blunt scissors.

✔ If the hair at its hock is very long or straggly, make it neater by holding a straight scissors pointing down and then trimming the hair around the hock to no more than 1 inch (2.5 cm) long.

✔ Trim its ears by cutting around the ear, especially the hair behind the fold. To make the look more professional, blend the edges with the thinning sheers.

Proper Care of Nails, Ears, and Eyes

Nails: We've already discussed how to trim your Newf's nails but it's also necessary to stress the importance of keeping them cut. And don't forget the dewclaws (vestiginal toes). Leaving

When grooming the adult Newf, you will need to use thinning shears to remove the hair between its toes.

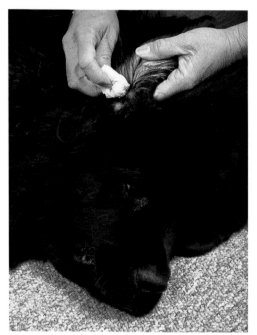

Keep your Newf's ears clean with a weekly wash.

If your Newf's eyes become watery or inflamed, try treating them with a mild eyewash.

them uncut can cause the nail to curve back and grow into the skin of the leg. Also remember to file your Newfoundland's nails after trimming. If you leave jagged edges, your dog can hurt itself if it scratches a part of its body. It will also give you a nasty scratch if it playfully hits you with its paw. You can use any heavy-duty nail file to get the job done.

Ears: Always keep your Newf's ears clean. There are many commercial ear washes on the market that will do the job, or you can make your own. There are also pet ear swabs on the market that release a gentle cleanser and help protect ear infections with regular use.

✔ Routinely dampen a cotton ball with hydrogen peroxide and alcohol and gently clean the inside of the dog's ear.

✔ Use another cotton ball to dry the ear. If you use a commercial drying powder, be sure the ear is completely dry before dusting it.

✔ Administering powder to a moist ear can cause the powder to cake and obstruct the air flow, which can precipitate waxing or scratching. Never use a swab or Q-Tip to clean or probe inside your Newf's ear; you could cause damage.

With regular care, your Newf's ears should remain clean, healthy, and odor-free.

Eyes: Since your Newf will probably spend a great deal of time outdoors, its eyes are particularly prone to injury and/or infection. Keep a careful watch on its eyes and, should they appear red or watery, you can treat them with a mild eyewash that is commercially available over the counter at drugstores. A baby eyewash is recommended. There are also sterile eyewashes available that are designed specifically for pets. These washes can help remove air pollutants and stray hairs from your dog's eyes. If the condition worsens, consult your veterinarian.

Your puppy needs to be vaccinated against rabies when it is between 4–6 months old.

PROPER HEALTH CARE FOR YOUR NEWFOUNDLAND

After you bring your Newf home and integrate it into your family life, you must also make sure that it has a safe and healthy environment in which to grow and thrive. Remember, it's easier and far less costly to prevent common injuries and health problems before they arise.

Keeping Your Newf Healthy

The first thing you'll have to learn is to protect your pet from the common diseases, parasites, and medical problems that will confront it during its life.

Proper medical care is the best way to insure that your Newf will lead a happy, healthy, and long life. As a dog owner, it's helpful to have a support system. Friends with dogs and breeders will be an invaluable part of that system. One of the most important relationships you and your Newf will establish is with your veterinarian.

Mom would never let me out without my Lyme disease shot!

Diseases Controlled by Immunizations

Throughout your Newf's life, you will have to make sure that it is vaccinated against some common canine diseases such as distemper, rabies, parainfluenza, leptospirosis, hepatitis, coronavirus, and parvovirus. Immunization for these and other diseases is usually given in a series, beginning in early puppyhood. Your Newf should have received its first shots at the breeder's kennel when it was approximately six weeks old. Your veterinarian will then schedule follow-up vaccinations usually at the eight- to ten-week mark and then again at twelve weeks. The veterinarian will also immunize your Newf against bordatella (kennel cough).

The Veterinarian

Once your Newf has had a week to acclimate to its new environment, schedule an appointment with your local veterinarian.

✔ If you don't have a veterinarian, ask your friends who have dogs for their recommendations.

✔ Don't be afraid to "interview" prospective veterinarians before deciding on the one you and your Newf will feel most comfortable with. You'll find most veterinarians are happy to answer any of your questions.

✔ Get your Newf used to visiting the veterinarian's office during an unstressful time. That way, it will associate going there will pleasant things. When your Newf is full grown you'll appreciate having a calm, well-behaved dog at the veterinarian's office instead of a giant dog that is unmanageable, frightened, and uncooperative.

After completing its puppy series, your Newf will have to be revaccinated every year. It will also receive a rabies shot when it is between four to six months of age and, depending on the laws of the state in which you live, it'll need to be revaccinated every one to two years, according to local ordinances.

Distemper

Distemper is a viral disease that in its early stages most closely resembles a cold. Its symptoms include a runny nose, fever, loss of appetite, and listlessness, often accompanied by diarrhea. Occasionally, it causes the pads of the feet to thicken. As in any virus, its symptoms appear rapidly, within a week after exposure to an infected animal. Even if an affected dog appears to recover, the virus lingers, later manifesting itself in the form of convulsions, paralysis, twitching, and eventually, death.

Because of the pernicious nature of the disease, it was one of the chief killers of puppies. However, with advances in modern medicine, and now that more and more animals are receiving vaccinations, the disease is nowhere near as common as it once was.

Rabies

Rabies is probably one of the most feared diseases known to afflict dogs and other mammals. It is an infectious disease that destroys the nerve cells of part of the brain and causes death. In Latin, the word means *rage* or *fury* and probably got that name because infected animals appeared mad and aggressive. However, contrary to popular belief, rabid dogs do not foam at the mouth. One of the symptoms of rabies is the inability to swallow water, resulting in saliva stringing from the mouth, due to paralysis of the jaw.

Rabies is not exclusively a canine disease, but affects all warm-blooded mammals, including humans. The most common carriers are wild animals like skunks, raccoons, foxes, and bats. It is transmitted by a bite from an infected animal and is always fatal.

Thanks to a vaccine first developed in 1885 by Louis Pasteur, the disease is under control in domestic animals in most developed countries and has been virtually eradicated in England because of a mandate for quarantine, but it still exists in many parts of the world. Occasionally,

The vet will put your Newf on a schedule for yearly vaccinations.

there will be outbreaks in parts of the United States among the wild animal population. The disease is endemic in various regions of the United States in wild carnivores.

Since the Newf is an active, outdoor dog, it is liable to come in contact with other animals. If it is not immunized against rabies and is bitten by a rabid animal, the consequences for it and even for you will be irreparable.

Infectious Canine Hepatitis

Infectious canine hepatitis, which is also a viral infection, can range from mild to severe. In its most virulent form, a sick dog can die within 24 hours of the first appearance of symptoms, which include: fever, listlessness, vomiting, abdominal tenderness and pain, tonsillitis, and hemorrhaging. Contact your veterinarian immediately if these symptoms appear.

Leptospirosis

Unlike distemper and hepatitis, leptospirosis is a spirochete disease. It is transmitted from dog to dog by exposure to an affected animal or by drinking water that has been contaminated with the urine of an infected animal. It can also be transmitted to many other mammals, including humans.

Early signs of the disease include: loss of appetite, vomiting, diarrhea, and fever. Other signs are jaundice, abdominal pain, sores in the oral cavity, and weakness in the hindquarters. Once the disease has been allowed to advance untreated, kidney and liver damage can occur. Consult your veterinarian immediately if your dog has these symptoms.

Parvovirus

This viral disease is most deadly in puppies. Its symptoms mimic many other canine diseases and include: diarrhea, which is sometimes bloody, fever, and vomiting. Because dehydration occurs so quickly, your Newf's survival will depend on how quickly a diagnosis is made and treatment begun. With parvo, as with many canine diseases, the best treatment is prevention. By having your Newf vaccinated, you save it from becoming a victim of this terribly contagious disease.

Coronavirus

This highly contagious disease is every bit as devastating as parvovirus and very similar in symptomatology. Though coronavirus can be

Examine your Newf's skin frequently.

deadly to puppies, it can affect dogs of any age. Most puppy vaccines now contain protection against this virus; however, if your Newf has not been vaccinated and begins to exhibit symptoms that include an insidious and often foul-smelling, watery diarrhea that can be tinged with blood, isolate it and then take it to your veterinarian immediately.

Parainfluenza

Another highly contagious viral disease, parainfluenza can spread rapidly from one dog to another. It has often been erroneously termed "kennel cough" because of the dry hacking cough that develops. In fact, it causes an infectious tracheobronchitis characterized by a cough and retching to expel mucus. While it is not a fatal disease, parainfluenza can become debilitating and lowers the dog's resistance to secondary infections that can cause more serious medical problems. If your Newf becomes infected, your veterinarian will have to treat it and isolate it from other dogs to keep the disease from spreading. As with other contagious canine diseases, the best cure is vaccination before the fact.

Bordetella

Bordetella is a bacterial infection that is often put under the generalized term "kennel cough." Its symptoms include a hacking cough, runny nose, and weepy eyes. In fact, it is often seen in conjunction with tracheobronchitis.

To immunize your Newf, the veterinarian will squirt the vaccine into the dog's nostrils rather than inject it. While your pet probably won't like the sensation, the protection it will get is worth the momentary discomfort.

Make sure your Newf is protected against common parasites such as fleas and ticks before taking him or her outdoors.

Some dogs have been known to come down with mild symptoms within 10 days after vaccination. If this happens, don't worry. Your pet isn't contagious—it will just look and sound like it is!

Lyme Disease

Since the Newf loves the outdoors, it is very likely that you and your pet will spend time romping in parks, woods, or around lakes. Unfortunately, these are all breeding grounds for the minuscule deer tick that can carry Lyme disease. First identified in the town of Lyme, Connecticut, Lyme disease is a serious malady that can affect both you and your Newf. It is transmitted by a bite from a carrier tick. In dogs, the disease is usually characterized by tenderness and swelling in the joints. In humans, the symptoms are not always so recognizable and can mimic other illnesses, particularly flu.

If you suspect you have been bitten by a tick and notice a small, circular rash developing at the site of the bite, see your physician or call a Lyme disease hotline immediately. While there is no vaccine available for humans at present, there is one for your pet. Your veterinarian will administer the Lyme vaccination in an initial series of two injections, spaced over a three-week period. Thereafter, your Newf will need a yearly booster.

Parasites

The blight of parasites poses one of the greatest annoyances to both pets and their owners. A parasite is an animal that lives in or on an organism of another species that acts as

its host. External parasites such as fleas and ticks, as well as internal ones such as worms can make your Newf's life and yours miserable. Fortunately, you can get a handle on the situation by following a regimen that begins with keeping your pet's quarters clean. No matter how conscientious you are, however, the reality is that at some time during your Newf's life, it will be infected with parasites. Knowing what to look for and understanding how to eliminate the problem is half the battle.

External Parasites

Fleas: The word alone sends chills up many a dog owner's spine! It's easy to understand why, since this pest causes more skin and coat problems among dogs than any other parasite. Just consider this: There are 11,000 different types of fleas! In cases of severe infestation, the flea, which feeds on the dog's blood supply, can cause your Newf to develop anemia. Your Newf can also contract tapeworm by ingesting a single flea.

Always check your Newf for ticks after he or she has been out in the woods.

Some dogs also develop an allergic reaction to fleas. For this reason, you should consult your veterinarian and decide on a course of prevention and treatment before the problem gets out of hand. Once the flea gets in the house and into carpets, cracks, or crevices, it's total war!

The lifecycle of the flea explains why. A single female flea can lay hundreds of eggs that hatch and become adults in under three weeks. As the mating process continues and multiplies, it won't take long for your home to become infested. In order to combat the problem, you must launch an attack on every front. Flea dips, shampoos, and powders, as well as flea collars can kill fleas on your dog. Monthly prevention such as Frontline and Advantage applied directly to the dog's coat are highly effective against both fleas and ticks. However, you must also treat your house and the rest of the dog's environment at the same time or your efforts will be useless. Flea foggers can be used in the house, but for cases of severe infestation, particularly in warmer cli-

mates, a professional exterminator may be needed. There are also other flea control products on the market, including a nontoxic borax-based powder that breaks the lifecycle of the flea by preventing it from reproducing. The product, sold under a variety of generic names, is brushed into the carpet once a year and is highly effective.

Flea pills are also available from your veterinarian, as well as a new series of flea shots. However, before using any flea product, consult your veterinarian who will advise you on the best method of prevention.

Ticks: Since your Newf loves the outdoors and particularly enjoys a romp in the woods, it may pick up ticks. There are many types of ticks, including the deer tick that carries Lyme disease, as discussed on page 79, but by far the most common is the brown dog tick. These insidious parasites are found in woods and fields where they cling to vegetation and then attach themselves to animals.

If you live in a wooded area, make sure to check your Newf after walks or exercise periods by running your hands up and down its extremities and around its neck and ears, which are the most common places for ticks to congregate. If you find a tick burrowed in, you can remove it yourself by dabbing it with alcohol or nail polish remover. This may cause the tick to loosen its hold momentarily. Then take a tweezers and grab it as close to the skin as possible and pull it out. Be careful to disengage it completely and not leave any of the mouthpiece in the dog's skin because infection can result. Dispose of the tick and then treat the bite with a dab of alcohol or antibiotic cream.

Ear mites: If you notice your Newf scratching or rubbing its ears with its paws, or shaking its head, ear mites could be the problem. Check the ears and, if you see dark, waxy, foul-smelling matter, take the dog to the veterinarian so a definitive diagnosis can be made.

Mites are microscopic bugs that live in your dog's ear canal. By examining the residue in the dog's ear, your veterinarian will easily be able to identify the problem. If your Newf does have mites, your veterinarian will clean out the ears and give you medication to correct the problem. Since mites can be transmitted from one animal to another, if you have other pets in the house, including cats, you must have them checked as well.

Mange: At one time, the word "mange" was enough to make many a dog owner shudder. This skin disorder, characterized by scaly, oozing patches, is caused by another type of mite that burrows into the epidermis and causes the dog to scratch, bite, and lose its hair. There are several types of mange, but the most common are: red mange, also called demodectic, and scabies, also called sarcoptic.

While all dogs carry mites in the pores of their skin, they almost never become "active" and cause problems unless the dog is under stress. Red mange is seen more frequently in puppies and older dogs. In its early stages, it is easily treatable and may even disappear by itself. Scabies, on the other hand, requires immediate treatment and is contagious. Regardless of the type of mange you suspect, consult your veterinarian so the problem can be correctly identified and treated, if necessary.

Internal Parasites

During the course of its life, your Newf will probably have worms. The four most common types are: roundworms, hookworms, whipworms, and tapeworms. The first three can eas-ily be diagnosed by your veterinarian by examination of a fecal specimen under a microscope.

Tapeworms are transmitted when a dog swallows an infected flea or rodent and can be seen by the naked eye in the dog's stool or attached to hair around the anal area. Tapeworm segments detach from the worm. They are pale pink in color and resemble flattened grains of rice. If untreated, tapeworms can cause your dog to lose weight and become generally debilitated.

Roundworms are found more commonly in puppies than in older dogs. Puppies can be born with this parasite if the mother is infected. They are passed on to other dogs through the excreted feces where the eggs are present. Suspect roundworms if your Newf's coat becomes dull or its abdomen seems to hang like a pot belly. It may also expel the worms in vomit or in stool. They resemble long, whitish, spaghetti-like strands.

Whipworms are found in the large intestine. Symptoms include diarrhea, loss of weight, rest-

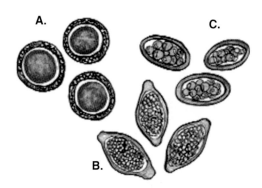

Microscopic view of worms:
A: Roundworm eggs;
B: Whipworm eggs;
C: Hookworm eggs.

During mosquito season, be sure to keep your Newf on heartworm preventative medications.

lessness, and anemia if the infestation goes untreated. Keeping your Newf's kennel clean is imperative to prevent it from contracting this parasite. However, while whipworms and others are contagious, they don't self-generate because of a dirty kennel; they are passed from dog to dog.

Hookworms can affect dogs of any age, but they affect puppies more dramatically. They attach themselves inside the small intestine and suck blood from the intestinal wall. A puppy with hookworms will lose appetite and weight and will often have bloody or black stools. If untreated, anemia can result and in puppies this can be fatal.

Heartworms are transmitted to your dog by a mosquito bite. The carrier mosquito deposits microfilariae that are then transported through the dog's bloodstream, finally lodging in the heart where they mature and reproduce. When the carrier dog is bitten by an uninfected mosquito, the mosquito then becomes infected and bites another dog and the vicious cycle continues.

If not diagnosed and treated, heart failure will be the end result. However, diagnosis is difficult and treatment is risky so the safest path is prevention. Before your veterinarian puts your Newf on a program, it must first be given a simple blood test to be sure no heartworms are present. Once that is determined, your Newf

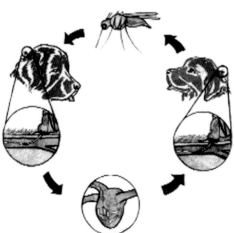

The lifecycle of the heartworm. Your Newf can contract heartworm after being bitten by an infected mosquito.

will be put on a heartworm preventive medication. Three different types are currently available: a tablet (Filaribits), given once daily during mosquito season; a liquid (Caricide), added to the food daily; or a tablet (Heartguard) given monthly. Most dogs should remain on a preventative throughout the mosquito season (spring, summer, fall). But if you live in a warm, moist climate, you should keep your Newf on preventive all year-round. Every year, your veterinarian will give your Newf an occult blood test to make sure it is heartworm free.

Coccidia and giardia are commonly found in puppies. Both are more difficult to identify than most common worms. Diagnosis requires a careful examination of a fresh fecal sample by your veterinarian. Signs to watch for that may signal the presence of these protozoas are weight loss, watery diarrhea, and dullness of coat.

A wise rule of thumb is to have your Newf routinely checked for the presence of worms during its yearly visit to the veterinarian's office.

Common Illnesses and Medical Problems

No matter how diligent a "parent" you are, at one time or another during its life, your Newfy "child" will encounter common medical problems—so don't panic. Fortunately, most illnesses can be treated and you and your Newf can get back to the business of living, loving, and playing together.

Constipation, Diarrhea, and Vomiting

Occasionally, your Newf may experience a change in its bowel movements. This can be brought on by something as simple as changing its diet or stress. If the dog suddenly appears to be straining, suspect constipation. This is usually a nonemergency problem that will correct itself. If it persists, or if the dog appears to be in pain when it tries to defecate, call your veterinarian at once.

Like constipation, diarrhea and vomiting can be triggered by a change in diet or stress. Worms can also be the culprit. If either diarrhea or vomiting becomes severe and lasts more than 12 hours, suspect a more serious condition and call your veterinarian. Both conditions can lead to extreme dehydration that is often fatal in puppies. Until you are thoroughly familiar with what is normal for your Newf, don't hesitate to call the veterinarian at the first sign of a change in its daily behavior.

Impacted Anal Sacs

If your Newf starts "scooting" its rear end on the ground, suspect impacted anal sacs. These two glands lie on either side of the rectum, just inside the anus. Occasionally, they can become clogged or impacted. When that happens, they must be emptied out manually to avoid more serious conditions such as infection or abscess.

The first time it happens, take your dog to the veterinarian and let him or her show you what to do if the problem arises again. To empty the anal sacs, you must apply pressure to both sides of each gland. A thick, odoriferous secretion will then be expelled. Repeat the same procedure with the other sac. It may not be the most pleasant job in the house, but as the saying goes, somebody's got to do it!

Gastric Torsion or Bloat

A serious and often fatal problem is gastric torsion, also known as bloat. In fact, they are

Deep-chested dogs like the Newf are predisposed to bloat, so learn to recognize the symptoms.

Bloat

Though research continues about the causes of bloat, there is still no clear-cut answer. Current data seems to suggest there may be a link between food and bloat. The condition is triggered when the stomach swells up from gas, fluid, or a combination of the two. Once the stomach becomes distended, it has a tendency to twist. Be on the lookout for the following signs:

✔ Swollen stomach and abdominal pain
✔ Excessive drooling
✔ Unsuccessful attempts to vomit or defecate
✔ Inability to find a comfortable position
✔ Cool, pale skin and gums

If you suspect bloat, don't waste a second—get your Newf to the veterinarian IMMEDIATELY. It's far better to be wrong about this condition than to risk losing your beloved pet to this horrible and painful killer.

As a preventive measure, it's wise to divide your Newf's daily food allotment into at least two separate meals per day. Don't exercise your Newf an hour before or after eating and limit its intake of water after exercise.

two separate conditions. A dog whose stomach bloats often "twists" as well; thus the term "gastric torsion."

Unfortunately, bloat is being seen more and more among dogs of all breeds; however, it is believed that large, deep-chested dogs such as the Newfoundland are at a much greater risk. There is no way to predict whether a dog will bloat at some time during its life. At best, you can only exercise preventive measures based on current information available and learn to recognize the danger signs because, if your Newf does bloat, your quick action can save its life.

Tumors

Like the human population, the dog world is also plagued with another potential killer—cancer.

Giant breeds can develop hip dysplasia. An X-ray can determine whether or not your Newf is dysplastic.

However, it is important to realize that not every growth, lump, or bump you may find on your dog is cancer. In fact, most are benign growths or cysts. As a breed, Newfoundlands are prone to all kinds of lumps and bumps, both internally and externally, but fortunately, most are noncancerous. Just to be sure, any time you notice a lump or swelling on any part of its body, let your veterinarian check it out. You should get into the habit of manually going over your Newf's body once a week. Make it a regular part of its grooming. That way, you will know its body and be alerted to any irregularities.

If your Newf should develop cancer during its lifetime, don't lose heart. As with humans, cancer isn't necessarily a death sentence. Depending on the type of tumor your dog has, your veterinarian can advise you of the types of treatment available.

Common Health Problems in Newfoundlands

Hip Dysplasia

Since the Newfoundland is considered a giant breed, it is particularly prone to orthopedic problems. One of the more prevalent is hip dysplasia, which can take many forms. The most common form is a condition in which the ball of the hip joint doesn't fit securely into the socket. The resulting friction causes the ball and socket to wear down in some places and build

A Newf pup should be checked for subvalvular aortic stenosis (SAS), which can manifest itself as early as nine weeks of age.

up abnormally in others. To make matters worse, arthritis often sets in as well, and the pet becomes increasingly uncomfortable as the condition deteriorates. While many dysplastic dogs can live long, productive lives with very little distress, others will require antiinflammatory painkillers. In some cases, the dysplasia is so crippling that the dog may have to be euthanized. Surgery is another option, but is not successful in every case.

Evaluation: The best way to avoid dysplasia is to choose your Newf puppy carefully. Since research has shown that dysplasia is primarily genetic, study your prospective pup's ancestry. If its parents and grandparents are nondysplastic, there's a fairly good chance it will be, too. The only way to be sure your Newf is not dysplastic is to have its hips X-rayed after it reaches two years of age. Your veterinarian can evaluate the films but you can also have them checked by an independent agency called the Orthopedic Foundation for Animals (OFA), which is composed of expert veterinary radiologists who examine the dog's hip X-rays and then determine if they are within the normal range for the breed. If the OFA determines that your dog is nondysplastic, it will assign it an OFA number.

OFA and PENNHIP: Before buying your Newf, it is wise to be certain both its parents have OFA numbers. An alternative to the OFA X-rays is a new method developed at the University of Pennsylvania called PENNHIP. With this method, a dog can be X-rayed as young as six months old and the owner can be given a fairly accurate description of the hips. If you are buying a dog for show, or breeding dogs, PENNHIP may be the best way to be assured your Newf does not have hip dysplasia.

Obesity: You can also take precautions to insure that your Newf doesn't develop other orthopedic problems by not allowing it to put on extra weight at any age. Be especially mindful of extra pounds while it's still a puppy and its bones are forming. If your Newf is dysplastic, obesity will only compound the problem.

Heart Disease

Another serious problem that can affect the Newfoundland breed is heart disease, particularly subvalvular aortic stenosis (SAS). This disease is also prevalent in other breeds. Like hip dysplasia, studies have found that SAS is inherited, but even a Newf that's declared clear of the disease can still produce it in the progeny. The reason is unclear. We do know that SAS is not present at birth, but develops as the puppy grows. This is another reason you should have your Newf checked by your veterinarian early, preferably after nine weeks of age.

If SAS is present, it is detectable as a murmur ranging from slight to severe. Responsible breeders will have their litters evaluated by a veterinary cardiologist before the puppies leave their kennel for their new homes. Unfortunately, there are no guarantees with SAS. Newfoundlands diagnosed with a mild form of the disease can live long, productive lives or they can die at an early age.

Functional murmurs: Even though many murmurs in Newfs turn out to be SAS, many others are functional murmurs, which are temporary and not harmful to the dog. A functional murmur can sound like SAS, but unlike SAS, it will disappear within a few weeks to a few months. Only your veterinarian can make the proper diagnosis.

Eye Problems

Entropion, or the turning in of the eyelid, is another genetic problem sometimes found in the Newfoundland breed. As the lid turns in, it allows the eyelashes to rub against the cornea, which causes inflammation, irritation, and pain. Surgery is necessary to correct the condition.

Ectropion is a problem in which the opposite occurs: the eyelid turns outward, sagging and exposing the eye to irritants such as dirt and dust and other pollutants. Most ectropic dogs

TIP

Administering Medicine

At different times during your Newf's life, you will invariably have to administer medication.

If you need to give it liquid medicine, use a small syringe, which you can fill with the prescribed amount of medication. Then pull the lips away from the side of your Newf's mouth, insert the syringe, and dispense the medicine.

To administer tablets, open your Newf's mouth, hold its head slightly back, and place the pill as far to the rear of the tongue as possible. Then hold its mouth closed with one hand and stroke its neck with the other to activate the swallowing impulse. Be sure not to hold its head too far back because the pill could become lodged in the windpipe rather than down the throat.

Often, giving the dog a bit of cheese or other treat immediately afterward will assure that the pill has been swallowed. Most important, make sure it doesn't spit it out!

can function very well without corrective surgery.

Cherry eye: All dogs have three eyelids: an upper, a lower, and a third inner eyelid that is usually out of sight. Sometimes the third eyelid can prolapse or pop out and a mass of red tissue will be seen at the inside corner of the eye. This condition, aptly named "cherry eye," is usually seen more in young dogs. Initially it affects

only one eye, but the other eye often becomes infected within a few weeks. Cherry eye can be caused by a trauma, but it is also a common congenital defect that can be passed on from one generation to another. The condition can be permanently corrected by surgically removing the gland of the third eyelid.

Emergency Care

One of the most important things to learn is what to do if a medical emergency should arise. The first rule: Don't panic; then seek immediate advice from your veterinarian.

Poisoning

In our efforts to protect our canine friends from parasites, we have unfortunately introduced more and more toxic substances into the household. Products such as flea dips, flea collars, sprays, and disinfectants can cause skin irritations and sometimes a dangerously toxic condition. For this reason, it's best to check with your veterinarian before using a pesticide in your home or on your lawn.

Accidents

Every year, road accidents claim an enormous number of animal lives. Most of these can be prevented if pet owners exercised more diligence.

When you walk your Newf, always keep it on a lead. No matter how well trained you believe it is, a stimulus such as a rabbit or a squirrel scurrying by can send it across a street and into the path of a moving vehicle with fatal results.

Never open the door and allow it to take itself for a walk.

If you have a fenced yard, make sure gates are always latched before you let your dog out.

Precautions: Of course, accidents happen with even the most alert owners. If your Newf is injured in an accident of any kind, get it to the veterinarian immediately—but first exercise some simple precautions. Remember, an injured animal is a frightened animal. To avoid being bitten, secure a makeshift muzzle around its jaws. Use a belt, a tie, whatever is available, and gently wrap it around its mouth. Move the dog very carefully if internal injuries are suspected and take it right to the veterinarian.

Bleeding

If your Newf is hurt or is bleeding, determine the point of the bleeding and then apply firm, direct pressure to the spot. If the cut or wound is deep, your Newf will probably require sutures.

If there is profuse bleeding from any extremity, you can apply a tourniquet.

To make a tourniquet, wrap a cloth or belt or whatever else is handy, between the injury and the heart. Then loosen it for 15 to 30 seconds every 15 minutes. Be aware that tourniquets can be dangerous if you don't know what you're doing. If in doubt, apply direct pressure to the wound. Anything but minor bleeding should be treated as a medical emergency and your Newf should be taken to the veterinarian immediately.

Heatstroke

You and your Newf will undoubtedly get used to traveling together, but be forewarned that the car can be a potential death trap for a dog in hot weather in less than ten minutes. Don't be fooled by the weather outside. It doesn't have to be 90°F (32°C) for your dog to succumb to heatstroke inside the car. Even if you leave the windows open several inches, in direct sunlight on a pleasant 60°F (15.6°C) day, the car can heat up enough to kill your beloved pet.

You should also never leave your Newf outside in hot weather without some form of shelter from the sun. Be alert to the signs of heatstroke, which include rapid panting, bright red gums, a dazed look, and high fever. If you observe any of these symptoms, take immediate action. Place cool, moist compresses or towels all over its body, accompanied by an ice pack to get the temperature down. Then rush it to the veterinarian.

CPR

If your Newf is injured in an accident, it may require artificial respiration.

✔ Administer CPR by first opening its mouth and checking for any obstructions.

CHECKLIST

Potentially Lethal Products

Some common household products can be lethal to your pet, if ingested. Keep all of the following locked away from your Newf's reach:

✔ Antifreeze: the liquid is sweet-tasting and appealing to dogs and dangerously poisonous.

✔ Soap, detergents, and boric acid can also be lethal, as well as paint, fertilizer, and other garden supplies.

✔ For safety's sake, childproof all of your kitchen cabinets and keep your garage or tool shed locked at all times.

✔ Never leave your Newf unattended in a garage where many of these items are likely to be stored.

Since your Newf will be outdoors a lot, it could also pick up something without your knowing it. Be alert to signs of poisoning that include

• vomiting
• labored breathing
• stomach cramps
• trembling
• disorientation
• a change in the color of the mucous membranes.

If you suspect poisoning, call your veterinarian immediately or call the Poison Control Center, which operates a 24-hour-a-day hotline: 1-888-426-4435

✔ Then pull out its tongue to make sure nothing is caught in the pharynx.

✔ Next, clear the mouth of any mucus or blood.

✔ Keep the mouth slightly open and with one hand, hold the tongue firmly to the bottom of the mouth and, with the other hand, cover the nostrils. Then begin blowing air into the mouth. Make sure the chest is expanding with every breath.

✔ Repeat every five to six seconds until it is breathing on its own, then get it to the veterinarian.

Note: If your dog has a head, neck, or spinal injury, using the above method can cause a violent reaction. Also be aware that reaching into the mouth of an injured animal that is conscious can pose a danger to you in the form of a bite.

Proper Dental Care

No discussion about how to care for your Newf's health would be complete without mentioning dental hygiene. Remember, your Newf's teeth and gums need just as much attention as the rest of its body does; a dental exam should be a part of its yearly medical checkup. Fortunately, dogs' teeth are usually in better condition than human teeth because they don't usually snack on candy bars and other sweets. However, dogs do build up calculus and tartar on their teeth and, if left untreated, periodontal problems can result. Chew toys and nylon bones will help keep your Newf's teeth clean, but only daily brushing will prevent tartar buildup.

Brushing: If you get your Newf used to having its teeth brushed from puppyhood, it will soon regard it as a pleasant part of its daily grooming ritual. Your veterinarian will instruct you on the proper method of brushing your dog's teeth and give you a special brush and toothpaste to use. Do not attempt to use human toothpaste as it can be harmful to your pet. There are also several antiplaque gels on the market that you can rub into your Newf's gums on a regular basis. This will keep plaque and calculus from building up and save you the expense of professional cleanings.

You can also purchase a professional tooth scaler from wholesale dog catalogs. Your veterinarian or veterinary technician can demonstrate the proper way to scale your dog's teeth between visits.

Also keep in mind that puppies love to chew just about anything, so be sure to supervise what goes into its mouth. Don't allow it to chew hard objects such as rocks because a broken or chipped tooth is likely to result.

Once again, common sense and prevention are the keys. If you keep your Newf's teeth and gums healthy, it won't be plagued by decaying teeth that can cause other health problems as it gets older.

Caring for the Older Newfoundland

When your Newf reaches the age of seven, by dog standards it will be well into middle age. As it ages, it will become less active and its nutritional needs will change (see page 61). Generally, it will need a diet with less, though higher-quality protein. But make no mistake—your Newf is still capable of being a vital member of the family and, if you've cared for it well during its younger years, there is no reason why it shouldn't live to a ripe old age, which for a Newfoundland is around 12 years.

A Newfoundland will be your beloved friend and companion for its entire life.

Changes: You should be aware of physical changes that occur as your dog gets older. Pay particular attention to its teeth and gums and any changes in its bladder or bowel habits. Its eyesight and hearing may also become impaired as it ages. Dogs, like humans, are also afflicted with arthritis and rheumatism, but these conditions are often managed with little difficulty. Since your Newf has been your faithful friend and companion for so many years, you will be happy to make its advanced years as enjoyable and comfortable as possible.

Remember, the worst disease that can afflict your Newf as it ages is neglect. Good preventive care throughout its lifetime is the best way to assure it of a long and healthy life.

Euthanasia

It has been called the ultimate kindness. Nonetheless, when and if the time comes to put your Newf down, it will be one of the saddest moments in your life. If your dog, either because of advanced age or terminal illness, has reached a point where it is in pain or can no longer enjoy a good quality of life, putting it to sleep is probably the kindest thing you can do. Most Newfs, unless stricken by fatal illness or accident, will live long, healthy lives. As the years go by, you will watch it go from a young ball of fire to a robust adult to a more mellow senior citizen. Finally, at some point, you will realize that every day is a struggle for it.

Making the decision to say good-bye is the hardest, as well as the most unselfish one, you will ever have to face. Don't try to make it alone. Seek the support of the whole family and, most importantly, seek the advice of your veterinarian. Often, there are options besides euthanasia and your veterinarian can best advise you if treating your pet is possible or realistic. Whatever your decision, be comforted that you have made it completely out of love for your beloved Newfy.

Clubs

The American Kennel Club
51 Madison Avenue
New York, NY 10038

The Canadian Kennel Club
100-89 Skyway Avenue
Etobicoke, Ontario
Canada M9W 6R4

The Newfoundland Club of America
Official Web site: *www.newfdogclub.org*
   You will find information on the breed, as
well as how to apply for membership, and how
to subscribe to the NCA's official quarterly
magazine, *NEWF TIDE.*

Epitaph to a Dog

*Near this spot
are deposited the remains
of one who possessed beauty
without vanity,
strength without insolence,
courage without ferocity,
and all the virtues of man
without his vices.
This praise, which would be
unmeaning flattery
if inscribed over human ashes,
is but a just tribute to the
memory of Boatswain,
a dog who was born
at Newfoundland
May, 1803
and died at Newstead Abbey
Nov. 18, 1808*

Associations

American Veterinary Medical Association
930 North Meacham Road
Schaumburg, IL 60173

Orthopedic Foundation for Animals (OFA)
2300 E. Nifong Boulevard
Columbia, MO 65201

Books

Adler, Judi. *The Newfoundland Puppy: Early
   Care, Early Training.* Third Edition, (1993).
   From the author, 12320 SW Malloy,
   Sherwood, Oregon 97140.

–––. *The Audible Nose.* From the author,
   12320 SW Malloy, Sherwood, Oregon 97140.

–––. *Water Work, Water Play.* From the
   author, 12320 SW Malloy, Sherwood, Oregon
   97140.

Bendure, Joan C. *The Newfoundland, Companion Dog–Water Dog.* Howell House, Inc., New
   York, New York: 1994.

Klever, Ulrich. *The Complete Book of Dog Care.*
   Barron's Educational Series, Inc., Hauppauge,
   New York: 1989.

Powell, Consie. *Newfoundland Draft Work:
   A Guide for Training.* From the author, 5208
   Olive Rd., Raleigh, North Carolina: 27606.

Ullmann, Hans. *The New Dog Handbook.*
   Barron's Educational Series, Inc., Hauppauge,
   New York: 1984.

Here I come, ready or not!

94 INDEX

edication

This book is dedicated to my most beloved boys: a Foi's Dylan Malloy de Tomas and Ch. Fleetwood Farm's Jamie O'Dyl.

About the Author

Joanna Kosloff is a novelist and television writer and has owned and loved Newfoundlands for more than 25 years.

Acknowledgments

To those fanciers of the breed who have so generously shared their time, stories, and precious Newfs with me, I am exceedingly grateful. Special thanks to Newf owner, Dawn Hockman; to Judie Adler of Sweetbay Newfoundlands for her beautiful books and photographs; to my editor, Mary Falcon; to Joe Stahlkuppe, a fellow fancier and writer; to Dr. Theodore Leif and Dr. Dan Rice for their expert advice; and finally, to my husband, George, and my beloved Irish Setters: Ch Fleetwood's Jamie O'Dyl—Dylan, Fleetwood's Right About You—Brandy, and Sweet Baby James—Jamie, and last but not least, Fleetwood's Dangerous Heart—Dylan IV, who waited patiently for this revision to be completed.

Important Note

This pet owner's manual tells the reader how to buy or adopt, and care for a Newfoundland. The author and publisher consider it important to point out that the advice given in the book is meant primarily for normally developed dogs of excellent physical health and sound temperament.

Anyone who acquires a fully-grown dog should be aware that the animal has already formed its basic impressions of human beings. The new owner should watch the animal carefully, including its behavior toward humans, and, whenever possible, should meet the previous owner. If the dog comes from a shelter or was acquired through rescue, it should be possible to get some information on the dog's background and peculiarities there. There are dogs that, as a result of bad experiences with humans, behave in an unnatural manner or may even bite. Only people that have experience with dogs should take in such animals.

Caution is further advised in the association of children with dogs, in meeting with other dogs, and in exercising the dog without a leash.

Even well-behaved, carefully supervised dogs sometimes do damage to someone else's property or cause accidents. It is therefore in the owner's interest to be adequately insured against such eventualities, and we strongly urge all dog owners to purchase a liability policy that covers their dog.

Cover Photos

Isabelle Francais: front cover, back cover, inside front cover, and inside back cover.

Photo Credits

Kent Dannen: 7, 14, 15, 19, 22, 23, 27, 28, 33, 37, 59, 60 (bottom left), 61, 74, 77, 78, 85, and 86; Tara Darling: 4, 12, 20, 21 (top and bottom), 31, 39 (top right), 43, 47, 49, 50 (top right), 62, 64 (top), 67, 75, 82, 88, 91, and 93; Isabelle Francais: 2, 3, 5, 6, 9, 11, 16, 24, 25, 29, 30, 32, 34, 40, 46, 50 (top left), 56, 65, 72 (bottom left), and 79; Daniel Johnson: 8, 13, 38, 39 (bottom right), 41, 64 (bottom left), 69 (top and bottom), 72 (top left), and 80; Pets by Paulette: 10, 35, 36, 52, 53, 57, 60 (top), 66, 73, and 84.

© Copyright 2006, 1996 by Barron's Educational Series, Inc.

All inquiries should be addressed to:
Barron's Educational Series, Inc.
250 Wireless Boulevard
Hauppauge, NY 11788
www.barronseduc.com

ISBN-13: 978-0-7641-3399-2
ISBN-10: 0-7641-3399-3

Library of Congress Catalog Card No. 2006013570

Library of Congress Cataloging-in-Publication Data
Kosloff, Joanna.
    Newfoundlands : everything about purchase, care, nutrition, behavior, and training / Joanna Kosloff ; Illustrations by Tana Hakanson.
        p. cm. — (A complete pet owner's manual)
    Includes bibliographical references and index.
    ISBN-13: 978-0-7641-3399-2 (alk. paper)
    ISBN-10: 0-7641-3399-3 (alk. paper)
    1. Newfoundland dog. I. Title. II. Series.

SF429.N4K67   2006
636.73—dc22   2006013570

Printed in China
9 8 7 6 5 4 3 2